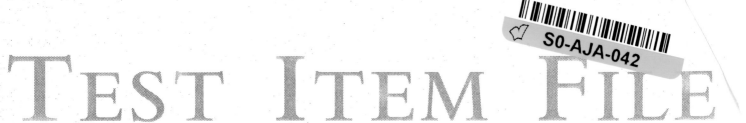

TEST ITEM FILE

DELENA BELL GATCH
GEORGIA SOUTHERN UNIVERSITY

Sixth Edition

PHYSICS

Principles with Applications

GIANCOLI

Upper Saddle River, NJ 07458

Associate Editor: Christian Botting
Senior Editor: Erik Fahlgren
Editor-in-Chief, Science: John Challice
Vice President of Production & Manufacturing: David W. Riccardi
Executive Managing Editor: Kathleen Schiaparelli
Assistant Managing Editor: Becca Richter
Production Editor: Dana Dunn
Supplement Cover Management/Design: Paul Gourhan
Supplement Cover Designer: Christopher Kossa
Manufacturing Buyer: Ilene Kahn

Pearson Prentice Hall
Pearson Education, Inc.
Upper Saddle River, NJ 07458

Printed in the United States of America

10 9 8

ISBN 0-13-047311-1

Pearson Education Ltd., *London*
Pearson Education Australia Pty. Ltd., *Sydney*
Pearson Education Singapore, Pte. Ltd.
Pearson Education North Asia Ltd., *Hong Kong*
Pearson Education Canada, Inc., *Toronto*
Pearson Educación de Mexico, S.A. de C.V.
Pearson Education—Japan, *Tokyo*
Pearson Education Malaysia, Pte. Ltd.

Contents

Test Item File

to accompany

Physics: Principles with Applications

Sixth Edition

Douglas Giancoli

Delena Bell Gatch

Georgia Southern University

Preface

This test bank is a revision and update of the ***Test Item File*** accompanying the fifth edition of Douglas Giancoli's ***Physics: Principles with Applications***. The sixth edition test bank was created with TestGenerator, a networkable program for creating quizzes and exams. TestGenerator allows users to modify existing questions/problems, including algorithmic versions, as well as create and input new questions/problems.

This test bank contains approximately 2500 multiple choice, short answer, and essay questions. The majority of the multiple choice questions and problems could also be given as free response questions or problems. Like the end of chapter of ***Physics: Principles with Applications***, each chapter of the test bank is divided into two sections: **Conceptual Questions** and **Quantitative Problems**. Thus, nearly 50% of the material in the test bank is conceptual in nature. All questions and problems are ranked by level of difficulty and are referenced to the corresponding section in the textbook. The notation in the sixth edition test bank has been updated to reflect the notation used in the sixth edition of ***Physics: Principles with Applications***.

About the Author

Dr. Delena Bell Gatch has taught introductory physics at Georgia Southern University since early 2001. She completed her Ph.D. at the University of Georgia in September of 2000, and remained at the University of Georgia as a post doctorial assistant before accepting the assistant professor position Georgia Southern University. Her field of specialty is experimental condensed matter physics. Her research ventures have included the study of the properties of powder phosphors for flat panel displays, the development of new infrared detection schemes utilizing visible emission from crystals, and the investigation of the shifts in energy levels of crystals due to the application of hydrostatic pressure.

During a typical semester, Dr. Gatch teaches three or four introductory physics classes, in addition to one-to-three introductory physics labs. She works with students in the University Honors Program who desire to study physics in greater depth. She also spends time outside of the classroom assisting her premedical students who are preparing to take the MCAT.

Chapter 1 Introduction, Measurement, Estimating

Conceptual Questions

1) Four students measure the mass of an object, each using a different scale. They record their results as follows:

Student	A	B	C	D
Mass (g)	49.06	49	50	49.2

Which student used the least precise scale?

A) A

B) B

C) C

D) D

Answer: C

Diff: 1 *Page Ref:* Sec. 1.4

2) Four students measure the mass of an object, each using a different scale. They record their results as follows:

Student	A	B	C	D
Mass (g)	49.06	49	50	49.2

Which student used the most precise scale?

A) A

B) B

C) C

D) D

Answer: A

Diff: 1 *Page Ref:* Sec. 1.4

3) A useful method of expressing very small or very large numbers is

A) scientific notation.

B) arabic numerals.

C) the metric system.

D) roman numerals.

Answer: A

Diff: 1 *Page Ref:* Sec. 1.4

4) All of the following are base units of the SI system except:
   A) kilogram.
   B) kelvin.
   C) meter.
   D) volt.

   Answer: D
   Diff: 1   *Page Ref: Sec. 15–1.6*

5) Select the list which contains only SI basic units.
   A) liter, meter, second, watt
   B) joule, kelvin, kilogram, watt
   C) candela, kelvin, meter, second
   D) joule, newton, second, watt

   Answer: C
   Diff: 1   *Page Ref: Sec. 1.5–1.6*

6) How many basic units does the SI system have?
   A) four
   B) five
   C) seven
   D) ten

   Answer: C
   Diff: 1   *Page Ref: Sec. 1.5–1.6*

7) The base SI unit of time is
   A) hour.
   B) minute.
   C) second.
   D) millisecond.

   Answer: C
   Diff: 1   *Page Ref: Sec. 1.5–1.6*

8) In the CGS system, what are the fundamental units?
   A) Newton, centimeter, second
   B) kilogram, meter, second
   C) gram, centimeter, minute
   D) gram, centimeter, second

   Answer: D
   Diff: 2   *Page Ref: Sec. 1.5–1.6*

9) The metric prefix for one one-thousandth is

A) milli.

B) centi.

C) kilo.

D) mega.

Answer: A
Diff: 1 *Page Ref: Sec. 1.5-1.6*

10) The metric prefix for one one-hundredth is

A) milli.

B) centi.

C) kilo.

D) mega.

Answer: B
Diff: 1 *Page Ref: Sec. 1.5-1.6*

11) The metric prefix for one thousand is

A) milli.

B) centi.

C) kilo.

D) mega.

Answer: C
Diff: 1 *Page Ref: Sec. 1.5-1.6*

12) Express the number 0.02 days using a prefix of Table 1-4.

A) 2 decidays

B) 2 centidays

C) 2 millidays

D) 2 microdays

Answer: B
Diff: 1 *Page Ref: Sec. 1.5-1.6*

13) What is the conversion factor between km/h and m/s?

A) 0.0278 m/s

B) 0.278 m/s

C) 3.60 m/s

D) 16.7 m/s

Answer: B
Diff: 1 *Page Ref: Sec. 1.5-1.6*

14) What is the conversion factor between km/h^2 and m/s^2?

A) 7.72×10^{-6} m/s^2

B) 2.78×10^{-1} m/s^2

C) 1.30×10^{4} m/s^2

D) 3.60 m/s^2

Answer: A
Diff: 1 *Page Ref: Sec. 1.5–1.6*

15) What is the conversion factor between cm^2 and m^2?

A) 0.01 m^2/cm^2

B) 0.0001 m^2/cm^2

C) 100 m^2/cm^2

D) 10000 m^2/cm^2

Answer: B
Diff: 1 *Page Ref: Sec. 1.5–1.6*

16) The position, x, of an object is given by the equation $x = A + Bt + Ct^2$, where t refers to time. What are the dimensions of A, B, and C?

A) distance, distance, distance

B) distance, time, time^2

C) distance, distance/time, distance/time^2

D) distance/time, distance/time^2, distance/time^3

Answer: C
Diff: 2 *Page Ref: Sec. 1.8*

Quantitative Problems

1) What is the percent uncertainty in the measurement 2.58 ± 0.15 cm?

A) 2.9%

B) 5.8%

C) 8.7%

D) 12%

Answer: B
Diff: 2 *Page Ref: Sec. 1.4*

2) What, approximately, is the percent uncertainty for the measurement 5.2?

A) 1%

B) 2%

C) 3%

D) 4%

Answer: B
Diff: 2 *Page Ref: Sec. 1.4*

3) What is the percent uncertainty in the area of a circle whose radius is 1.8×10^4 cm?

A) 1.1%

B) 5.6%

C) 11%

D) 56%

Answer: C
Diff: 3 *Page Ref: Sec. 1.4*

4) What is the volume, and its approximate uncertainty, of a sphere of radius 1.96 ± 0.01 m?

A) 31.5 ± 0.2 m2

B) 31.5 ± 0.3 m2

C) 31.5 ± 0.4 m2

D) 31.5 ± 0.5 m2

Answer: D
Diff: 3 *Page Ref: Sec. 1.4*

5) The number of significant figures in 10001 is

A) two.

B) three.

C) five.

D) six.

Answer: C
Diff: 1 *Page Ref: Sec. 1.4*

6) The number of significant figures in 0.01500 is

A) two.

B) three.

C) four.

D) five.

Answer: C
Diff: 1 *Page Ref: Sec. 1.4*

7) The number of significant figures in 0.040 is

A) one.

B) two.

C) three.

D) four.

Answer: B
Diff: 1 *Page Ref: Sec. 1.4*

8) Which of the following has three significant figures?

A) 305.0 cm

B) 0.0500 mm

C) 1.00081 kg

D) 8.060×10^{11} m^2

Answer: B
Diff: 1 *Page Ref: Sec. 1.4*

9) What is the sum of 2.67 + 1.976 + 2.1?

A) 6.7

B) 6.75

C) 6.746

D) 6.7460

Answer: A
Diff: 1 *Page Ref: Sec. 1.4*

10) What is the difference between 103.5 and 102.24?

A) 1.3

B) 1.26

C) 1.260

D) 1.2600

Answer: A
Diff: 1 *Page Ref: Sec. 1.4*

11) What is the product of 12.56 and 2.12?

A) 27

B) 26.6

C) 26.23

D) 26.627

Answer: B
Diff: 1 *Page Ref: Sec. 1.4*

12) What is the result of 2.43 ÷ 4.561?

A) 5.3278×10^{-1}

B) 5.328×10^{-1}

C) 5.33×10^{-1}

D) 5.3×10^{-1}

Answer: C
Diff: 1 *Page Ref: Sec. 1.4*

13) What is the cosine of 55°?

A) 0.6

B) 0.57

C) 0.574

D) 0.5736

Answer: B
Diff: 1 *Page Ref: Sec. 1.4*

14) The length and width of a rectangle are 1.125 m and 0.606 m, respectively. Multiplying, your calculator gives the product as 0.68175. Rounding properly to the correct number of significant figures, the area should be written as

A) 0.68 m^2.

B) 0.682 m^2.

C) 0.6818 m^2.

D) 0.68175 m^2.

Answer: B
Diff: 1 *Page Ref: Sec. 1.4*

15) The length and width of a rectangle are 1.125 m and 0.606 m, respectively. You calculate the rectangle's perimeter by adding these and multiplying by two. Your calculator's display reads 3.462. To the correct number of significant figures, this should be written as

A) 3.5 m.

B) 3.46 m.

C) 3.462 m.

D) 3.4620 m.

Answer: C
Diff: 1 *Page Ref: Sec. 1.4*

16) A rectangle is 3.25 m long and 1.5 m wide. What is its area?

A) 4.875 m^2

B) 4.87 m^2

C) 4.80 m^2

D) 4.9 m^2

Answer: D
Diff: 2 *Page Ref: Sec. 1.4*

17) A rectangular garden measures 15 m long and 13.7 m wide. What is the length of a diagonal from one corner of the garden to the other?

A) 18 m

B) 19 m

C) 20 m

D) 4.1×10^2 m

Answer: C
Diff: 2 *Page Ref: Sec. 1.4*

18) Select the smallest value.

A) 15×10^{-3}

B) 0.15×10^0

C) 0.00015×10^3

D) 0.00000015×10^6

Answer: A
Diff: 1 *Page Ref: Sec. 1.4*

19) Write the number 0.00045 in power of ten notation.

A) 4.5×10^{-4}

B) 4.5×10^{-3}

C) 4.5×10^{-2}

D) 4.5×10^{-1}

Answer: A
Diff: 1 *Page Ref: Sec. 1.4*

20) 0.0001776 can also be expressed as

A) 1.776×10^{-4}.

B) 17.72×10^4.

C) 1772×10^5.

D) 177.2×10^7.

Answer: A
Diff: 1 *Page Ref: Sec. 1.4*

21) 4567.89 is properly expressed in scientific notation as

A) 4.56789×10^3.

B) 45.6789×10^2.

C) 456.789×10^1.

D) 4567.89×10^0.

Answer: A
Diff: 1 *Page Ref: Sec. 1.4*

22) Convert 1.2×10^{-3} to decimal notation.

A) 1.200

B) 0.1200

C) 0.0120

D) 0.0012

Answer: D
Diff: 1 *Page Ref: Sec. 1.4*

23) Write out the number 8.42×10^{-5} in full with a decimal point and correct number of zeros.

A) 0.00000842

B) 0.0000842

C) 0.000842

D) 0.00842

Answer: B
Diff: 1 *Page Ref: Sec. 1.4*

24) What is the result of $(0.410 + 0.021) \times (2.20 \times 10^{3})$?

A) 880

B) 946

C) 948

D) 950

Answer: C
Diff: 2 *Page Ref: Sec. 1.4*

25) Write the number 13.5 gigameters as full (decimal) numbers with standard units.

A) 135,000 m

B) 135,000,000 m

C) 135,000,000,000 m

D) 13,500,000,000 m

Answer: D
Diff: 1 *Page Ref: Sec. 1.5–1.6*

26) 100 mL is equivalent to which of the following?

A) 1 kL

B) 10^{-6} μL

C) 0.1 L

D) 0.01 ML

Answer: C
Diff: 1 *Page Ref: Sec. 1.5–1.6*

27) How many grams is forty milligrams?

A) 0.000040 g

B) 0.00040 g

C) 0.040 g

D) 40000 g

Answer: C
Diff: 1 *Page Ref: Sec. 1.5–1.6*

28) How many meters is sixty kilometers?

A) 600,000 m

B) 60,000 m

C) 60 m

D) 0.06 m

Answer: B
Diff: 1 *Page Ref: Sec. 1.5–1.6*

29) 1 angstrom = 10^{-10} m and 1 fermi = 10^{-15} m, what is the relationship between these units?

A) 1 angstrom = 10^{5} fermi

B) 1 angstrom = 10^{-5} fermi

C) 1 angstrom = 10^{-25} fermi

D) 1 angstrom = 10^{+25} fermi

Answer: A
Diff: 1 *Page Ref: Sec. 1.5–1.6*

30) 0.00325×10^{-8} cm can also be expressed in mm as

A) 3.25×10^{-12} mm.

B) 3.25×10^{-11} mm.

C) 3.25×10^{-10} mm.

D) 3.25×10^{-9} mm.

Answer: C
Diff: 2 *Page Ref: Sec. 1.5–1.6*

31) Which one of the following is not equivalent to 2.50 miles? (1 mi = 1.609 km = 5280 ft, 1 ft = 12 in.)

A) 1.32×10^{4} ft

B) 1.58×10^{5} in.

C) 4.02×10^{3} km

D) 4.40×10^{3} yd

Answer: C
Diff: 1 *Page Ref: Sec. 1.5–1.6*

32) If you are 5'10" tall, what is your height in meters? (1 in = 2.54 cm.)
A) 1.5 m
B) 1.6 m
C) 1.7 m
D) 1.8 m

Answer: D
Diff: 1 *Page Ref: Sec. 1.5–1.6*

33) If 1 inch = 2.54 cm, and 1 yd = 36 in., how many meters are in 7.00 yd?
A) 6.40 m
B) 36.3 m
C) 640 m
D) 1.78×10^3 m

Answer: A
Diff: 2 *Page Ref: Sec. 1.5–1.6*

34) A hot air balloon rises to an altitude of 600 fathoms. What is this height, in feet? (1 fathom = 6 ft.)
A) 100 ft
B) 600 ft
C) 1200 ft
D) 3600 ft

Answer: D
Diff: 1 *Page Ref: Sec. 1.5–1.6*

35) The average life of an animal is 70 years. Assume one numerical figure, write this in power of ten in seconds.
A) 3×10^7 s
B) 2×10^7 s
C) 2×10^9 s
D) 3×10^9 s

Answer: C
Diff: 1 *Page Ref: Sec. 1.5–1.6*

36) The mass of an electron is 9.1×10^{-31} kg. How many electrons will make a mass of 1.0 kg?
A) 9.1×10^{30}
B) 1.1×10^{30}
C) 9.1×10^{31}
D) 1.1×10^{31}

Answer: B
Diff: 1 *Page Ref: Sec. 15–1.6*

37) How many m/s is 50 mi/h equivalent to? (1 mi = 1609 m.)

A) 49 m/s

B) 2.2 m/s

C) 22 m/s

D) 45 m/s

Answer: C
Diff: 1 *Page Ref: Sec. 1.5–1.6*

38) How much longer (percentage) is a 100 m dash than a 100 yd dash? (1 yd = 0.9146 m.)

A) 3.5%

B) 6.5%

C) 8.5%

D) 12%

Answer: C
Diff: 1 *Page Ref: Sec. 1.5–1.6*

39) Which is the largest area?

A) 2,500,000 cm^2

B) 100,000 cm^2

C) 7.5 m^2

D) 0.75 m^2

Answer: B
Diff: 1 *Page Ref: Sec. 1.5–1.6*

40) If 1 inch = 2.54 cm, how many square centimeters are in 1.00 square in.?

A) 1.59

B) 2.54

C) 5.08

D) 6.45

Answer: D
Diff: 2 *Page Ref: Sec. 1.5–1.6*

41) Express the following sum with the correct number of significant figures: 1.00 kg + 1531 g + 2.54×10^4 mg.

A) 2.56 kg

B) 27.9 kg

C) 2.53 kg

D) 2.79 kg

Answer: A
Diff: 2 *Page Ref: Sec. 1.5–1.6*

42) A football field is 120 yd long and 50 yd wide. What is the area of the football field, in m^2, if 1 yd = 91.44 cm?

A) 2.4×10^3 m^2

B) 3.7×10^3 m^2

C) 4.2×10^3 m^2

D) 5.0×10^3 m^2

Answer: D
Diff: 2 *Page Ref: Sec. 1.5-1.6*

43) A ball has a radius of 3.23 cm. What is the volume of the ball in m^3?

A) 1.41×10^{-4}

B) 1.41

C) 4.23×10^{-4}

D) 4.23

Answer: A
Diff: 2 *Page Ref: Sec. 1.5-1.6*

44) A thick-walled metal pipe of length 20.0 cm has an inside diameter of 2.00 cm and an outside diameter of 2.40 cm. What is the total surface area of the pipe, counting the ends, in m^2?

A) 276

B) 277

C) 278

D) 279

Answer: D
Diff: 3 *Page Ref: Sec. 1.5-1.6*

45) The radius of the Earth is 3963 mi. What is the surface area of the Earth in square meters? (1 mi = 1609 m.)

A) 4.9×10^7 m^2

B) 1.3×10^{14} m^2

C) 2.6×10^{14} m^2

D) 5.1×10^{14} m^2

Answer: D
Diff: 2 *Page Ref: Sec. 1.5-1.6*

46) The average density of blood is 1.06×10^3 kg/m^3. If you donate a pint of blood to the Red Cross, what mass of blood have you donated, in grams? (1 pt = 1/2 L, 1 L = 1000 cm^3.)

A) 530 g

B) 0.530 g

C) 5300 g

D) 5.30×10^5 g

Answer: A
Diff: 2 *Page Ref: Sec. 1.5-1.6*

47) The mass of Mars, 6.40×10^{23} kg, is about one-tenth that of the Earth, and its radius, 3395 km, is about half that of Earth. What is the mean density of Mars in kg/m^3?

A) 9.76×10^2

B) 1.95×10^3

C) 3.90×10^3

D) 7.81×10^3

Answer: C
Diff: 2 *Page Ref: Sec. 1.5-1.6*

48) Concrete is sold by the cubic yard. What is the mass, in kilograms, of one cubic yard of concrete that is five times as dense as water? (1 m = 1.094 yd, and 1 m^3 of water has a mass of 1,000 kg.)

A) 764 kg

B) 2.42×10^3 kg

C) 3.82×10^3 kg

D) 6.55×10^3 kg

Answer: C
Diff: 2 *Page Ref: Sec. 1.5-1.6*

49) An average human has a heart rate of 70 beats per minute. If someone's heart beats at that average rate over a 70-yr lifetime, how many times would it beat?

A) 7×10^5

B) 2×10^6

C) 2×10^7

D) 3×10^9

Answer: D
Diff: 2 *Page Ref: Sec. 1.7*

50) A large school district has 300 school buses. If each school bus is used 3 hours each day, the average speed of the school buses is 15 mi/h, and the fuel economy of the buses is 10 mi/gal. How much does it cost to run these buses in 22 school days if gasoline costs $1.20 a gallon?

A) $600

B) $1200

C) $1800

D) $2400

Answer: B
Diff: 2 *Page Ref: Sec. 1.7*

51) A person stands 35.0 m from a flag pole. With a protractor at eye level, he finds that the angle at the top of the flag pole makes with the horizontal is 25.0 degrees. How high is the flag pole? (The distance from his feet to his eyes is 1.7 m.)

A) 10 m

B) 20 m

C) 30 m

D) 80 m

Answer: B
Diff: 2 *Page Ref: Sec. 1.7*

52) Starting from city A, a car drives 250 miles east to city B, then 300 miles north to city C, and finally 700 miles west to city D. What is the distance between city A and city D?

A) 300 mi

B) 400 mi

C) 500 mi

D) 600 mi

Answer: C
Diff: 2 *Page Ref: Sec. 1.7*

53) The last page of a book is numbered 764. The book is 3.00 cm thick. What is the average thickness of a sheet of paper in the book, in centimeters?

A) 4×10^{-3}

B) 8×10^{-3}

C) 100

D) 200

Answer: B
Diff: 2 *Page Ref: Sec. 1.7*

54) Wall posters are usually sold curled up in cylindrical cardboard tubes. If the length of the tube is 84.5 cm, and the diameter of the tube is 2.40 cm, what is the area of the poster, in cm^2? (Assume the poster doesn't overlap itself.)

A) 200 cm^2

B) 400 cm^2

C) 600 cm^2

D) 2000 cm^2

Answer: C
Diff: 2 *Page Ref: Sec. 1.7*

Chapter 2 Describing Motion: Kinematics in One Dimension

Conceptual Questions

1) Suppose that an object travels from one point in space to another. Make a comparison between the displacement and the distance traveled.

A) The displacement is either greater than or equal to the distance traveled.

B) The displacement is always equal to the distance traveled.

C) The displacement is either less than or equal to the distance traveled.

D) The displacement can be either greater than, smaller than, or equal to the distance traveled.

Answer: C
Diff: 2 *Page Ref: Sec. 2.1*

2) When is the average velocity of an object equal to the instantaneous velocity?

A) always

B) never

C) only when the velocity is constant

D) only when the velocity is increasing at a constant rate

Answer: C
Diff: 2 *Page Ref: Sec. 2.2–2.3*

3) A new car manufacturer advertises that their car can go "from zero to sixty in 8 s". This is a description of

A) average speed.

B) instantaneous speed.

C) average acceleration.

D) instantaneous acceleration.

Answer: C
Diff: 1 *Page Ref: Sec. 2.4*

4) An object moving in the +x axis experiences an acceleration of 2.0 m/s^2. This means the object is

   A) traveling at 2.0 m in every second.

   B) traveling at 2.0 m/s in every second.

   C) changing its velocity by 2.0 m/s.

   D) increasing its velocity by 2.0 m/s in every second.

   Answer: D
   Diff: 1 *Page Ref: Sec. 2.4*

5) Suppose that a car traveling to the East (+x direction) begins to slow down as it approaches a traffic light. Make a statement concerning its acceleration.

   A) The car is decelerating, and its acceleration is positive.

   B) The car is decelerating, and its acceleration is negative.

   C) The acceleration is zero.

   D) A statement cannot be made using the information given.

   Answer: B
   Diff: 1 *Page Ref: Sec. 2.4*

6) Suppose that a car traveling to the West (−x direction) begins to slow down as it approaches a traffic light. Make a statement concerning its acceleration.

   A) The car is decelerating, and its acceleration is positive.

   B) The car is decelerating, and its acceleration is negative.

   C) The acceleration is zero.

   D) A statement cannot be made using the information given.

   Answer: A
   Diff: 2 *Page Ref: Sec. 2.4*

7) Suppose that an object is moving with a constant velocity. Make a statement concerning its acceleration.

   A) The acceleration must be constantly increasing.

   B) The acceleration must be constantly decreasing.

   C) The acceleration must be a constant non-zero value.

   D) The acceleration must be equal to zero.

   Answer: D
   Diff: 1 *Page Ref: Sec. 2.4*

8) If the velocity of an object is zero, does it mean that the acceleration is zero? Support your answer with an example.

A) no, and an example would be an object starting from rest

B) no, and an example would be an object coming to a stop

C) yes, because of the way in which velocity is defined

D) yes, because of the way in which acceleration is defined

Answer: A
Diff: 1 *Page Ref: Sec. 2.4*

9) Can an object's velocity change direction when its acceleration is constant? Support your answer with an example.

A) No, this is not possible because it is always speeding up.

B) No, this is not possible because it is always speeding up or always slowing down, but it can never turn around.

C) Yes, this is possible, and a rock thrown straight up is an example.

D) Yes, this is possible, and a car that starts from rest, speeds up, slows to a stop, and then backs up is an example.

Answer: C
Diff: 2 *Page Ref: Sec. 2.4*

10) Suppose that an object is moving with constant acceleration. Make a statement concerning its motion with respect to time.

A) In equal times its speed increases by equal amounts.

B) In equal times its velocity changes by equal amounts.

C) In equal times it moves equal distances.

D) A statement cannot be made using the information given.

Answer: B
Diff: 2 *Page Ref: Sec. 2.4*

11) Can an object have increasing speed while its acceleration is decreasing? Support your answer with an example.

A) No, this is impossible because of the way in which acceleration is defined.

B) No, because if acceleration is decreasing the object will be slowing down.

C) Yes, and an example would be an object falling in the absence of air friction.

D) Yes, and an example would be an object released from rest in the presence of air friction.

Answer: D
Diff: 2 *Page Ref: Sec. 2.4*

12) Suppose a can, after an initial kick, moves up along a smooth hill of ice. Make a statement concerning its acceleration.

A) It will travel at constant velocity with zero acceleration.

B) It will have a constant acceleration up the hill, but a different constant acceleration when it comes back down the hill.

C) It will have the same acceleration, both up the hill and down the hill.

D) It will have a varying acceleration along the hill.

Answer: C
Diff: 3 *Page Ref: Sec. 2.4*

13) Under what condition is average velocity equal to the average of the object's initial and final velocity?

A) The acceleration must be constantly changing.

B) The acceleration must be constant.

C) This can only occur if there is no acceleration.

D) This is impossible.

Answer: B
Diff: 2 *Page Ref: Sec. 2.4*

14) Objects A and B both start at rest. They both accelerate at the same rate. However, object A accelerates for twice the time as object B. What is the final speed of object A compared to that of object B?

A) the same speed

B) twice as fast

C) three times as fast

D) four times as fast

Answer: B
Diff: 2 *Page Ref: Sec. 2.5–2.6*

15) Objects A and B both start from rest. They both accelerate at the same rate. However, object A accelerates for twice the time as object B. What is the distance traveled by object A compared to that of object B?

A) the same distance

B) twice as far

C) three times as far

D) four times as far

Answer: D
Diff: 2 *Page Ref: Sec. 2.5–2.6*

16) When an object is released from rest and falls in the absence of friction, which of the following is true concerning its motion?

A) The speed of the falling object is proportional to its mass.

B) The speed of the falling object is proportional to its weight.

C) The speed of the falling object is inversely proportional to its surface area.

D) None of the above is true.

Answer: D
Diff: 1 *Page Ref: Sec. 2.7*

17) When an object is released from rest and falls in the absence of friction, which of the following is true concerning its motion?

A) Its acceleration is constant.

B) Its velocity is constant.

C) Neither its acceleration nor its velocity is constant.

D) Both its acceleration and its velocity are constant.

Answer: A
Diff: 1 *Page Ref: Sec. 2.7*

18) Suppose a ball is thrown straight up. Make a statement about the velocity and the acceleration when the ball reaches the highest point.

A) Both its velocity and its acceleration are zero.

B) Its velocity is zero and its acceleration is not zero.

C) Its velocity is not zero and its acceleration is zero.

D) Neither its velocity nor its acceleration is zero.

Answer: B
Diff: 1 *Page Ref: Sec. 2.7*

19) Suppose a ball is thrown straight up. What is its acceleration just before it reaches its highest point?

A) zero

B) slightly less than g

C) exactly g

D) slightly greater than g

Answer: C
Diff: 1 *Page Ref: Sec. 2.7*

20) Suppose a ball is thrown straight up, reaches a maximum height, then falls to its initial height. Make a statement about the direction of the velocity and acceleration as the ball is going up.

A) Both its velocity and its acceleration point upward.

B) Its velocity points upward and its acceleration points downward.

C) Its velocity points downward and its acceleration points upward.

D) Both its velocity and its acceleration points downward.

Answer: B
Diff: 1 *Page Ref: Sec. 2.7*

21) A ball is thrown straight up, reaches a maximum height, then falls to its initial height. Make a statement about the direction of the velocity and acceleration as the ball is coming down.

A) Both its velocity and its acceleration point upward.

B) Its velocity points upward and its acceleration points downward.

C) Its velocity points downward and its acceleration points upward.

D) Both its velocity and its acceleration point downward.

Answer: D
Diff: 1 *Page Ref: Sec. 2.7*

22) Suppose a ball is thrown downward in the absence of air resistance. Make a statement concerning its acceleration.

A) Its acceleration is constantly increasing.

B) Its acceleration is constant.

C) Its acceleration is constantly decreasing.

D) Its acceleration is zero.

Answer: B
Diff: 1 *Page Ref: Sec. 2.7*

23) Suppose a skydiver jumps from a high-flying plane. What is her acceleration when she she reaches terminal velocity?

A) It is essentially zero.

B) It is in the upward direction.

C) It is approximately 9.8 m/s^2 downward.

D) It is a constant pointing upward.

Answer: A
Diff: 2 *Page Ref: Sec. 2.7*

24) A ball is thrown vertically upward with a speed v. An identical second ball is thrown upward with a speed 2v (twice as fast). What is the ratio of the maximum height of the second ball to that of the first ball? (How many times higher does the second ball go than the first ball?)

A) 4:1

B) 2:1

C) 1.7:1

D) 1.4:1

Answer: A
Diff: 2 *Page Ref: Sec. 2.7*

25) Ball A is dropped from the top of a building. One second later, ball B is dropped from the same building. As time progresses, the distance between them

A) increases.

B) remains constant.

C) decreases.

D) cannot be determined from the information given.

Answer: A
Diff: 3 *Page Ref: Sec. 2.7*

26) Ball A is dropped from the top of a building. One second later, ball B is dropped from the same building. As time progresses, the difference in their speeds

A) increases.

B) remains constant.

C) decreases.

D) cannot be determined from the information given.

Answer: B
Diff: 3 *Page Ref: Sec. 2.7*

27) Two objects are thrown from the top of a tall building. One is thrown up, and the other is thrown down, both with the same initial speed. What are their speeds when they hit the street?

A) The one thrown up is traveling faster.

B) The one thrown down is traveling faster.

C) They are traveling at the same speed.

D) It is impossible to tell because the height of the building is not given.

Answer: C
Diff: 2 *Page Ref: Sec. 2.7*

28) A brick is dropped from the top of a building. A second brick is thrown straight down from the same building. They are released at the same time. Neglect air resistance. Compare the accelerations of the two bricks.

A) The first brick accelerates faster.

B) The second brick accelerates faster.

C) The two bricks accelerate at the same rate.

D) It is impossible to determine from the information given.

Answer: C
Diff: 2 *Page Ref: Sec. 2.7*

29) An object is moving with constant non-zero velocity in the +x axis. The position versus time graph of this object is

A) a horizontal straight line.

B) a vertical straight line.

C) a straight line making an angle with the time axis.

D) a parabolic curve.

Answer: C
Diff: 1 *Page Ref: Sec. 2.8*

30) An object is moving with constant non-zero acceleration in the +x axis. The position versus time graph of this object is

A) a horizontal straight line.

B) a vertical straight line.

C) a straight line making an angle with the time axis.

D) a parabolic curve.

Answer: D
Diff: 1 *Page Ref: Sec. 2.8*

31) An object is moving with constant non-zero velocity in the +x axis. The velocity versus time graph of this object is

A) a horizontal straight line.

B) a vertical straight line.

C) a straight line making an angle with the time axis.

D) a parabolic curve.

Answer: A
Diff: 1 *Page Ref: Sec. 2.8*

32) An object is moving with constant non–zero acceleration in the +x axis. The velocity versus time graph of this object is

A) a horizontal straight line.

B) a vertical straight line.

C) a straight line making an angle with the time axis.

D) a parabolic curve.

Answer: C
Diff: 1 *Page Ref: Sec. 2.8*

33) The slope of a position versus time graph gives

A) position.

B) velocity.

C) acceleration.

D) displacement.

Answer: B
Diff: 1 *Page Ref: Sec. 2.8*

34) The slope of a velocity versus time graph gives

A) position.

B) velocity.

C) acceleration.

D) displacement.

Answer: C
Diff: 1 *Page Ref: Sec. 2.8*

35) The area under a curve in an acceleration versus time graph gives

A) acceleration.

B) velocity.

C) displacement.

D) position.

Answer: B
Diff: 2 *Page Ref: Sec. 2.8*

36) The area under a curve in a velocity versus time graph gives

A) acceleration.

B) velocity.

C) displacement.

D) position.

Answer: C
Diff: 2 *Page Ref: Sec. 2.8*

37) If the position versus time graph of an object is a horizontal line, the object is

A) moving with constant non-zero speed.

B) moving with constant non-zero acceleration.

C) at rest.

D) moving with infinite speed.

Answer: C
Diff: 1 *Page Ref: Sec. 2.8*

38) If the position versus time graph of an object is a vertical line, the object is

A) moving with constant non-zero speed.

B) moving with constant non-zero acceleration.

C) at rest.

D) moving with infinite speed.

Answer: D
Diff: 1 *Page Ref: Sec. 2.8*

39) If the velocity versus time graph of an object is a horizontal line, the object is

A) moving with constant non-zero speed.

B) moving with constant non-zero acceleration.

C) at rest.

D) moving with infinite speed.

Answer: A
Diff: 1 *Page Ref: Sec. 2.8*

40) If the velocity versus time graph of an object is a straight line making an angle of 30 degrees with the time axis, the object is

A) moving with constant non-zero speed.

B) moving with constant non-zero acceleration.

C) at rest.

D) moving with infinite speed.

Answer: B
Diff: 1 *Page Ref: Sec. 2.8*

Quantitative Problems

1) An object moves 15.0 m north and then 11.0 m south. Find both the distance traveled and the magnitude of the displacement vector.

A) 6.0 m, 26.0 m

B) 26.0 m, 6.0 m

C) 26.0 m, 26.0 m

D) 6.0 m, 6.0 m

Answer: B
Diff: 1 *Page Ref: Sec 2.1*

2) A boat can move at 30 km/h in still water. How long will it take to move 12 km upstream in a river flowing 6.0 km/h?

A) 20 min

B) 22 min

C) 24 min

D) 30 min

Answer: D
Diff: 2 *Page Ref: Sec. 2.1-2.3*

3) 55 mi/h is how many m/s? (1 mi = 1609 m.)

A) 25 m/s

B) 49 m/s

C) 90 m/s

D) 120 m/s

Answer: A
Diff: 1 *Page Ref: Sec. 2.2-2.3*

4) What must be your average speed in order to travel 350 km in 5.15 h?

A) 66.0 km/h

B) 67.0 km/h

C) 68.0 km/h

D) 69.0 km/h

Answer: C
Diff: 1 *Page Ref: Sec. 2.2-2.3*

5) A runner ran the marathon (approximately 42.0 km) in 2 hours and 57 min. What is the average speed of the runner in m/s?

A) 14.2×10^3 m/s

B) 124 m/s

C) 3.95 m/s

D) 14.2 m/s

Answer: C
Diff: 2 *Page Ref: Sec. 2.2–2.3*

6) A car travels 90 km/h. How long does it take for it to travel 400 km?

A) 4.1 h

B) 4.2 h

C) 4.3 h

D) 4.4 h

Answer: D
Diff: 1 *Page Ref: Sec. 2.2–2.3*

7) A ly (light year) is the distance that light travels in one year. The speed of light is 3.00×10^8 m/s. How many miles are there in a ly? (1 mi = 1609 m, 1 yr = 365 d.)

A) 9.46×10^{12} mi

B) 9.46×10^{15} mi

C) 5.88×10^{12} mi

D) 5.88×10^{15} mi

Answer: C
Diff: 2 *Page Ref: Sec. 2.2–2.3*

8) If you are driving 72 km/h along a straight road and you look to the side for 4.0 s, how far do you travel during this inattentive period?

A) 18 m

B) 20 m

C) 40 m

D) 80 m

Answer: D
Diff: 1 *Page Ref: Sec. 2.2–2.3*

9) If you run a complete loop around an outdoor track (400 m), in 100 s, your average velocity is

A) 0.25 m/s.

B) 4.0 m/s.

C) 40,000 m/s.

D) zero.

Answer: D
Diff: 2 *Page Ref: Sec. 2.2–2.3*

10) A polar bear starts at the North Pole. It travels 1.0 km south, then 1.0 km east, then 1.0 km north, then 1.0 km west to return to its starting point. This trip takes 45 min. What was the bear's average speed?

A) 0 km/h

B) 0.09 km/h

C) 4.5 km/h

D) 5.3 km/h

Answer: D
Diff: 1 *Page Ref: Sec. 2.2–2.3*

11) A polar bear starts at the North Pole. It travels 1.0 km south, then 1.0 km east, then 1.0 km north, then 1.0 km west to return to its starting point. This trip takes 45 min. What was the bear's average velocity?

A) 0 km/h

B) 0.09 km/h

C) 4.5 km/h

D) 5.3 km/h

Answer: A
Diff: 2 *Page Ref: Sec. 2.2–2.3*

12) You are driving home on a weekend from school at 55 mi/h for 110 miles. It then starts to snow and you slow to 35 mi/h. You arrive home after driving 4 hours and 15 minutes. How far is your hometown from school?

A) 180 mi

B) 190 mi

C) 200 mi

D) 210 mi

Answer: B
Diff: 2 *Page Ref: Sec. 2.2–2.3*

13) A motorist travels 160 km at 80 km/h and 160 km at 100 km/h. What is the average speed of the motorist for this trip?

A) 84 km/h

B) 89 km/h

C) 90 km/h

D) 91 km/h

Answer: B
Diff: 2 *Page Ref: Sec. 2.2–2.3*

14) A motorist travels for 3.0 h at 80 km/h and 2.0 h at 100 km/h. What is her average speed for the trip?

A) 85 km/h

B) 88 km/h

C) 90 km/h

D) 92 km/h

Answer: B
Diff: 2 *Page Ref: Sec. 2.2–2.3*

15) An airplane travels at 300 mi/h south for 2.00 h and then at 250 mi/h north for 750 miles. What is the average speed for the trip?

A) 260 mi/h

B) 270 mi/h

C) 275 mi/h

D) 280 mi/h

Answer: B
Diff: 2 *Page Ref: Sec. 2.2–2.3*

16) In a 400–m relay race the anchorman (the person who runs the last 100 m) for team A can run 100 m in 9.8 s. His rival, the anchorman for team B, can cover 100 m in 10.1 s. What is the largest lead the team B runner can have when the team A runner starts the final leg of the race, in order that the team A runner not lose the race?

A) 2.0 m

B) 3.0 m

C) 4.0 m

D) 5.0 m

Answer: B
Diff: 3 *Page Ref: Sec. 2.2–2.3*

17) A car decelerates uniformly and comes to a stop after 10 s. The car's average velocity during deceleration was 50 km/h. What was the car's deceleration while slowing down?

A) 10 km/h–s

B) 8.0 km/h–s

C) 5.0 km/h–s

D) 4.0 km/h–s

Answer: A
Diff: 1 *Page Ref: Sec. 2.4*

18) An airplane increases its speed from 100 m/s to 160 m/s, at the average rate of 15 m/s^2. How much time does it take for the complete increase in speed?

A) 17 s

B) 0.058 s

C) 4.0 s

D) 0.25 s

Answer: C
Diff: 1 *Page Ref: Sec. 2.4*

19) A car traveling 60 km/h accelerates at the rate of 2.0 m/s^2. How much time is required for the car to reach a speed of 90 km/h?

A) 15 s

B) 30 s

C) 45 s

D) 4.2 s

Answer: D
Diff: 1 *Page Ref: Sec. 2.4*

20) A cart starts from rest and accelerates at 4.0 m/s^2 for 5.0 s, then maintain that velocity for 10 s, and then decelerates at the rate of 2.0 m/s^2 for 4.0 s. What is the final speed of the car?

A) 20 m/s

B) 16 m/s

C) 12 m/s

D) 10 m/s

Answer: C
Diff: 2 *Page Ref: Sec. 2.4*

21) A car travels at 15 m/s for 10 s. It then speeds up with a constant acceleration of 2.0 m/s^2 for 15 s. At the end of this time, what is its velocity?

A) 15 m/s

B) 30 m/s

C) 45 m/s

D) 375 m/s

Answer: C
Diff: 2 *Page Ref: Sec. 2.4*

22) A cart with an initial velocity of 5.0 m/s experiences a constant acceleration of 2.0 m/s^2. What is the cart's displacement during the first 6.0 s of its motion?

A) 10 m

B) 55 m

C) 66 m

D) 80 m

Answer: C
Diff: 1 *Page Ref: Sec 2.5–2.6*

23) A bullet moving horizontally to the right (+*x* direction) with a speed of 500 m/s strikes a sandbag and penetrates a distance of 10.0 cm. What is the average acceleration, in m/s^2, of the bullet?

A) -1.25×10^6

B) -2.50×10^6

C) -1.25×10^3

D) -2.50×10^3

Answer: A
Diff: 2 *Page Ref: Sec. 2.5–2.6*

24) A jet fighter plane is launched from a catapult on an aircraft carrier. It reaches a speed of 42 m/s at the end of the catapult, and this requires 2.0 s. Assuming the acceleration is constant, what is the length of the catapult?

A) 16 m

B) 24 m

C) 42 m

D) 84 m

Answer: C
Diff: 2 *Page Ref: Sec. 2.5–2.6*

25) A car starting from rest moves with constant acceleration of 2.0 m/s^2 for 10 s, then travels with constant speed for another 10 s, and then finally slows to a stop with constant acceleration of -2.0 m/s^2. How far does it travel?

A) 200 m

B) 300 m

C) 400 m

D) 500 m

Answer: C
Diff: 2 *Page Ref: Sec. 2.5–2.6*

26) A car goes from 40 m/s to 80 m/s in a distance of 200 m. What is its average acceleration?

A) 8.0 m/s^2

B) 9.6 m/s^2

C) 12 m/s^2

D) 24 m/s^2

Answer: C

Diff: 2 *Page Ref: Sec. 2.5–2.6*

27) An object starts from rest and undergoes uniform acceleration. During the first second it travels 5.0 m. How far will it travel during the third second?

A) 5.0 m

B) 15 m

C) 25 m

D) 45 m

Answer: C

Diff: 2 *Page Ref: Sec. 2.5–2.6*

28) An object is moving in a straight line with constant acceleration. Initially it is traveling at 16 m/s. Three seconds later it is traveling at 10 m/s. How far does it move during this time?

A) 30 m

B) 39 m

C) 48 m

D) 57 m

Answer: B

Diff: 2 *Page Ref: Sec. 2.5–2.6*

29) A car starts from rest and accelerates uniformly at 3.0 m/s^2. A second car starts from rest 6.0 s later at the same point and accelerates uniformly at 5.0 m/s^2. How long does it take the second car to overtake the first car?

A) 12 s

B) 19 s

C) 21 s

D) 24 s

Answer: C

Diff: 3 *Page Ref: Sec. 2.5–2.6*

30) A car with good tires on a dry road can decelerate at about 5.0 m/s^2 when braking. Suppose a car is initially traveling at 55 mi/h.

(a.) How much time does it take the car to stop?

(b.) What is the stopping distance?

Answer: (a.) 4.9 s

(b.) 60 m

Diff: 1 *Page Ref: Sec. 2.5–2.6*

31) At the instant a traffic light turns green, a car that has been waiting at the intersection starts ahead with a constant acceleration of 2.00 m/s^2. At that moment a truck traveling with a constant velocity of 15.0 m/s overtakes and passes the car.
(a.) Calculate the time necessary for the car to reach the truck.
(b.) Calculate the distance beyond the traffic light that the car will pass the truck.
(c.) Determine the speed of the car when it passes the truck.

Answer: (a.) 15.0 s
(b.) 225 m
(c.) 30.0 m/s
Diff: 3 *Page Ref: Sec. 2.5–2.6*

32) An object is thrown upward with a speed of 12 m/s on the surface of planet X where the acceleration due to gravity is 1.5 m/s^2. What is the maximum height reached by the object?

A) 8.0 m
B) 18 m
C) 48 m
D) 144 m

Answer: C
Diff: 1 *Page Ref: Sec. 2.7*

33) An object is thrown upward with a speed of 12 m/s on the surface of planet X where the acceleration due to gravity is 1.5 m/s^2. How long does it take for the object to reach the maximum height?

A) 8.0 s
B) 11 s
C) 14 s
D) 16 s

Answer: A
Diff: 1 *Page Ref: Sec. 2.7*

34) An object is thrown upward with a speed of 15 m/s on the surface of planet X where the acceleration due to gravity is 2.5 m/s^2. How long does it take for the object to return to where it is thrown?

A) 6.0 s
B) 8.0 s
C) 10 s
D) 12 s

Answer: D
Diff: 1 *Page Ref: Sec. 2.7*

35) An object is thrown upward with a speed of 14 m/s on the surface of planet X where the acceleration due to gravity is 3.5 m/s^2. What is the speed of the object after 8.0 s?

A) 7.0 m/s

B) 14 m/s

C) 21 m/s

D) 64 m/s

Answer: B
Diff: 1 *Page Ref: Sec. 2.7*

36) Human reaction time is usually greater than 0.10 s. If your friend holds a ruler between your fingers and releases it without warning, how far can you expect the ruler to fall before you catch it?

A) at least 3.0 cm

B) at least 4.9 cm

C) at least 6.8 cm

D) at least 9.8 cm

Answer: B
Diff: 1 *Page Ref: Sec. 2.7*

37) A ball is thrown upward at a velocity of 19.6 m/s. What is its velocity after 3.00 s?

A) 9.8 m/s upward

B) 9.8 m/s downward

C) zero

D) 19.6 downward

Answer: B
Diff: 1 *Page Ref: Sec. 2.7*

38) A bullet shot straight up returns to its starting point in 10 s. What is the initial speed of the bullet?

A) 9.8 m/s

B) 25 m/s

C) 49 m/s

D) 98 m/s

Answer: C
Diff: 1 *Page Ref: Sec. 2.7*

39) A ball is thrown straight up with a speed of 36.0 m/s. How long does it take to return to its starting point?

A) 3.67 s

B) 7.35 s

C) 11.0 s

D) 14.7 s

Answer: B
Diff: 1 *Page Ref: Sec. 2.7*

40) A ball is thrown downward from the top of a building with an initial speed of 25 m/s. It strikes the ground after 2.0 s. How high is the building?

A) 20 m

B) 30 m

C) 50 m

D) 70 m

Answer: D
Diff: 2 *Page Ref: Sec. 2.7*

41) A ball is thrown straight up with a speed of 30 m/s.
(a.) How long does it take the ball to reach the maximum height?
(b.) What is the maximum height reached by the ball?
(c.) What is its speed after 4.2 s?

Answer: (a.) 3.1 s
(b.) 46 m
(c.) 11 m/s
Diff: 1 *Page Ref: Sec. 2.7*

42) A foul ball is hit straight up into the air with a speed of 30.0 m/s.
(a.) Calculate the time required for the ball to rise to its maximum height.
(b.) Calculate the maximum height reached by the ball.
(c.) Determine the time at which the ball pass a point 25.0 m above the point of contact between the bat and ball.
(d.) Explain why there are two answers to part c.

Answer: (a.) 3.06 s
(b.) 45.9 m
(c.) 0.995 s and 5.13 s
(d.) One value for the ball traveling upward; one value for the ball traveling downward.
Diff: 2 *Page Ref: Sec. 2.7*

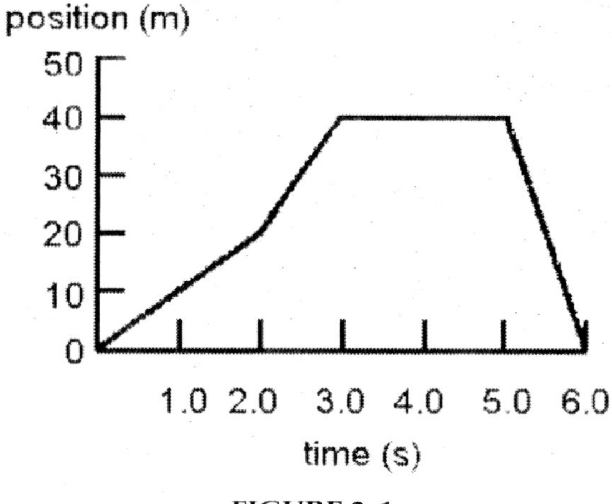

FIGURE 2-1

43) In Fig. 2-1, what is the velocity at t = 1.0 s?

A) 0

B) 10 m/s

C) 20 m/s

D) -40 m/s

Answer: B

Diff: 1 *Page Ref: Sec. 2.8*

44) In Fig. 2-1, what is the velocity at t = 2.5 s?

A) 0

B) 10 m/s

C) 20 m/s

D) -40 m/s

Answer: C

Diff: 1 *Page Ref: Sec. 2.8*

45) In Fig. 2-1, what is the velocity at t = 4.0 s?

A) 0

B) 10 m/s

C) 20 m/s

D) -40 m/s

Answer: A

Diff: 1 *Page Ref: Sec. 2.8*

46) In Fig. 2-1, what is the velocity at t = 5.5 s?

A) 0

B) 10 m/s

C) 20 m/s

D) -40 m/s

Answer: D
Diff: 1 *Page Ref: Sec. 2.8*

47) In Fig. 2-1, what is the average velocity from 0 to 4.0 s?

A) 0

B) 10 m/s

C) 20 m/s

D) -40 m/s

Answer: B
Diff: 1 *Page Ref: Sec. 2.8*

48) In Fig. 2-1, what is the average velocity from 0 to 6.0 s?

A) 0

B) 10 m/s

C) 20 m/s

D) -40 m/s

Answer: A
Diff: 1 *Page Ref: Sec. 2.8*

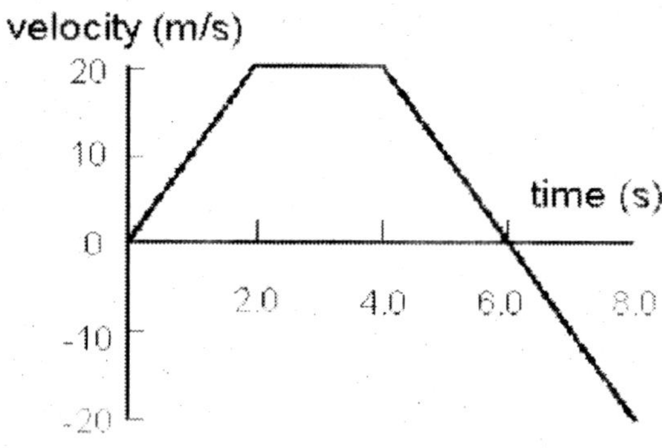

FIGURE 2-2

49) In Fig. 2-2, what is the acceleration at 1.0 s?

A) 0

B) 2.0 m/s^2

C) -2.5 m/s^2

D) 10 m/s^2

Answer: D

Diff: 1 *Page Ref: Sec. 2.8*

50) In Fig. 2-2, what is the acceleration at 3.0 s?

A) 0

B) 2.0 m/s^2

C) -2.5 m/s^2

D) 10 m/s^2

Answer: A

Diff: 1 *Page Ref: Sec. 2.8*

51) In Fig. 2-2, what is the average acceleration from 0 to 5.0 s?

A) 0

B) 2.0 m/s^2

C) -2.5 m/s^2

D) 10 m/s^2

Answer: B

Diff: 1 *Page Ref: Sec. 2.8*

52) In Fig. 2-2, what is the average acceleration from 0 to 8.0 s?

A) 0

B) 2.0 m/s^2

C) -2.5 m/s^2

D) 10 m/s^2

Answer: C
Diff: 1 *Page Ref: Sec. 2.8*

53) In Fig. 2-2, what is the displacement from 0 to 8.0 s?

A) 20 m

B) 40 m

C) 60 m

D) 80 m

Answer: C
Diff: 1 *Page Ref: Sec. 2.8*

Chapter 3 Kinematics in Two Dimensions; Vectors

Conceptual Questions

1) Which one of the following is an example of a vector quantity?

A) distance

B) velocity

C) mass

D) area

Answer: B
Diff: 1 *Page Ref: Sec. 3.1*

2) Which of the following operations will not change a vector?

A) Translate it parallel to itself.

B) Rotate it.

C) Multiply it by a constant factor.

D) Add a constant vector to it.

Answer: A
Diff: 1 *Page Ref: Sec. 3.2–3.4*

3) Which of the following is an accurate statement?

A) A vector cannot have zero magnitude if one of its components is not zero.

B) The magnitude of a vector can be less than the magnitude of one of its components.

C) If the magnitude of vector A is less than the magnitude of vector B, then the x–component of A is less than the x–component of B.

D) The magnitude of a vector can be positive or negative.

Answer: A
Diff: 1 *Page Ref: Sec. 3.2–3.4*

4) The resultant of two vectors is the smallest when the angle between them is

A) $0°$.

B) $45°$.

C) $90°$.

D) $180°$.

Answer: D
Diff: 1 *Page Ref: Sec. 3.2–3.4*

5) Two displacement vectors have magnitudes of 5.0 m and 7.0 m, respectively. When these two vectors are added, the magnitude of the sum

A) is 2.0 m.

B) could be as small as 2.0 m, or as large as 12 m.

C) is 12 m.

D) is larger than 12 m.

Answer: B
Diff: 1 *Page Ref: Sec. 3.2–3.4*

6) Two vectors, of magnitudes 20 and 50, are added. Which one of the following is a possible answer for the magnitude of the resultant?

A) 10

B) 20

C) 40

D) 80

Answer: C
Diff: 1 *Page Ref: Sec. 3.2–3.4*

7) Three forces, each having a magnitude of 30 N, pull on an object in directions that are 120° apart from each other. Make a statement concerning the resultant force.

A) The resultant force is zero.

B) The resultant force is greater than 30 N.

C) The resultant force is equal to 30 N.

D) The resultant force is less than 30 N.

Answer: A
Diff: 2 *Page Ref: Sec. 3.2–3.4*

8) In the diagram shown, the unknown vector is

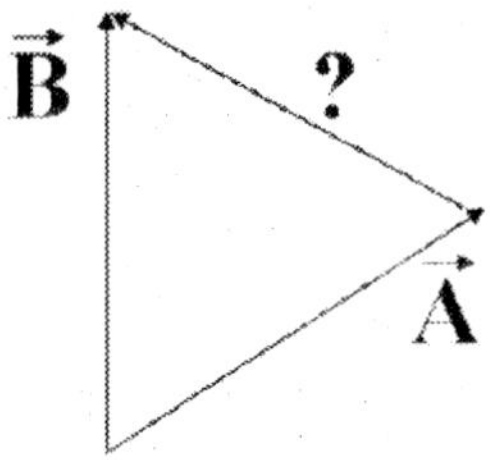

Diagram 1

A) $\vec{A} + \vec{B}$.

B) $\vec{A} - \vec{B}$.

C) $\vec{B} - \vec{A}$.

D) $\vec{A} \times \vec{B}$.

Answer: C
Diff: 1 *Page Ref: Sec. 3.2–3.4*

9) Ignoring air resistance, the horizontal component of a projectile's velocity

A) is zero.

B) remains constant.

C) continuously increases.

D) continuously decreases.

Answer: B
Diff: 1 *Page Ref: Sec. 3.5–3.6*

10) A ball is thrown with a velocity of 20 m/s at an angle of 60° above the horizontal. What is the horizontal component of its instantaneous velocity at the exact top of its trajectory?

A) 10 m/s

B) 17 m/s

C) 20 m/s

D) zero

Answer: A
Diff: 1 *Page Ref: Sec. 3.5–3.6*

11) Ignoring air resistance, the horizontal component of a projectile's acceleration

A) is zero.

B) remains a non-zero constant.

C) continuously increases.

D) continuously decreases.

Answer: A
Diff: 1 *Page Ref: Sec. 3.5–3.6*

12) A soccer ball is kicked with a velocity of 25 m/s at an angle of 45° above the horizontal. What is the vertical component of its acceleration as it travels along its trajectory?

A) 9.80 m/s^2 downward

B) (9.80 m/s^2) × sin (45°) downward

C) (9.80 m/s^2) × sin (45°) upward

D) (9.80 m/s^2) upward

Answer: A

Diff: 1 *Page Ref: Sec. 3.5–3.6*

13) If the acceleration vector of an object is directed anti-parallel to the velocity vector,

A) the object is turning.

B) the object is speeding up.

C) the object is slowing down.

D) the object is moving in the negative x-direction.

Answer: C

Diff: 1 *Page Ref: Sec. 3.5–3.6*

14) If the acceleration of an object is always directed perpendicular to its velocity,

A) the object is speeding up.

B) the object is slowing down.

C) the object is turning.

D) this situation would not be physically possible.

Answer: C

Diff: 2 *Page Ref: Sec. 3.5–3.6*

15) At what angle should a water-gun be aimed in order for the water to land with the greatest horizontal range?

A) 0°

B) 30°

C) 45°

D) 60°

Answer: C

Diff: 1 *Page Ref: Sec. 3.5–3.6*

16) An Olympic athlete throws a javelin at four different angles above the horizontal, each with the same speed: 30°, 40°, 60°, and 80°. Which two throws cause the javelin to land the same distance away?

A) 30° and 80°

B) 40° and 60°

C) 40° and 80°

D) 30° and 60°

Answer: D
Diff: 2 *Page Ref:* Sec. 3.5–3.6

17) You are throwing a ball for the second time. If the ball leaves your hand with twice the velocity it had on your first throw, its horizontal range R (compared to your first serve) would be

A) 1.4 times as much.

B) half as much.

C) twice as much.

D) four times as much.

Answer: D
Diff: 2 *Page Ref:* Sec. 3.5–3.6

18) A ball is thrown at an original speed of 8.0 m/s at an angle of 35° above the horizontal. What is the speed of the ball when it returns to the same horizontal level?

A) 4.0 m/s

B) 8.0 m/s

C) 16 m/s

D) 9.8 m/s

Answer: B
Diff: 1 *Page Ref:* Sec. 3.5–3.6

19) When a football in a field goal attempt reaches its maximum height, how does its speed compare to its initial speed?

A) It is zero.

B) It is less than its initial speed.

C) It is equal to its initial speed.

D) It is greater than its initial speed.

Answer: B
Diff: 2 *Page Ref:* Sec. 3.5–3.6

20) A stone is thrown horizontally from the top of a tower at the same instant a ball is dropped vertically. Which object is traveling faster when it hits the level ground below?

A) It is impossible to tell from the information given.

B) the stone

C) the ball

D) Neither, since both are traveling at the same speed.

Answer: B
Diff: 2 *Page Ref: Sec. 3.5–3.6*

21) A bullet is fired horizontally, and at the same instant a second bullet is dropped from the same height. Ignore air resistance. Compare the times of fall of the two bullets.

A) The fired bullet hits first.

B) The dropped bullet hits first.

C) They hit at the same time.

D) cannot tell without knowing the masses

Answer: C
Diff: 1 *Page Ref: Sec. 3.5–3.6*

22) A plane flying horizontally at a speed of 50.0 m/s and at an elevation of 160 m drops a package. Two seconds later it drops a second package. How far apart will the two packages land on the ground?

A) 100 m

B) 162 m

C) 177 m

D) 283 m

Answer: A
Diff: 2 *Page Ref: Sec. 3.5–3.6*

23) A package of supplies is dropped from a plane, and one second later a second package is dropped. Neglecting air resistance, the distance between the falling packages will

A) be constant.

B) decrease.

C) increase.

D) depend on their weight.

Answer: C
Diff: 2 *Page Ref: Sec. 3.5–3.6*

24) A pilot drops a bomb from a plane flying horizontally at a constant speed. Neglecting air resistance, when the bomb hits the ground the horizontal location of the plane will

A) be behind the bomb.

B) be over the bomb.

C) be in front of the bomb.

D) depend on the speed of the plane when the bomb was released.

Answer: B
Diff: 2   *Page Ref: Sec. 3.5–3.6*

25) The acceleration of gravity on the Moon is only one-sixth of that on Earth. If you hit a baseball on the Moon with the same effort (and at the speed and angle) that you would on Earth, the ball would land

A) the same distance away.

B) one-sixth as far.

C) 6 times as far.

D) 36 times as far.

Answer: C
Diff: 2   *Page Ref: Sec. 3.5–3.6*

26) You are traveling at 55 mi/h in the +x axis relative to a straight, level road and pass a car traveling at 45 mi/h. The relative velocity of your car to the other car is

A) -10 mi/h.

B) 10 mi/h.

C) 65 mi/h.

D) 35 mi/h.

Answer: B
Diff: 1   *Page Ref: Sec. 3.8*

27) You are trying to cross a river that flows due south with a strong current. You start out in your motorboat on the east bank desiring to reach the west bank directly west from your starting point. You should head your motorboat

A) due west.

B) due north.

C) in a southwesterly direction.

D) in a northwesterly direction.

Answer: D
Diff: 2   *Page Ref: Sec. 3.8*

28) Your motorboat can move at 30 km/h in still water. How much time will it take you to move 12 km downstream, in a river flowing at 6.0 km/h?

A) 20 min

B) 22 min

C) 24 min

D) 30 min

Answer: A
Diff: 1 *Page Ref: Sec. 3.8*

Quantitative Problems

1) Vector $\vec{\mathbf{A}}$ has magnitude 8.0 m at an angle of 30 degrees below the $+x$ axis. The y component of $\vec{\mathbf{A}}$ is

A) 6.9 m.

B) -6.9 m.

C) 4.0 m.

D) -4.0 m.

Answer: D
Diff: 1 *Page Ref: Sec. 3.2-3.4*

2) If a ball is thrown with a velocity of 25 m/s at an angle of 37° above the horizontal, what is the vertical component of the velocity?

A) 12 m/s

B) 15 m/s

C) 19 m/s

D) 25 m/s

Answer: B
Diff: 1 *Page Ref: Sec. 3.2-3.4*

3) If you walk 6.0 km in a straight line in a direction north of east and you end up 2.0 km north and several kilometers east. How many degrees north of east have you walked?

A) 19°

B) 45°

C) 60°

D) 71°

Answer: A
Diff: 2 *Page Ref: Sec. 3.2-3.4*

4) A butterfly moves with a speed of 12.0 m/s. The x component of its velocity is 8.00 m/s. The angle between the direction of its motion and the *x* axis must be

A) 30.0°.

B) 41.8°.

C) 48.2°.

D) 53.0°.

Answer: C
Diff: 2 *Page Ref: Sec. 3.2–3.4*

5) A 400–m tall tower casts a 600–m long shadow over a level ground. At what angle is the Sun elevated above the horizon?

A) 34°

B) 42°

C) 48°

D) can't be found; not enough information

Answer: A
Diff: 2 *Page Ref: Sec. 3.2–3.4*

6) Two vectors $\vec{\mathbf{A}}$ and $\vec{\mathbf{B}}$ have components (0, 1) and (–1, 3), respectively. What are the components of the sum of these two vectors?

A) (1, 4)

B) (–1, 4)

C) (1, 2)

D) (–1, 2)

Answer: B
Diff: 1 *Page Ref: Sec. 3.2–3.4*

7) Two vectors $\vec{\mathbf{A}}$ and $\vec{\mathbf{B}}$ have components (0, 1) and (–1, 3), respectively. What is magnitude of the sum of these two vectors?

A) 2.8

B) 3.2

C) 3.9

D) 4.1

Answer: D
Diff: 1 *Page Ref: Sec. 3.2–3.4*

8) Vector $\vec{\mathbf{A}} = (1, 3)$. Vector $\vec{\mathbf{B}} = (3, 0)$. Vector $\vec{\mathbf{C}} = \vec{\mathbf{A}} + \vec{\mathbf{B}}$. What is the magnitude of $\vec{\mathbf{C}}$?

A) 3

B) 4

C) 5

D) 7

Answer: C
Diff: 1 *Page Ref: Sec. 3.2–3.4*

9) A car travels 20 km West, then 20 km South. What is the magnitude of its displacement?

A) 0 km

B) 20 km

C) 28 km

D) 40 km

Answer: C
Diff: 1 *Page Ref: Sec. 3.2–3.4*

10) Three vectors, expressed in Cartesian coordinates, are

	x comp	*y* comp
$\vec{\mathbf{S}}$	-3.5	+4.5
$\vec{\mathbf{T}}$	0	-6.5
$\vec{\mathbf{U}}$	+5.5	-2.5

What is the magnitude of the resultant vector $\vec{\mathbf{S}} + \vec{\mathbf{T}} + \vec{\mathbf{U}}$?

A) 4.9

B) 24

C) 16

D) 18

Answer: A
Diff: 2 *Page Ref: Sec. 3.2–3.4*

11) Three vectors, expressed in Cartesian coordinates, are

	x comp	*y* comp
$\vec{\mathbf{S}}$	-3.5	+4.5
$\vec{\mathbf{T}}$	0	-6.5
$\vec{\mathbf{U}}$	+5.5	-2.5

What is the angle of the resultant vector $\vec{\mathbf{S}} + \vec{\mathbf{T}} + \vec{\mathbf{U}}$ measured from the positive *x* axis?

A) 24° above

B) 24° below

C) 66° above

D) 66° below

Answer: D
Diff: 2 *Page Ref: Sec. 3.2–3.4*

12) If vector $\vec{\mathbf{A}}$ = (-3.0, -4.0) and vector $\vec{\mathbf{B}}$ = (+3.0, -8.0), what is the magnitude of vector $\vec{\mathbf{C}} = \vec{\mathbf{A}} - \vec{\mathbf{B}}$?

A) 13

B) 16

C) 144

D) 7.2

Answer: D
Diff: 2 *Page Ref: Sec. 3.2–3.4*

13) A runner runs halfway around a circular path of radius 10 m. What is the displacement of the jogger?

A) 0

B) 5 m

C) 10 m

D) 20 m

Answer: D
Diff: 1 *Page Ref: Sec. 3.2–3.4*

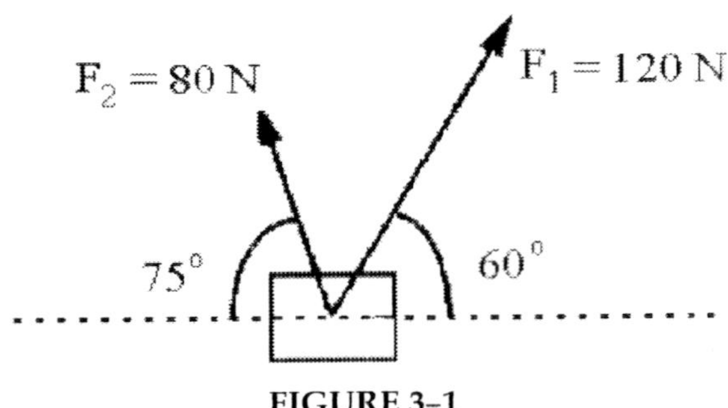

FIGURE 3–1

14) Two forces are acting on an object as shown in Fig. 3–1. What is the magnitude of the resultant force?

A) 47.5 N

B) 185 N

C) 198 N

D) 200 N

Answer: B
Diff: 2 *Page Ref: Sec. 3.2–3.4*

15) Two forces are acting on an object as shown in Fig. 3–1. What is the direction of the resultant force?

A) 12° above $-x$

B) 78° above $-x$

C) 12° above $+x$

D) 78° above $+x$

Answer: D
Diff: 2 *Page Ref: Sec. 3.2–3.4*

16) Vector $\vec{\mathbf{A}}$ is 5.5 cm long and points along the x axis. Vector $\vec{\mathbf{B}}$ is 7.5 cm long and points at +30° to the negative x axis.

(a) Determine the x and y components of Vector $\vec{\mathbf{A}}$.

(b) Determine the x and y components of Vector $\vec{\mathbf{B}}$.

(c) Determine the sum of these two vectors in terms of components.

(d) Determine the sum of these two vectors in terms of magnitude and direction.

Answer: (a) $A_x = 5.5$ cm, $A_y = 0$
(b) $B_x = -6.5$ cm, $B_y = 3.8$ cm
(c) $R_x = -1.0$ cm, $R_y = 3.8$ cm
(d) 3.9 cm at 75° above $-x$ axis
Diff: 2 *Page Ref: Sec. 3.2–3.4*

17) Vector $\vec{\mathbf{A}}$ is 75.0 cm long and points at 30° above the positive x axis. Vector $\vec{\mathbf{B}}$ is 25.0 cm long and points along the negative x axis. Vector $\vec{\mathbf{C}}$ is 40.0 cm long and points at 45° below the negative x axis.

(a) Determine the x and y components of Vector $\vec{\mathbf{A}}$.
(b) Determine the x and y components of Vector $\vec{\mathbf{B}}$.
(c) Determine the x and y components of Vector $\vec{\mathbf{C}}$.
(d) Determine the sum of these three vectors in terms of components.
(e) Determine the sum of these three vectors in terms of magnitude and direction.

Answer: (a) $A_x = 65$ cm, $A_y = 38$ cm
(b) $B_x = -25$ cm, $B_y = 0$
(c) $C_x = 21$ cm, $C_y = -21$ cm
(d) $R_x = 61$ cm, $R_y = 17$ cm
(e) 63 cm at 20° above x axis

Diff: 2 *Page Ref: Sec. 32–3.4*

18) A stone is thrown horizontally with an initial speed of 10 m/s from the edge of a cliff. A stop watch measures the stone's trajectory time from the top of the cliff to the bottom to be 4.3 s. What is the height of the cliff?

A) 22 m
B) 43 m
C) 77 m
D) 91 m

Answer: D
Diff: 1 *Page Ref: Sec. 3.5–3.6*

19) A girl throws a rock horizontally, with a velocity of 10 m/s, from a bridge. It falls 20 m to the water below. How far does the rock travel horizontally before striking the water?

A) 14 m
B) 16 m
C) 20 m
D) 24 m

Answer: C
Diff: 2 *Page Ref: Sec. 3.5–3.6*

20) A ball thrown horizontally from a point 24 m above the ground, strikes the ground after traveling horizontally a distance of 18 m. With what speed was it thrown?

A) 6.1 m/s
B) 7.4 m/s
C) 8.1 m/s
D) 8.9 m/s

Answer: C
Diff: 2 *Page Ref: Sec. 3.5–3.6*

21) A jumper in the long-jump goes into the jump with a speed of 12 m/s at an angle of 20° above the horizontal. How long is the jumper in the air before returning to the Earth?

A) 0.21 s

B) 0.42 s

C) 0.84 s

D) 1.3 s

Answer: C
Diff: 2 *Page Ref: Sec. 3.5-3.6*

22) A jumper in the long-jump goes into the jump with a speed of 12 m/s at an angle of 20° above the horizontal. How far does the jumper jump?

A) 3.4 m

B) 6.2 m

C) 9.4 m

D) 15 m

Answer: C
Diff: 2 *Page Ref: Sec. 3.5-3.6*

23) A projectile is launched with an initial velocity of 60.0 m/s at an angle of 30.0° above the horizontal. How far does it travel?

A) 152 m

B) 160 m

C) 184 m

D) 318 m

Answer: D
Diff: 2 *Page Ref: Sec. 3.5-3.6*

24) A projectile is launched with an initial velocity of 60.0 m/s at an angle of 30.0° above the horizontal. What is the maximum height reached by the projectile?

A) 23 m

B) 46 m

C) 69 m

D) 92 m

Answer: B
Diff: 2 *Page Ref: Sec. 3.5-3.6*

25) A rifle bullet is fired at an angle of 30° below the horizontal with an initial velocity of 800 m/s from the top of a cliff 80 m high. How far from the base of the cliff does it strike the level ground below?

A) 130 m

B) 140 m

C) 150 m

D) 160 m

Answer: B
Diff: 3 *Page Ref: Sec 3.5–3.6*

26) A projectile is shot horizontally at 23.4 m/s from the roof of a building 55.0 m tall.
(a) Determine the time necessary for the projectile to reach the ground below.
(b) Determine the distance from the base of the building that the projectile lands.
(c) Determine the horizontal and vertical components of the velocity just before the projectile reaches the ground.

Answer: (a) 3.35 s
(b) 78.4 m
(c) $v_{horizontal} = 23.4$ m/s, $v_{vertical} = 32.8$ m/s
Diff: 2 *Page Ref: Sec. 3.5–3.6*

27) A projectile is fired from ground level with an initial speed of 55.6 m/s at an angle of 41.2° above the horizontal.
(a) Determine the time necessary for the projectile to reach its maximum height.
(b) Determine the maximum height reached by the projectile.
(c) Determine the horizontal and vertical components of the velocity vector at the maximum height.
(d) Determine the horizontal and vertical components of the acceleration vector at the maximum height.

Answer: (a) 3.73 s
(b) 68.3 m
(c) $v_{horizontal} = 41.8$ m/s, $v_{vertical} = 0$
(d) $a_{horizontal} = 0$, $a_{vertical} = -9.8$ m/s2
Diff: 2 *Page Ref: Sec. 3.4–3.5*

28) On a calm day (no wind), you can run a 1500-m race at a velocity of 4.0 m/s. If you ran the same race on a day when you had a constant headwind which slows your speed by 2.0 m/s, the time it would take you to finish would be

A) 250 s.

B) 750 s.

C) 1125 s.

D) 9000 s.

Answer: B
Diff: 1 *Page Ref: Sec. 3.8*

29) A plane has an air speed of 200 m/s due North, and is in a wind of 50.0 m/s to the West. The plane's speed relative to the ground is

A) 150 m/s.

B) 200 m/s.

C) 206 m/s.

D) 250 m/s.

Answer: C
Diff: 1 *Page Ref: Sec. 3.8*

30) A plane is flying due South (270°) at 500 km/h. A wind blows from East to West (180°) at 45.0 km/h. Find the plane's velocity with respect to the ground.

A) 502 km/h at 265°

B) 502 km/h at 85°

C) 520 km/h at 5°

D) 545 km/h at 265°

Answer: A
Diff: 2 *Page Ref: Sec. 3.8*

31) An airplane with a speed of 120 km/h is headed 30.0° east of north in a wind blowing due west at 30.0 km/h. What is the speed of the plane relative to the ground?

A) 90.0 km/h

B) 110 km/h

C) 137 km/h

D) 150 km/h

Answer: B
Diff: 2 *Page Ref: Sec. 3.8*

32) A fighter plane moving 200 m/s horizontally fires a projectile with speed 50.0 m/s in a forward direction 30.0° below the horizontal. What is the speed of the projectile with respect to a stationary observer on the ground?

A) 245 m/s

B) 250 m/s

C) 268 m/s

D) 293 m/s

Answer: A
Diff: 2 *Page Ref: Sec. 3.8*

33) A boat, whose speed in still water is 8.0 m/s, is directed across a river with a current of 6.0 m/s. What is the speed of the boat as it crosses the river?

A) 5.3 m/s

B) 6.0 m/s

C) 8.0 m/s

D) 10.0 m/s

Answer: D
Diff: 1 *Page Ref: Sec. 3.8*

34) The driver of a motorboat that can move at 10 m/s in still water wishes to travel directly across a river 1.6 km wide in which the current flows at 5.0 m/s. How long will it take to cross the river?

A) 5.3 min

B) 2.7 min

C) 2.4 min

D) 1.8 min

Answer: C
Diff: 2 *Page Ref: Sec. 3.8*

35) The driver of a motorboat that can move at 10 m/s in still water wishes to travel directly across a narrow strait in which the current flows at 5.0 m/s. At what angle upstream should the driver head the boat?

A) 27°

B) 30°

C) 60°

D) 63°

Answer: B
Diff: 2 *Page Ref: Sec. 3.8*

36) A swimmer heading directly across a river 200 m wide reaches the opposite bank in 6 min 40 s. She is swept downstream 480 m. How fast can she swim in still water?

A) 0.50 m/s

B) 1.2 m/s

C) 1.4 m/s

D) 1.8 m/s

Answer: A
Diff: 3 *Page Ref: Sec. 3.8*

37) A swimmer heading directly across a river 200 m wide reaches the opposite bank in 6 min 40 s. She is swept downstream 480 m. What is the speed of the current?

A) 0.50 m/s

B) 1.2 m/s

C) 1.4 m/s

D) 1.8 m/s

Answer: B
Diff: 3 *Page Ref: Sec. 3.8*

38) A boat, whose speed in still water is 1.75 m/s, must aim upstream at an angle of 26.3° (with respect to a line perpendicular to the shore) in order to travel directly across the stream.
(a) Determine the speed of the current.
(b) Determine the resultant speed of the boat with respect to the shore.

Answer: (a) 0.775 m/s
(b) 1.57 m/s
Diff: 2 *Page Ref: Sec. 3.8*

Chapter 4 Dynamics: Newton's Laws of Motion

Conceptual Questions

1) Which of Newton's laws best explains why motorists should buckle-up?

A) the first law

B) the second law

C) the third law

D) the law of gravitation

Answer: A
Diff: 1 *Page Ref: Sec. 4.1-4.5*

2) When you sit on a chair, the resultant force on you is

A) zero.

B) up.

C) down.

D) depending on your weight.

Answer: A
Diff: 1 *Page Ref: Sec. 4.1-4.5*

3) In the absence of an external force, a moving object will

A) stop immediately.

B) slow down and eventually come to a stop.

C) go faster and faster.

D) move with constant velocity.

Answer: D
Diff: 1 *Page Ref: Sec. 4.1-4.5*

4) When the rocket engines on the starship NO-PAIN-NO-GAIN are suddenly turned off, while traveling in empty space, the starship will

A) stop immediately.

B) slowly slow down, and then stop.

C) go faster and faster.

D) move with constant speed.

Answer: D
Diff: 1 *Page Ref: Sec. 4.1-4.5*

5) A rocket moves through empty space in a straight line with constant speed. It is far from the gravitational effect of any star or planet. Under these conditions, the force that must be applied to the rocket in order to sustain its motion is

A) equal to its weight.

B) equal to its mass.

C) dependent on how fast it is moving.

D) zero.

Answer: D
Diff: 1 *Page Ref: Sec. 4.1–4.5*

6) You are standing in a moving bus, facing forward, and you suddenly fall forward. You can imply from this that the bus's

A) velocity decreased.

B) velocity increased.

C) speed remained the same, but it's turning to the right.

D) speed remained the same, but it's turning to the left.

Answer: A
Diff: 1 *Page Ref: Sec. 4.1–4.5*

7) You are standing in a moving bus, facing forward, and you suddenly fall forward as the bus comes to an immediate stop. What force caused you to fall forward?

A) gravity

B) normal force due to your contact with the floor of the bus

C) force due to friction between you and the floor of the bus

D) There is **not** a force leading to your fall.

Answer: D
Diff: 2 *Page Ref: Sec. 4.1–4.5*

8) A constant net force acts on an object. Describe the motion of the object.

A) constant acceleration

B) constant speed

C) constant velocity

D) increasing acceleration

Answer: A
Diff: 1 *Page Ref: Sec. 4.1–4.5*

9) The acceleration of an object is inversely proportional to

A) the net force acting on it.

B) its position.

C) its velocity.

D) its mass.

Answer: D
Diff: 1 *Page Ref: Sec. 4.1-4.6*

10) A net force F accelerates a mass m with an acceleration a. If the same net force is applied to mass 2m, then the acceleration will be

A) 4a.

B) 2a.

C) a/2.

D) a/4.

Answer: C
Diff: 1 *Page Ref: Sec. 4.1-4.5*

11) A net force F acts on a mass m and produces an acceleration a. What acceleration results if a net force 2F acts on mass 4m?

A) a/2

B) 8a

C) 4a

D) 2a

Answer: D
Diff: 1 *Page Ref: Sec. 4.1-4.5*

12) If you blow up a balloon, and then release it, the balloon will fly away. This is an illustration of

A) Newton's first law.

B) Newton's second law.

C) Newton's third law.

D) Galileo's law of inertia.

Answer: C
Diff: 1 *Page Ref: Sec. 4.1-4.5*

13) Two cars collide head-on. At every moment during the collision, the magnitude of the force the first car exerts on the second is exactly equal to the magnitude of the force the second car exerts on the first. This is an example of

A) Newton's first law.

B) Newton's second law.

C) Newton's third law.

D) Newton's law of gravitation.

Answer: C
Diff: 1 *Page Ref: Sec. 4.1-4.5*

14) If you exert a force F on an object, the force which the object exerts on you will

A) depend on whether or not the object is moving.

B) depend on whether or not you are moving.

C) depend on the relative masses of you and the object.

D) always be F.

Answer: D
Diff: 1 *Page Ref: Sec. 4.1-4.5*

15) Action-reaction forces

A) sometimes act on the same object.

B) always act on the same object.

C) may be at right angles.

D) always act on different objects.

Answer: D
Diff: 1 *Page Ref: Sec. 4.1-4.5*

16) Action-reaction forces are

A) equal in magnitude and point in the same direction.

B) equal in magnitude but point in opposite directions.

C) unequal in magnitude but point in the same direction.

D) unequal in magnitude and point in opposite directions

Answer: B
Diff: 1 *Page Ref: Sec. 4.1-4.5*

17) A 20-ton truck collides with a 1500-lb car and causes a lot of damage to the car. Since a lot of damage is done on the car

A) the force on the truck is greater then the force on the car.

B) the force on the truck is equal to the force on the car.

C) the force on the truck is smaller than the force on the car.

D) the truck did not slow down during the collision.

Answer: B
Diff: 1 *Page Ref: Sec. 4.1-4.5*

18) An object of mass m sits on a flat table. The Earth pulls on this object with force mg, which we will call the action force. What is the reaction force?

A) The table pushing up on the object with force mg.

B) The object pushing down on the table with force mg.

C) The table pushing down on the floor with force mg.

D) The object pulling upward on the Earth with force mg.

Answer: D
Diff: 2 *Page Ref: Sec. 4.1–4.5*

19) A child's toy is suspended from the ceiling by means of a string. The Earth pulls downward on the toy with its weight force of 8.0 N. If this is the "action force," what is the "reaction force"?

A) The string pulling upward on the toy with an 8.0-N force.

B) The ceiling pulling upward on the string with an 8.0-N force.

C) The string pulling downward on the ceiling with an 8.0-N force.

D) The toy pulling upward on the Earth with an 8.0-N force.

Answer: D
Diff: 2 *Page Ref: Sec. 4.1–4.5*

20) A golf club hits a golf ball with a force of 2400 N. The golf ball hits the club with a force

A) slightly less than 2400 N.

B) exactly 2400 N.

C) slightly more than 2400 N.

D) close to 0 N.

Answer: B
Diff: 1 *Page Ref: Sec. 4.1–4.5*

21) Your bat hits the ball pitched to you with a 1500-N instantaneous force. The ball hits the bat with an instantaneous force, whose magnitude is

A) somewhat less than 1500 N.

B) somewhat greater than 1500 N.

C) exactly equal to 1500 N.

D) essentially zero.

Answer: C
Diff: 1 *Page Ref: Sec. 4.1–4.5*

22) State Newton's three laws.

Answer: Newton's first law: Every object continues in its state of rest, or of uniform velocity in a straight line, as long as no net force acts on it.

Newton's second law: The acceleration of an object is directly proportional to the net force acting on it, and is inversely proportional to its mass. The direction of the acceleration is in the direction of the net force acting on the object.

Newton's third law: Whenever one object exerts a force on a second object, the second exerts an equal force in the opposite direction on the first.

Diff: 1 *Page Ref: Sec. 4.1–4.5*

23) Mass and weight

A) both measure the same thing.

B) are exactly equal.

C) are two different quantities.

D) are both measured in kilograms.

Answer: C

Diff: 1 *Page Ref: Sec. 4.6*

24) The acceleration due to gravity is lower on the Moon than on Earth. Which of the following is true about the mass and weight of an astronaut on the Moon's surface, compared to Earth?

A) Mass is less, weight is same.

B) Mass is same, weight is less.

C) Both mass and weight are less.

D) Both mass and weight are the same.

Answer: B

Diff: 2 *Page Ref: Sec. 4.6*

25) An example of a force which acts at a distance is

A) tension.

B) weight.

C) static friction.

D) kinetic friction.

Answer: B

Diff: 1 *Page Ref: Sec. 4.6*

26) Who has a greater weight to mass ratio, a person weighing 400 N or a person weighing 600 N?

A) the person weighing 400 N

B) the person weighing 600 N

C) Neither; their ratios are the same.

D) The question can't be answered; not enough information is given.

Answer: C
Diff: 1 *Page Ref: Sec. 4.6*

27) A stone is thrown straight up. At the top of its path, the net force acting on it is

A) greater than its weight.

B) greater than zero, but less than its weight.

C) instantaneously equal to zero.

D) equal to its weight.

Answer: D
Diff: 1 *Page Ref: Sec. 4.6*

28) A 20-N weight and a 5.0-N weight are dropped simultaneously from the same height. Ignore air resistance. Compare their accelerations.

A) The 20 N weight accelerates faster because it is heavier.

B) The 20 N weight accelerates faster because it has more inertia.

C) The 5.0 N weight accelerates faster because it has a smaller mass.

D) They both accelerate at the same rate because they have the same weight to mass ratio.

Answer: D
Diff: 2 *Page Ref: Sec. 4.6*

29) A brick and a feather fall to the earth at their respective terminal velocities. Which object experiences the greater force of air friction?

A) the feather

B) the brick

C) Neither, both experience the same amount of air friction.

D) It cannot be determined because there is not enough information given.

Answer: B
Diff: 2 *Page Ref: Sec. 4.6*

30) An object of mass m is hanging by a string from the ceiling of an elevator. The elevator is moving up at constant speed. What is the tension in the string?

A) less than mg

B) exactly mg

C) greater than mg

D) cannot be determined without knowing the speed

Answer: B
Diff: 2 *Page Ref: Sec. 4.6*

31) An object of mass m is hanging by a string from the ceiling of an elevator. The elevator is moving upward, but slowing down. What is the tension in the string?

A) less than mg

B) exactly mg

C) greater than mg

D) zero

Answer: A
Diff: 2 *Page Ref: Sec. 4.6*

32) The force that keeps you from sliding on an icy sidewalk is

A) weight.

B) kinetic friction.

C) static friction.

D) normal force.

Answer: C
Diff: 2 *Page Ref: Sec. 4.8*

33) It's more difficult to start moving a heavy carton from rest than it is to keep pushing it with constant velocity, because

A) the normal force is greater when the carton is at rest.

B) $\mu_s < \mu_k$.

C) initially, the normal force is not perpendicular to the applied force.

D) $\mu_k < \mu_s$.

Answer: D
Diff: 1 *Page Ref: Sec. 4.8*

34) A horizontal force accelerates a box from rest across a horizontal surface (friction is present) at a constant rate. The experiment is repeated, and all conditions remain the same with the exception that the horizontal force is doubled. What happens to the box's acceleration?

A) It increases to more than double its original value.

B) It increases to exactly double its original value.

C) It increases to less than double its original value.

D) It increases somewhat.

Answer: A
Diff: 2 *Page Ref: Sec. 4.8*

35) A packing crate slides down an inclined ramp at constant velocity. Thus we can deduce that

A) a frictional force is acting on it.

B) a net downward force is acting on it.

C) it may be accelerating.

D) it is not acted on by appreciable gravitational force.

Answer: A
Diff: 1 *Page Ref: Sec. 4.8*

36) A block of mass M slides down a frictionless plane inclined at an angle θ with the horizontal. The normal reaction force exerted by the plane on the block is

A) Mg.

B) Mg sin θ.

C) Mg cos θ.

D) zero, since the plane is frictionless.

Answer: C
Diff: 1 *Page Ref: Sec. 4.8*

37) A block of mass M slides down a frictionless plane inclined at an angle θ with the horizontal. The normal reaction force exerted by the plane on the block is directed

A) parallel to the plane in the same direction as the movement of the block.

B) parallel to the plane in the opposite direction as the movement of the block

C) perpendicular to the plane.

D) toward the center of the Earth.

Answer: C
Diff: 1 *Page Ref: Sec. 4.8*

38) A block of mass M slides down a frictionless plane inclined at an angle θ with the horizontal. The gravitational force is directed

A) parallel to the plane in the same direction as the movement of the block.

B) parallel to the plane in the opposite direction as the movement of the block

C) perpendicular to the plane.

D) toward the center of the Earth.

Answer: D
Diff: 1 *Page Ref: Sec. 4.8*

39) Two toy cars (16 kg and 2.0 kg) are released simultaneously on an inclined plane that makes an angle of 30° with the horizontal. Make a statement which best describes their acceleration after being released.

A) The 16-kg car accelerates 8 times faster than the 2.0-kg car.

B) The 2.0-kg car accelerates 8 times faster than the 16-kg car.

C) Both cars accelerate at the same rate.

D) none of the above

Answer: C
Diff: 2 *Page Ref: Sec. 4.8*

Quantitative Problems

1) An object sits on a frictionless surface. A 16-N force is applied to the object, and it accelerates at 2.0 m/s^2. What is the mass of the object?

A) 4.0 kg

B) 8.0 kg

C) 32 kg

D) 78 N

Answer: B
Diff: 1 *Page Ref: Sec. 4.4-4.6*

2) A sports car of mass 1000 kg can accelerate from rest to 27 m/s in 7.0 s. What is the average forward force on the car?

A) 2.6×10^2 N

B) 3.9×10^3 N

C) 2.7×10^4 N

D) 1.9×10^5 N

Answer: B
Diff: 1 *Page Ref: Sec. 4.4-4.6*

3) Starting from rest, a 4.0-kg body reaches a speed of 8.0 m/s in 2.0 s. What is the net force acting on the body?

A) 4.0 N

B) 8.0 N

C) 16 N

D) 32 N

Answer: C
Diff: 2 *Page Ref: Sec. 4.4-4.6*

4) An antitank weapon fires a 3.00-kg rocket which acquires a speed of 50.0 m/s after traveling 90.0 cm down a launching tube. Assuming the rocket was accelerated uniformly, what is the average force acted on it?

A) 4.17×10^3 N

B) 3.62×10^3 N

C) 2.82×10^3 N

D) 2.00×10^3 N

Answer: A
Diff: 2 *Page Ref: Sec. 4.4-4.6*

5) If you push a 4.0-kg mass with the same force that you push a 10-kg mass from rest,

A) the 10-kg mass accelerates 2.5 times faster than the 4.0-kg mass.

B) the 4.0-kg mass accelerates 2.5 times faster than the 10-kg mass.

C) both masses accelerate at the same rate.

D) None of the above is true.

Answer: B
Diff: 1 *Page Ref: Sec. 4.4-4.6*

6) What is the mass of a person who weighs 110 lb?

A) 50 kg

B) 55 kg

C) 110 kg

D) 242 kg

Answer: A
Diff: 1 *Page Ref: Sec. 4.4-4.6*

7) What is the mass of an object that weighs 250 N on the surface of the Earth where the acceleration due to gravity is 9.80 m/s^2?

A) 250 kg

B) 24.5 kg

C) 25.5 kg

D) 2,450 kg

Answer: C
Diff: 1 *Page Ref: Sec. 4.4-4.6*

8) An object has a mass of 60 kg on the Earth. What is the mass of the object on the surface of the Moon where the acceleration due to gravity is only 1/6 of that on the Earth?

A) 6.0 kg

B) 10 kg

C) 60 kg

D) 360 kg

Answer: C
Diff: 1 Page Ref: Sec. 4.4-4.6

9) Object A weighs 40 N on Earth, and object B weighs 40 N on the Moon. The Moon's gravity is one sixth of Earth's. Compare the masses of the objects.

A) A has 6 times the mass of B.

B) B has 6 times the mass of A.

C) A and B have equal mass.

D) The situation as stated is impossible.

Answer: B
Diff: 2 Page Ref: Sec. 4.4-4.6

10) Sue and Sean are having a tug-of-war by pulling on opposite ends of a 5.0-kg rope. Sue pulls with a 15-N force. What is Sean's force if the rope accelerates toward Sue at 2.0 m/s^2?

A) 3.0 N

B) 5.0 N

C) 25 N

D) 50 N

Answer: B
Diff: 2 Page Ref: Sec. 4.4-4.6

11) A stack of books rests on a level frictionless surface. A force F acts on the stack, and it accelerates at 3.0 m/s^2. A 1.0 kg book is then added to the stack. The same force is applied, and now the stack accelerates at 2.0 m/s^2. What was the mass of the original stack?

A) 1.0 kg

B) 2.0 kg

C) 3.0 kg

D) none of the above

Answer: B
Diff: 2 Page Ref: Sec. 4.4-4.6

12) A person of weight 480 N stands on a scale in an elevator. What will the scale be reading when the elevator is accelerating downward at 4.00 m/s2?

A) 196 N

B) 284 N

C) 676 N

D) 480 N

Answer: B
Diff: 2 *Page Ref: Sec. 4.4–4.6*

13) A person on a scale rides in an elevator. If the mass of the person is 60.0 kg and the elevator accelerates downward with an acceleration of 4.90 m/s2, what is the reading on the scale?

A) 147 N

B) 294 N

C) 588 N

D) 882 N

Answer: B
Diff: 2 *Page Ref: Sec. 4.4–4.6*

14) A person on a scale rides in an elevator. If the mass of the person is 60.0 kg and the elevator accelerates upward with an acceleration of 4.90 m/s2, what is the reading on the scale?

A) 147 N

B) 294 N

C) 588 N

D) 882 N

Answer: D
Diff: 2 *Page Ref: Sec. 4.4–4.6*

15) Two horizontal forces act on a 5.0-kg mass. One force has a magnitude of 8.0 N and is directed due north. The second force toward the east has a magnitude of 6.0 N. What is the acceleration of the mass?

A) 1.6 m/s2 due north

B) 1.2 m/s2 due east

C) 2.0 m/s2 at 53° N of E

D) 2.0 m/s2 at 53 m E of N

Answer: C
Diff: 1 *Page Ref: Sec. 4.7*

16) An object of mass 6000 kg rests on the flatbed of a truck. It is held in place by metal brackets that can exert a maximum horizontal force of 9000 N. When the truck is traveling 15 m/s, what is the minimum stopping distance if the load is not to slide forward into the cab?

A) 15 m

B) 30 m

C) 75 m

D) 150 m

Answer: C

Diff: 2 Page Ref: Sec. 4.7

17) An object of mass 6000 kg rests on the flatbed of a truck. It is held in place by metal brackets that can exert a maximum horizontal force of 9000 N. When the truck is traveling 15 m/s, what is the minimum stopping time if the load is not to slide forward into the cab?

A) 5.0 s

B) 10 s

C) 13 s

D) 23 s

Answer: B

Diff: 2 Page Ref: Sec. 4.7

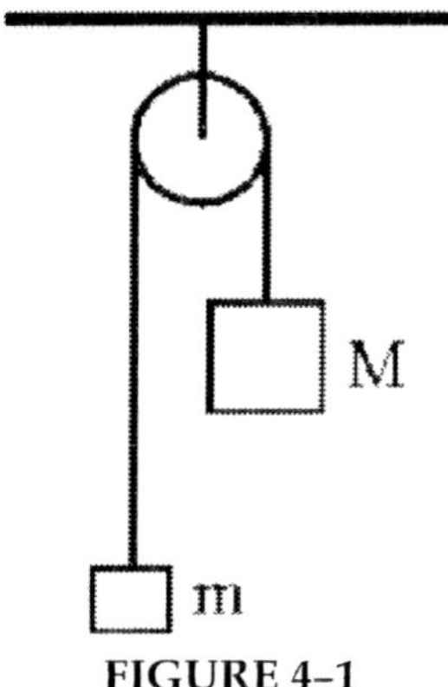

FIGURE 4–1

18) In the Atwood machine shown in Fig. 4–1, if M = 0.60 kg and m = 0.40 kg, what is the magnitude of the acceleration of the system? (Ignore friction and the mass of the pulley.)

A) 5.3 m/s^2

B) 3.9 m/s^2

C) 2.0 m/s^2

D) 0.98 m/s^2

Answer: C

Diff: 2 Page Ref: Sec. 4.7

19) In the Atwood machine shown in Fig. 4-1, if M = 0.60 kg and m = 0.40 kg, what is the tension in the string? (Ignore friction and the mass of the pulley.)

A) 3.1 N

B) 4.7 N

C) 7.1 N

D) 7.5 N

Answer: B
Diff: 2 *Page Ref: Sec. 4.7*

20) A student pulls a box of books on a smooth horizontal floor with a force of 100 N in a direction of 37° above the horizontal. If the mass of the box and the books is 40.0 kg, what is the acceleration of the box?

A) 1.5 m/s^2

B) 1.9 m/s^2

C) 2.0 m/s^2

D) 3.3 m/s^2

Answer: C
Diff: 2 *Page Ref: Sec. 4.7*

21) A student pulls a box of books on a smooth horizontal floor with a force of 100 N in a direction of 37.0° above the horizontal. If the mass of the box and the books is 40.0 kg, what is the normal force on the box?

A) 292 N

B) 312 N

C) 332 N

D) 392 N

Answer: C
Diff: 2 *Page Ref: Sec. 4.7*

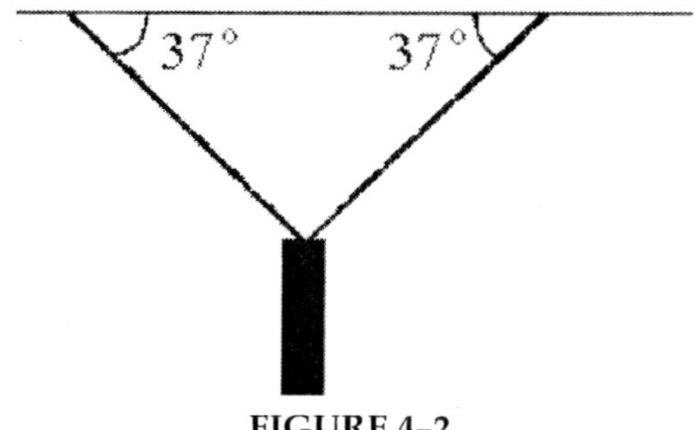

FIGURE 4-2

22) A traffic light of weight 100 N is supported by two ropes as shown in Fig. 4-2. What are the tensions in the ropes?

A) 50 N

B) 63 N

C) 66 N

D) 83 N

Answer: D
Diff: 2 *Page Ref: Sec. 4.7*

23) In Fig. 4-2, if the tensions in the ropes are 50 N, what is the mass of the traffic light?

A) 3.1 kg

B) 4.1 kg

C) 6.1 kg

D) 8.1 kg

Answer: C
Diff: 2 *Page Ref: Sec. 4.7*

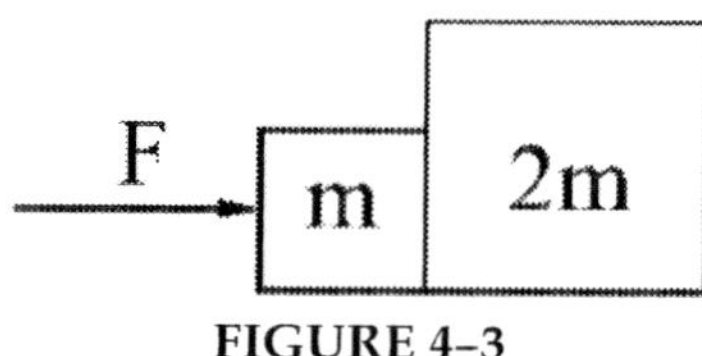

FIGURE 4-3

24) Two boxes of masses m and 2m are in contact with each other on a frictionless surface. (See Fig. 4-3.) What is the acceleration of the more massive box?

A) F/m

B) F/(2m)

C) F/(3m)

D) F/(4m)

Answer: C
Diff: 2 *Page Ref: Sec. 4.7*

25) Two boxes of masses m and 2m are in contact with each other on a frictionless surface. (See Fig. 4-3.) What is the net force on the more massive box?

A) 2/3 F

B) F

C) 3/2 F

D) 2F

Answer: A

Diff: 2 *Page Ref: Sec. 4.7*

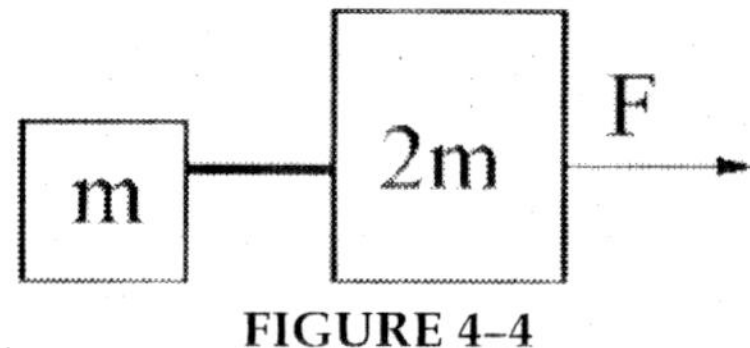

FIGURE 4-4

26) Two boxes of masses m and 2m are connected by a rope. (See Fig. 4-4.) If the forward force on the more massive box is F, what is the tension in the connecting rope?

A) 3F

B) F

C) F/2

D) F/3

Answer: D

Diff: 2 *Page Ref: Sec. 4.7*

27) Two boxes of masses m and 2m are connected by a rope. (See Fig. 4-4.) If the forward force on the more massive box is F, what is the acceleration of the less massive box?

A) F/(3m)

B) F/(2m)

C) F/m

D) 2F/m

Answer: A

Diff: 2 *Page Ref: Sec. 4.7*

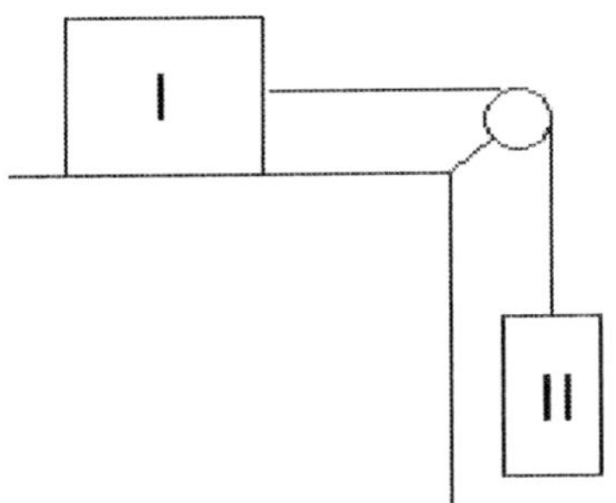

FIGURE 4–5

28) Two boxes are connected by a cord running over a pulley as shown in Fig. 4–5. Box I of mass 8.0 kg rest on the top of the table; the coefficient of kinetic friction between box I and the table is 0.10. Box II has a mass of 15.0 kg.
(a) Draw the free–body diagrams for the two boxes, identifying all of the forces acting on each of the masses.
(b) Calculate the acceleration of the system.
(c) Calculate the tension in the cord.

Answer: (a) Box one is acted on by the force of gravity in a downward direction, the normal force due to the table top in an upward direction, the tension in the string toward the right, and the force of friction due to the table top toward the left. Box two is acted on by the force of gravity in a downward direction and the tension in the string in an upward direction.
(b) 6.1 m/s^2
(c) 56 N

Diff: 2 *Page Ref: Sec. 4.7*

29) The coefficient of static and kinetic frictions between a 3.0–kg box and a desk are 0.40 and 0.30, respectively. What is the net force on the box when a 15 N horizontal force is applied to the box?

A) 6.2 N
B) 12 N
C) 8.8 N
D) zero

Answer: A
Diff: 1 *Page Ref: Sec. 4.8*

30) The coefficients of static and kinetic frictions for plastic on wood are 0.50 and 0.40, respectively. How much horizontal force would you need to apply to a 3.0 N plastic calculator to start it moving from rest?

A) 0.15 N

B) 1.2 N

C) 1.5 N

D) 2.7 N

Answer: C
Diff: 1 *Page Ref: Sec. 4.8*

31) An object slides on a level surface in the +x direction. It slows and comes to a stop with a constant acceleration of $-2.45\ m/s^2$. What is the coefficient of kinetic friction between the object and the floor?

A) 0.25

B) 0.50

C) 4.9

D) Impossible to determine without knowing the mass of the object.

Answer: A
Diff: 2 *Page Ref: Sec. 4.8*

32) A 10-kg box sitting on a horizontal surface is pulled by a 5.0-N force. A 3.0-N friction force retards the motion. What is the acceleration of the object?

A) $0.20\ m/s^2$

B) $0.30\ m/s^2$

C) $0.50\ m/s^2$

D) $5.0\ m/s^2$

Answer: A
Diff: 2 *Page Ref: Sec. 4.8*

33) A horizontal force of 5.0 N accelerates a 4.0-kg mass, from rest, at a rate of $0.50\ m/s^2$ in the positive direction. What friction force acts on the mass?

A) 2.0 N

B) 3.0 N

C) 4.0 N

D) 5.0 N

Answer: B
Diff: 2 *Page Ref: Sec. 4.8*

34) During a hockey game, a puck is given an initial speed of 10 m/s. It slides 50 m on the ice before it stops. What is the coefficient of kinetic friction between the puck and the ice?

A) 0.090

B) 0.10

C) 0.11

D) 0.12

Answer: B
Diff: 2 *Page Ref: Sec. 4.8*

35) During the investigation of a traffic accident, police find skid marks 90.0 m long. They determine the coefficient of friction between the car's tires and the roadway to be 0.500 for the prevailing conditions. Estimate the speed of the car when the brakes were applied.

A) 9.49 m/s

B) 21.0 m/s

C) 29.7 m/s

D) 42.0 m/s

Answer: C
Diff: 2 *Page Ref: Sec. 4.8*

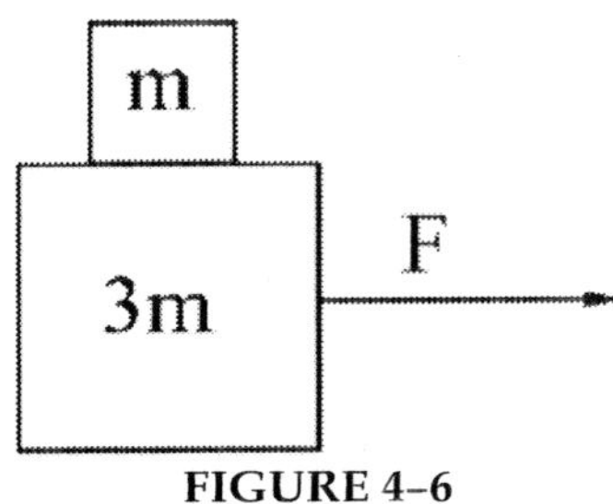

FIGURE 4-6

36) Two boxes of masses m and 3m are stacked. (See Fig. 4-6.) The surface between the more massive box and the horizontal surface is smooth and the surface between the boxes is rough. If the less massive box does not slide on the more massive box, what is the static friction force on the less massive box?

A) F

B) F/2

C) F/3

D) F/4

Answer: C
Diff: 3 *Page Ref: Sec. 4.8*

37) Two boxes of masses m and 3m are stacked. (See Fig. 4-6.) The surface between the more massive box and the horizontal surface is smooth and the surface between the boxes is rough. If the less massive box does not slide on the more massive box, what is the coefficient of static friction between the boxes?

A) F/(4mg)

B) F/(3mg)

C) F/(2mg)

D) F/(mg)

Answer: B
Diff: 3 *Page Ref: Sec. 4.8*

38) An object is on a frictionless inclined plane. The plane is inclined at an angle of 30° with the horizontal. What is the object's acceleration?

A) 0.50 g

B) 0.56 g

C) 0.87 g

D) 1.0 g

Answer: A
Diff: 2 *Page Ref: Sec. 4.8*

39) A 10-kg mass slides down a flat hill that makes an angle of 10° with the horizontal. If friction is negligible, what is the resultant force on the sled?

A) 1.7 N

B) 17 N

C) 97 N

D) 98 N

Answer: B
Diff: 2 *Page Ref: Sec. 4.8*

40) A mass is placed on a smooth inclined plane with an angle of 37° to the horizontal. If the inclined plane is 5.0-m long, how long does it take for the mass to reach the bottom of the inclined plane after it is released from rest?

A) 1.3 s

B) 1.2 s

C) 1.1 s

D) 1.0 s

Answer: A
Diff: 2 *Page Ref: Sec. 4.8*

41) A block lies on a smooth inclined plane tilted at an angle of 35° to the horizontal.
(a) Draw the free-body diagram for the block.
(b) Determine the block's acceleration as it slides down the inclined plane.
(c) If the block started from rest 8.5 m up the incline from its base, determine the block's speed when it reaches the bottom of the incline.
(d) How long did it take the block to reach the bottom of the inclined plane?

Answer: (a) The block is acted on by the force of gravity directed downward and the normal force due to the inclined plane directed perpendicular to the inclined surface.
(b) 5.6 m/s^2
(c) 9.7 m/s
(d) 1.7 s

Diff: 2 *Page Ref: Sec. 4.8*

42) A wooden block slides directly down an inclined plane, at a constant velocity of 6.0 m/s. What is the coefficient of kinetic friction, if the plane makes an angle of 25° with the horizontal?

A) 0.47
B) 0.42
C) 0.37
D) 0.91

Answer: A
Diff: 2 *Page Ref: Sec. 4.8*

43) An object with a mass m slides down a rough 37° inclined plane where the coefficient of kinetic friction is 0.20. What is the acceleration of the object?

A) 4.3 m/s^2
B) 5.9 m/s^2
C) 6.6 m/s^2
D) 7.8 m/s^2

Answer: A
Diff: 3 *Page Ref: Sec. 4.8*

44) An object with a mass m slides down a rough 37° inclined plane where the coefficient of kinetic friction is 0.20. If the plane is 10 m long and the mass starts from rest, what will be its speed at the bottom of the plane?

A) 12 m/s
B) 11 m/s
C) 9.7 m/s
D) 9.3 m/s

Answer: D
Diff: 3 *Page Ref: Sec. 4.8*

45) A bulldozer drags a log weighing 500 N along a rough surface. The cable attached to the log makes an angle of 30.0° with the ground. The coefficient of static friction between the log and the ground is 0.500. What minimum tension is required in the cable in order for the log to begin to move?

A) 224 N

B) 268 N

C) 289 N

D) 500 N

Answer: A
Diff: 3 *Page Ref: Sec. 4.8*

46) A 25.0-kg box is released from rest on a rough inclined plane tilted at an angle of 33.5° to the horizontal. The coefficient of kinetic friction between the box and the inclined plane is 0.200.
(a) Draw the free-body diagram for the box.
(b) Determine the force of kinetic friction acting on the box.
(c) Determine the acceleration of the box as it slides down the inclined plane.

Answer: (a) The box is acted on by the force of gravity directed downward, the normal force due to the inclined plane directed perpendicular to the surface of the incline, and the force of friction due to the inclined plane directed parallel to the inclined surface in the direction opposite of the motion.
(b) 40.9 N
(c) 3.77 m/s^2
Diff: 3 *Page Ref: Sec. 4.8*

47) An object is placed on an inclined plane. The angle of incline is gradually increased until the object begins to slide. The angle at which this occurs is θ. What is the coefficient of static friction between the object and the plane?

A) $\sin \theta$

B) $\cos \theta$

C) $\tan \theta$

D) $1/\tan \theta$

Answer: C
Diff: 3 *Page Ref: Sec. 4.8*

Chapter 5 Circular Motion; Gravitation

Conceptual Questions

1) Is it possible for an object moving with a constant speed to accelerate? Explain.

A) No, if the speed is constant then the acceleration is equal to zero.

B) No, an object can accelerate only if there is a net force acting on it.

C) Yes, although the speed is constant, the direction of the velocity can be changing.

D) Yes, if an object is moving it can experience acceleration

Answer: C
Diff: 1 *Page Ref: Sec. 5.1*

2) Consider a particle moving with constant speed such that its acceleration of constant magnitude is always perpendicular to its velocity.

A) It is moving in a straight line.

B) It is moving in a circle.

C) It is moving in a parabola.

D) None of the above is definitely true all of the time.

Answer: B
Diff: 2 *Page Ref: Sec. 5.1*

3) An object moves in a circular path at a constant speed. Compare the direction of the object's velocity and acceleration vectors.

A) Both vectors point in the same direction.

B) The vectors point in opposite directions.

C) The vectors are perpendicular.

D) The question is meaningless, since the acceleration is zero.

Answer: C
Diff: 2 *Page Ref: Sec. 5.1*

4) When an object experiences uniform circular motion, the direction of the acceleration is

A) in the same direction as the velocity vector.

B) in the opposite direction of the velocity vector.

C) is directed toward the center of the circular path.

D) is directed away from the center of the circular path.

Answer: C
Diff: 1 *Page Ref: Sec. 5.1*

5) Consider a particle moving with constant speed such that its acceleration of constant magnitude is always perpendicular to its velocity.

A) It is moving in a straight line.

B) It is moving in a circle.

C) It is moving in a parabola.

D) None of the above is definitely true all of the time.

Answer: B
Diff: 2 *Page Ref: Sec. 5.1*

6) What type of acceleration does an object moving with constant speed in a circular path experience?

A) free fall

B) constant acceleration

C) linear acceleration

D) centripetal acceleration

Answer: D
Diff: 1 *Page Ref: Sec. 5.1*

7) What force is needed to make an object move in a circle?

A) kinetic friction

B) static friction

C) centripetal force

D) weight

Answer: C
Diff: 1 *Page Ref: Sec. 5.2*

8) When an object experiences uniform circular motion, the direction of the net force is

A) in the same direction as the motion of the object.

B) in the opposite direction of the motion of the object.

C) is directed toward the center of the circular path.

D) is directed away from the center of the circular path.

Answer: C
Diff: 1 *Page Ref: Sec. 5.2*

9) A roller coaster car is on a track that forms a circular loop in the vertical plane. If the car is to just maintain contact with track at the top of the loop, what is the minimum value for its centripetal acceleration at this point?

A) g downward

B) 0.5g downward

C) g upward

D) 2g upward

Answer: A
Diff: 2 *Page Ref: Sec. 5.2*

10) A roller coaster car (mass = M) is on a track that forms a circular loop (radius = r) in the vertical plane. If the car is to just maintain contact with the track at the top of the loop, what is the minimum value for its speed at that point?

A) rg

B) $(rg)^{1/2}$

C) $(2rg)^{1/2}$

D) $(0.5rg)^{1/2}$

Answer: B
Diff: 2 *Page Ref: Sec. 5.2*

11) A pilot executes a vertical dive then follows a semi-circular arc until it is going straight up. Just as the plane is at its lowest point, the force on him is

A) less than mg, and pointing up.

B) less than mg, and pointing down.

C) more than mg, and pointing up.

D) more than mg, and pointing down.

Answer: C
Diff: 2 *Page Ref: Sec. 5.2*

12) A coin of mass m rests on a turntable a distance r from the axis of rotation. The turntable rotates with a frequency of f. What is the minimum coefficient of static friction between the turntable and the coin if the coin is not to slip?

A) $(4\pi^2 f^2 r)/g$

B) $(4\pi^2 f r^2)/g$

C) $(4\pi f^2 r)/g$

D) $(4\pi f r^2)/g$

Answer: A
Diff: 2 *Page Ref: Sec. 5.2*

13) A car goes around a curve of radius r at a constant speed v. What is the direction of the net force on the car?

A) toward the curve's center

B) away from the curve's center

C) toward the front of the car

D) toward the back of the car

Answer: A
Diff: 2 *Page Ref: Sec. 5.3*

14) A car goes around a curve of radius r at a constant speed v. Then it goes around the same curve at half of the original speed. What is the centripetal force on the car as it goes around the curve for the second time, compared to the first time?

A) twice as big

B) four times as big

C) half as big

D) one-fourth as big

Answer: D
Diff: 1 *Page Ref: Sec. 5.3*

15) A car goes around a curve of radius r at a constant speed v. Then it goes around a curve of radius 2r at speed 2v. What is the centripetal force on the car as it goes around the second curve, compared to the first?

A) four times as big

B) twice as big

C) one-half as big

D) one-fourth as big

Answer: B
Diff: 2 *Page Ref: Sec. 5.3*

16) A car of mass m goes around a banked curve of radius r with speed v. If the road is frictionless due to ice, the car can still negotiate the curve if the horizontal component of the normal force on the car from the road is equal in magnitude to

A) $mg/2$.

B) mg.

C) mv^2/r.

D) $\tan[v^2/(rg)]$.

Answer: C
Diff: 2 *Page Ref: Sec. 5.3*

17) Two horizontal curves on a bobsled run are banked at the same angle, but one has twice the radius of the other. The safe speed (no friction needed to stay on the run) for the smaller radius curve is v. What is the safe speed on the larger radius curve?

A) approximately 0.707v

B) 2v

C) approximately 1.41v

D) 0.5v

Answer: C
Diff: 2 *Page Ref: Sec. 5.3*

18) The banking angle in a turn on the Olympic bobsled track is not constant, but increases upward from the horizontal. Coming around a turn, the bobsled team will intentionally "climb the wall," then go lower coming out of the turn. Why do they do this?

A) to give the team better control, because they are able to see ahead of the turn

B) to prevent the bobsled from turning over

C) to take the turn at a faster speed

D) to reduce the g-force on them

Answer: C
Diff: 2 *Page Ref: Sec. 5.3*

19) Is it possible for an object moving around a circular path to have both centripetal and tangential acceleration?

A) No, because then the path would not be a circle.

B) No, an object can only have one or the other at any given time.

C) Yes, this is possible if the speed is constant.

D) Yes, this is possible if the speed is changing.

Answer: D
Diff: 2 *Page Ref: Sec. 5.4*

20) The gravitational force between two objects is proportional to

A) the distance between the two objects.

B) the square of the distance between the two objects.

C) the product of the two objects.

D) the square of the product of the two objects.

Answer: C
Diff: 2 *Page Ref: Sec. 5.6*

21) The gravitational force between two objects is inversely proportional to

A) the distance between the two objects.

B) the square of the distance between the two objects.

C) the product of the two objects.

D) the square of the product of the two objects.

Answer: B
Diff: 2 *Page Ref: Sec. 5.6*

22) Two objects attract each other gravitationally. If the distance between their centers is cut in half, the gravitational force

A) is cut to one fourth.

B) is cut in half.

C) doubles.

D) quadruples

Answer: D
Diff: 1 *Page Ref: Sec. 5.6*

23) Two objects, with masses m_1 and m_2, are originally a distance r apart. The gravitational force between them has magnitude F. The second object has its mass changed to $2m_2$, and the distance is changed to r/4. What is the magnitude of the new gravitational force?

A) F/32

B) F/16

C) 16F

D) 32F

Answer: D
Diff: 2 *Page Ref: Sec. 5.6*

24) Two objects, with masses m_1 and m_2, are originally a distance r apart. The magnitude of the gravitational force between them is F. The masses are changed to $2m_1$ and $2m_2$, and the distance is changed to 4r. What is the magnitude of the new gravitational force?

A) F/16

B) F/4

C) 16F

D) 4F

Answer: B
Diff: 2 *Page Ref: Sec. 5.6*

25) State Newton's law of universal gravitation.

Answer: Every particle in the universe attracts every other particle with a force that is proportional to the product of their masses and inversely proportional to the square of the distances between them. This force acts along the line joining the two particles.
Diff: 1 *Page Ref: Sec. 5.6*

26) Compared to its mass on the Earth, the mass of an object on the Moon is

A) less.

B) more.

C) the same.

D) half as much.

Answer: C
Diff: 1 *Page Ref: Sec. 5.7*

27) The acceleration of gravity on the Moon is one-sixth what it is on Earth. An object of mass 72 kg is taken to the Moon. What is its mass there?

A) 12 kg

B) 72 kg

C) 72 N

D) 12 N

Answer: B
Diff: 2 *Page Ref: Sec. 5.7*

28) As a rocket moves away from the Earth's surface, the rocket's weight

A) increases.

B) decreases.

C) remains the same.

D) depends on how fast it is moving.

Answer: B
Diff: 1 *Page Ref: Sec. 5.7*

29) A spaceship is traveling to the Moon. At what point is it beyond the pull of Earth's gravity?

A) when it gets above the atmosphere

B) when it is half-way there

C) when it is closer to the Moon than it is to Earth

D) It is never beyond the pull of Earth's gravity.

Answer: D
Diff: 2 *Page Ref: Sec. 5.7*

30) Suppose a satellite were orbiting the Earth just above the surface. What is its centripetal acceleration?

A) smaller than g

B) equal to g

C) larger than g

D) Impossible to say without knowing the mass.

Answer: B
Diff: 2 *Page Ref: Sec. 5.7*

31) A hypothetical planet has a mass of half that of the Earth and a radius of twice that of the Earth. What is the acceleration due to gravity on the planet in terms of g, the acceleration due to gravity at the Earth?

A) g

B) g/2

C) g/4

D) g/8

Answer: D
Diff: 2 *Page Ref: Sec. 5.7*

32) The acceleration of gravity on the Moon is one-sixth what it is on Earth. The radius of the Moon is one-fourth that of the Earth. What is the Moon's mass compared to the Earth's?

A) 1/6

B) 1/16

C) 1/24

D) 1/96

Answer: D
Diff: 2 *Page Ref: Sec. 5.7*

33) Two planets have the same surface gravity, but planet B has twice the radius of planet A. If planet A has mass m, what is the mass of planet B?

A) 0.707m

B) m

C) 1.41m

D) 4m

Answer: D
Diff: 2 *Page Ref: Sec. 5.7*

34) Two planets have the same surface gravity, but planet B has twice the mass of planet A. If planet A has radius r, what is the radius of planet B?

A) 0.707r

B) r

C) 1.41r

D) 4r

Answer: C
Diff: 2 *Page Ref: Sec. 5.7*

35) Consider a small satellite moving in a circular orbit (radius r) about a spherical planet (mass M). Which expression gives this satellite's orbital velocity?

A) $v = GM/r$

B) $(GM/r)^{1/2}$

C) GM/r^2

D) $(GM/r^2)^{1/2}$

Answer: B
Diff: 2 *Page Ref: Sec. 5.8*

36) Satellite A has twice the mass of satellite B, and rotates in the same orbit. Compare the two satellite's speeds.

A) The speed of B is twice the speed of A.

B) The speed of B is half the speed of A.

C) The speed of B is one-fourth the speed of A.

D) The speed of B is equal to the speed of A.

Answer: D
Diff: 1 *Page Ref: Sec. 5.8*

37) A person is standing on a scale in an elevator accelerating downward. Compare the reading on the scale to the person's true weight.

A) greater than their true weight

B) equal to their true weight

C) less than their true weight

D) zero

Answer: C
Diff: 2 *Page Ref: Sec. 5.8*

38) Who was the first person to realize that the planets move in elliptical paths around the Sun?

A) Kepler

B) Brahe

C) Einstein

D) Copernicus

Answer: A
Diff: 1 *Page Ref: Sec. 5.9*

39) The speed of Halley's Comet, while traveling in its elliptical orbit around the Sun,

A) is constant.

B) increases as it nears the Sun.

C) decreases as it nears the Sun.

D) is zero at two points in the orbit.

Answer: B
Diff: 2 *Page Ref: Sec. 5.9*

40) Let the average orbital radius of a planet be r. Let the orbital period be T. What quantity is constant for all planets orbiting the Sun?

A) T/R

B) T/R^2

C) T^2/R^3

D) T^3/R^2

Answer: C
Diff: 2 *Page Ref: Sec. 5.9*

41) A planet is discovered to orbit around a star in the galaxy Andromeda, with the same orbital diameter as the Earth around our Sun. If that star has 4 times the mass of our Sun, what will the period of revolution of that new planet be, compared to the Earth's orbital period?

A) one-fourth as much

B) one-half as much

C) twice as much

D) four times as much

Answer: B
Diff: 2 *Page Ref: Sec. 5.9*

42) The average distance from the Earth to the Sun is defined as one "astronomical unit" (AU). An asteroid orbits the Sun in one-third of a year. What is the asteroid's average distance from the Sun?

A) 0.19 AU

B) 0.48 AU

C) 2.1 AU

D) 5.2 AU

Answer: B
Diff: 2 *Page Ref: Sec. 5.9*

43) State Kepler's laws.

Answer: Kepler's first law: The path of each planet about the Sun is an ellipse with the Sun at one focus.
Kepler's second law: Each planet moves so that an imaginary line drawn from the Sun to the planet sweeps out equal areas in equal periods of time.
Kepler's third law: The ratio of the squares of the periods of any two planets revolving about the Sun is equal to the ratio of the cubes of their mean distances from the Sun.
Diff: 1 *Page Ref: Sec. 5.9*

44) List the four fundamental forces in nature.

A) gravitational, normal, tension, friction

B) gravitational, normal, kinetic friction, static friction

C) gravitational, electromagnetic, strong nuclear, weak nuclear

D) gravitational, electromagnetic, contact, nuclear

Answer: C
Diff: 1 *Page Ref: Sec. 5.10*

Quantitative Problems

1) An object moves with a constant speed of 30 m/s on a circular track of radius 150 m. What is the acceleration of the object?

A) zero

B) 0.17 m/s^2

C) 5.0 m/s^2

D) 6.0 m/s^2

Answer: D
Diff: 1 *Page Ref: Sec. 5.1-5.3*

2) The maximum speed around a level curve is 30.0 km/h. What is the maximum speed around a curve with twice the radius? (Assume all other factors remain unchanged.)

A) 42.4 km/h

B) 45.0 km/h

C) 60.0 km/h

D) 120 km/h

Answer: A
Diff: 2 *Page Ref: Sec. 5.1-5.3*

3) What is the centripetal acceleration of a point on the perimeter of a bicycle wheel of diameter 70 cm when the bike is moving 8.0 m/s?

A) 91 m/s^2

B) 1.8×10^2 m/s^2

C) 2.1×10^2 m/s^2

D) 2.7×10^2 m/s^2

Answer: B
Diff: 2 *Page Ref: Sec. 5.1-5.3*

4) A point on a wheel rotating at 5.00 rev/s is located 0.200 m from the axis. What is the centripetal acceleration?

A) 0.050 m/s^2

B) 1.35 m/s^2

C) 48.0 m/s^2

D) 198 m/s^2

Answer: D
Diff: 2 *Page Ref: Sec. 5.1-5.3*

5) How many revolutions per minute must a circular, rotating space station of radius 1000 m rotate to produce an artificial gravity of 9.80 m/s^2?

A) 0.65 rpm

B) 0.75 rpm

C) 0.85 rpm

D) 0.95 rpm

Answer: D
Diff: 2 *Page Ref: Sec. 5.1-5.3*

6) A motorcycle has a mass of 250 kg. It goes around a 13.7 m radius turn at 96.5 km/h. What is the centripetal force on the motorcycle?

A) 719 N

B) 2.95×10^3 N

C) 1.31×10^4 N

D) 4.31×10^4 N

Answer: C
Diff: 2 *Page Ref: Sec. 5.1-5.3*

7) A 0.50-kg mass is attached to the end of a 1.0-m string. The system is whirled in a horizontal circular path. If the maximum tension that the string can withstand is 350 N. What is the maximum speed of the mass if the string is not to break?

A) 700 m/s

B) 26 m/s

C) 19 m/s

D) 13 m/s

Answer: B
Diff: 2 *Page Ref: Sec. 5.1-5.3*

8) A stone, of mass m, is attached to a strong string and whirled in a vertical circle of radius r. At the exact top of the path the tension in the string is 3 times the stone's weight. The stone's speed at this point is given by

A) $2(gr)^{1/2}$.

B) $(2gr)^{1/2}$.

C) $(gr)^{1/2}$.

D) 2gr.

Answer: A
Diff: 2 *Page Ref: Sec. 5.1-5.3*

9) A stone, of mass m, is attached to a strong string and whirled in a vertical circle of radius r. At the exact bottom of the path the tension in the string is 3 times the stone's weight. The stone's speed at this point is given by

A) $2(gr)^{1/2}$.

B) $(2gr)^{1/2}$.

C) $(gr)^{1/2}$.

D) 2gr.

Answer: B
Diff: 2 *Page Ref: Sec. 5.1-5.3*

10) A jet plane flying 600 m/s experiences an acceleration of 4g when pulling out of the dive. What is the radius of curvature of the loop in which the plane is flying?

A) 640 m

B) 1200 m

C) 7100 m

D) 9200 m

Answer: D
Diff: 1 *Page Ref: Sec. 5.1-5.3*

11) A pilot makes an outside vertical loop (in which the center of the loop is beneath him) of radius 3200 m. At the top of his loop he is pushing down on his seat with only one-half of his normal weight. How fast is he going?

A) 5.0 m/s

B) 25 m/s

C) 125 m/s

D) 625 m/s

Answer: C
Diff: 1 *Page Ref: Sec. 5.1-5.3*

12) The maximum force a pilot can stand is about seven times his weight. What is the minimum radius of curvature that a jet plane's pilot, pulling out of a vertical dive, can tolerate at a speed of 250 m/s?

A) 4.25 m

B) 3.64 m

C) 1060 m

D) 911 m

Answer: C
Diff: 2 *Page Ref: Sec. 5.1-5.3*

13) A car traveling 20 m/s rounds an 80-m radius horizontal curve with the tires on the verge of slipping. How fast can this car round a second curve of radius 320 m? (Assume the same coefficient of friction between the car's tires and each road surface.)

A) 20 m/s

B) 40 m/s

C) 80 m/s

D) 160 m/s

Answer: B
Diff: 1 *Page Ref: Sec. 5.1-5.3*

14) A car is negotiating a flat curve of radius 50 m with a speed of 20 m/s. The centripetal force provided by friction is 1.2×10^4 N. What is the mass of the car?

A) 500 kg

B) 1000 kg

C) 1500 kg

D) 2000 kg

Answer: C
Diff: 2 *Page Ref: Sec. 5.1-5.3*

15) A car goes around a flat curve of radius 50 m at a speed of 14 m/s. What must be the minimum coefficient of friction between the tires and the road for the car to make the turn?

A) 0.20

B) 0.40

C) 0.60

D) 0.80

Answer: B
Diff: 2 *Page Ref: Sec. 5.1-5.3*

16) A car is moving with a constant speed v around a level curve. The coefficient of friction between the tires and the road is 0.40. What is the minimum radius of the curve if the car is to stay on the road?

A) $0.40v^2/g$

B) v^2/g

C) $2.5v^2/g$

D) $2v^2/g$

Answer: C
Diff: 2 *Page Ref: Sec. 5.1–5.3*

17) What minimum banking angle is required for an Olympic bobsled to negotiate a 100–m radius turn at 35 m/s without skidding? (Ignore friction.)

A) 31°

B) 41°

C) 51°

D) 61°

Answer: C
Diff: 2 *Page Ref: Sec. 5.1–5.3*

18) A horizontal curve on a bobsled run is banked at a 45° angle. When a bobsled rounds this curve at the curve's safe speed (no friction needed to stay on the run), what is its centripetal acceleration?

A) 1.0 g

B) 2.0 g

C) 0.5 g

D) none of the above

Answer: A
Diff: 2 *Page Ref: Sec. 5.1–5.3*

19) A frictionless curve of radius 100 m, banked at an angle of 45°, may be safely negotiated at a speed of

A) 22 m/s.

B) 31 m/s.

C) 44 m/s.

D) 67 m/s.

Answer: B
Diff: 2 *Page Ref: Sec. 5.1–5.3*

20) A curve of radius 80 m is banked at 45°. Suppose that an ice storm hits, and the curve is effectively frictionless. What is the safe speed with which to take the curve without either sliding up or down?

A) 9.4 m/s

B) 28 m/s

C) 7.8×10^2 m/s

D) The curve cannot be taken safely.

Answer: B

Diff: 2 *Page Ref: Sec. 5.1–5.3*

21) A 175-kg ball on the end of a string is revolving uniformly in a horizontal circle of radius 0.500 m. The ball makes 2.00 revolutions in a second.
(a) Determine the speed of the ball.
(b) Determine the ball's centripetal acceleration.
(c) Determine the force a person must exert on opposite end of the string.

Answer: (a) 6.28 m/s
(b) 79.0 m/s^2
(c) 13.8 N

Diff: 2 *Page Ref: Sec. 5.1–5.3*

22) Starting from rest in the pit area, a race car accelerates at a uniform rate to a speed of 45 m/s in 15 s, moving on a circular track of radius 500 m.
(a) Calculate the tangential acceleration.
(b) Calculate the radial acceleration when the instantaneous speed is equal to 30 m/s.

Answer: (a) 3.0 m/s^2
(b) 1.8 m/s^2

Diff: 2 *Page Ref: Sec. 5.4*

23) The hydrogen atom consists of a proton of mass 1.67×10^{-27} kg and an orbiting electron of mass 9.11×10^{-31} kg. In one of its orbits, the electron is 5.3×10^{-11} m from the proton. What is the mutual attractive force between the electron and proton?

A) 1.8×10^{-47} N

B) 3.6×10^{-47} N

C) 5.4×10^{-47} N

D) 7.0×10^{-47} N

Answer: B

Diff: 1 *Page Ref: Sec. 5.6–5.7*

24) What is the gravitational force on a 70-kg person standing on the Earth, due to the Moon? The mass of the Moon is 7.36×10^{22} kg and the distance to the Moon is 3.82×10^{8} m.

A) 0.24 N

B) 0.024 N

C) 0.0024 N

D) 0.00024 N

Answer: C
Diff: 1 *Page Ref: Sec. 5.6-5.7*

25) The gravitational attractive force between two masses is F. If the masses are moved to half of their initial distance, what is the gravitational attractive force?

A) 4F

B) 2F

C) F/2

D) F/4

Answer: A
Diff: 2 *Page Ref: Sec. 5.6-5.7*

26) For a spacecraft going from the Earth toward the Sun, at what distance from the Earth will the gravitational forces due to the Sun and the Earth cancel?
Earth's mass: $M_e = 5.98 \times 10^{24}$ kg
the Sun's mass: $M_s = 1.99 \times 10^{30}$ kg
Earth-Sun distance: $r = 1.50 \times 10^{11}$ m

A) 1.30×10^{8} m

B) 2.60×10^{8} m

C) 1.30×10^{10} m

D) 2.60×10^{10} m

Answer: B
Diff: 2 *Page Ref: Sec. 5.6-5.7*

27) The mass of the Moon is 7.4×10^{22} kg and its mean radius is 1.75×10^{3} km. What is the acceleration due to gravity at the surface of the Moon?

A) 2.8×10^{6} m/s^2

B) 9.80 m/s^2

C) 1.6 m/s^2

D) 0.80 m/s^2

Answer: C
Diff: 1 *Page Ref: Sec. 5.6-5.7*

28) An astronaut goes out for a "space-walk" at a distance above the Earth equal to the radius of the Earth. What is her acceleration due to gravity?

A) zero

B) g

C) g/2

D) g/4

Answer: D
Diff: 2 *Page Ref: Sec. 5.7*

29) The radius of the Earth is R. At what distance above the Earth's surface will the acceleration of gravity be 4.9 m/s^2?

A) 0.41 R

B) 0.50 R

C) 1.00 R

D) 1.41 R

Answer: A
Diff: 2 *Page Ref: Sec. 5.7*

30) A satellite encircles Mars at a distance above its surface equal to 3 times the radius of Mars. The acceleration of gravity of the satellite, as compared to the acceleration of gravity on the surface of Mars, is

A) zero.

B) the same.

C) one-third as much.

D) one-sixteenth as much.

Answer: D
Diff: 2 *Page Ref: Sec. 5.7*

31) At a distance of 14000 km from some planet's center, the acceleration of gravity is 32 m/s^2. What is the acceleration of gravity at a point 28000 km from the planet's center?

A) 8.0 m/s^2

B) 16 m/s^2

C) 128 m/s^2

D) cannot be determined from the information given

Answer: A
Diff: 2 *Page Ref: Sec. 5.6-5.7*

32) An object weighs 432 N on the surface of the Earth. The Earth has radius r. If the object is raised to a height of 3r above the Earth's surface, what is its weight?

A) 432 N

B) 48 N

C) 27 N

D) 0 N

Answer: C
Diff: 2 *Page Ref: Sec. 5.6–5.7*

33) By how many newtons does the weight of a 100-kg person change when he goes from sea level to an altitude of 5000 m? (The mean radius of the Earth is 6.38×10^6 m.)

A) 0.6 N

B) 1.6 N

C) 2.6 N

D) 3.6 N

Answer: B
Diff: 3 *Page Ref: Sec. 5.6–5.7*

34) The Earth has radius r. A satellite of mass 100 kg is at a point 3r above the Earth's surface. What is the satellite's weight?

A) 61 N

B) 110 N

C) 9000 N

D) 16000 N

Answer: A
Diff: 2 *Page Ref: Sec. 5.6–5.7*

35) A spherically symmetric planet has four times the Earth's mass and twice its radius. If a jar of peanut butter weighs 12 N on the surface of the Earth, how much would it weigh on the surface of this planet?

A) 6.0 N

B) 12 N

C) 24 N

D) 36 N

Answer: B
Diff: 2 *Page Ref: Sec. 5.6–5.7*

36) During a lunar eclipse, the Moon, Earth, and Sun all lie on the same line, with the Earth between the Moon and the Sun. The Moon has a mass of 7.36×10^{22} kg; the Earth has a mass of 5.98×10^{24} kg; and the Sun has a mass of 1.99×10^{30} kg. The separation between the Moon and the Earth is given by 3.84×10^{8} m; the separation between the Earth and the Sun is given by 1.496×10^{11} m.
(a) Calculate the force exerted on the Earth by the Moon.
(b) Calculate the force exerted on the Earth by the Sun.
(c) Calculate the net force exerted on the Earth by the Moon and the Sun.

Answer: (a) 1.99×10^{20} N, toward the Moon
(b) 3.55×10^{22} N, toward the Sun
(c) 3.53×10^{22} N, toward the Sun
Diff: 2 *Page Ref: Sec. 5.6–5.7*

37) A 2.10-kg brass ball is transported to the Moon.
(a) Calculate the acceleration due to gravity on the Moon. The radius of the Moon is 1.74×10^{6} m and the mass of the Moon is 7.35×10^{22} kg.
(b) Determine the mass of the brass ball on the Earth and on the Moon.
(c) Determine the weight of the brass ball on the Earth.
(d) Determine the weight of the brass ball on the Moon.

Answer: (a) 1.62 m/s^2
(b) 2.10 kg, 2.10 kg
(c) 20.6 N
(d) 3.40 N
Diff: 2 *Page Ref: Sec. 5.6–5.7*

38) A satellite is in a low circular orbit about the Earth (i.e., it just skims the surface of the Earth). What is the speed of the satellite? (The mean radius of the Earth is 6.38×10^{6} m.)

A) 5.9 km/s

B) 6.9 km/s

C) 7.9 km/s

D) 8.9 km/s

Answer: C
Diff: 2 *Page Ref: Sec. 5.8*

39) A satellite is in a low circular orbit about the Earth (i.e., it just skims the surface of the Earth). How long does it take to make one revolution around the Earth? (The mean radius of the Earth is 6.38×10^{6} m.)

A) 81 min

B) 85 min

C) 89 min

D) 93 min

Answer: B
Diff: 2 *Page Ref: Sec. 5.8*

40) A satellite is in circular orbit 230 km above the surface of the Earth. It is observed to have a period of 89 min. What is the mass of the Earth? (The mean radius of the Earth is 6.38×10^{6} m.)

A) 5.0×10^{24} kg

B) 5.5×10^{24} kg

C) 6.0×10^{24} kg

D) 6.5×10^{24} kg

Answer: C
Diff: 2 Page Ref: Sec. 5.8

41) Europa, a moon of Jupiter, has an orbital diameter of 1.34×10^{9} m, and a period of 3.55 days. What is the mass of Jupiter?

A) 1.83×10^{27} kg

B) 1.85×10^{27} kg

C) 1.87×10^{27} kg

D) 1.89×10^{27} kg

Answer: D
Diff: 2 Page Ref: Sec. 5.9

42) The innermost moon of Jupiter orbits the planet with a radius of 422×10^{3} km and a period of 1.77 days. What is the mass of Jupiter?

A) 1.3×10^{27} kg

B) 1.5×10^{27} kg

C) 1.7×10^{27} kg

D) 1.9×10^{27} kg

Answer: D
Diff: 2 Page Ref: Sec. 5.9

43) Two moons orbit a planet in nearly circular orbits. Moon A has orbital radius r, and moon B has orbital radius 4r. Moon A takes 20 days to complete one orbit. How long does it take moon B to complete an orbit?

A) 20 days

B) 80 days

C) 160 days

D) 320 days

Answer: C
Diff: 2 Page Ref: Sec. 5.9

44) The planet Jupiter is 7.78×10^{11} m from the Sun. How long does it take for Jupiter to orbit once about the Sun? (The distance from the Earth to the Sun is 1.50×10^{11} m.)

A) 1 yr

B) 3 yr

C) 6 yr

D) 12 yr

Answer: D
Diff: 2 *Page Ref: Sec. 5.9*

45) It takes the planet Jupiter 12 years to orbit the Sun once. What is the average distance from Jupiter to the Sun? (The distance from the Earth to the Sun is 1.5×10^{11} m.)

A) 3.9×10^{11} m

B) 5.2×10^{11} m

C) 7.9×10^{11} m

D) 9.7×10^{11} m

Answer: C
Diff: 2 *Page Ref: Sec. 5.9*

Chapter 6 Work and Energy

Conceptual Questions

1) What is the correct unit of work expressed in SI units?

A) kg m/s^2

B) kg m^2/s

C) kg m^2/s^2

D) kg^2 m/s^2

Answer: C
Diff: 1 *Page Ref: Sec. 6.1*

2) Can work be done on a system if there is no motion?

A) Yes, if an outside force is provided.

B) Yes, since motion is only relative.

C) No, since a system which is not moving has no energy.

D) No, because of the way work is defined.

Answer: D
Diff: 1 *Page Ref: Sec. 6.1*

3) If you push twice as hard against a stationary brick wall, the amount of work you do

A) doubles.

B) is cut in half.

C) remains constant but non-zero.

D) remains constant at zero.

Answer: D
Diff: 1 *Page Ref: Sec. 6.1*

4) A 50-N object was lifted 2.0 m vertically and is being held there. How much work is being done in holding the box in this position?

A) more than 100 J

B) 100 J

C) less than 100 J, but more than 0 J

D) 0 J

Answer: D
Diff: 2 *Page Ref: Sec. 6.1*

5) If you walk 5.0 m horizontally forward at a constant velocity carrying a 10-N object, the amount of work you do is

A) more than 50 J.

B) equal to 50 J.

C) less than 50 J, but more than 0 J.

D) zero.

Answer: D
Diff: 2 *Page Ref: Sec. 6.1*

6) A container of water is lifted vertically 3.0 m then returned to its original position. If the total weight is 30 N, how much work was done?

A) 45 J

B) 90 J

C) 180 J

D) No work was done.

Answer: D
Diff: 2 *Page Ref: Sec. 6.1*

7) Does the centripetal force acting on an object do work on the object?

A) Yes, since a force acts and the object moves, and work is force times distance.

B) Yes, since it takes energy to turn an object.

C) No, because the object has constant speed.

D) No, because the force and the displacement of the object are perpendicular.

Answer: D
Diff: 2 *Page Ref: Sec. 6.1*

8) You throw a ball straight up. Compare the sign of the work done by gravity while the ball goes up with the sign of the work done by gravity while it goes down.

A) Work is + on the way up and + on the way down.

B) Work is + on the way up and - on the way down.

C) Work is - on the way up and + on the way down.

D) Work is - on the way up and - on the way down.

Answer: C
Diff: 1 *Page Ref: Sec. 6.1*

9) The area under the curve, on a Force versus position (F vs. x) graph, represents

A) work.

B) kinetic energy.

C) power.

D) potential energy.

Answer: A
Diff: 1 *Page Ref: Sec. 6.2*

10) On a plot of Force versus position (F vs. x), what represents the work done by the force F?
   A) the slope of the curve
   B) the length of the curve
   C) the area under the curve
   D) the product of the maximum force times the maximum x

Answer: C
Diff: 1 *Page Ref: Sec. 6.2*

11) The quantity $1/2\ mv^2$ is
   A) the kinetic energy of the object.
   B) the potential energy of the object.
   C) the work done on the object by the force.
   D) the power supplied to the object by the force.

Answer: A
Diff: 1 *Page Ref: Sec. 6.3*

12) If the net work done on an object is positive, then the object's kinetic energy
   A) decreases.
   B) remains the same.
   C) increases.
   D) is zero.

Answer: C
Diff: 1 *Page Ref: Sec. 6.3*

13) If the net work done on an object is negative, then the object's kinetic energy
   A) decreases.
   B) remains the same.
   C) increases.
   D) is zero.

Answer: A
Diff: 1 *Page Ref: Sec. 6.3*

14) If the net work done on an object is zero, then the object's kinetic energy
   A) decreases.
   B) remains the same.
   C) increases.
   D) is zero.

Answer: B
Diff: 1 *Page Ref: Sec. 6.3*

15) A truck weighs twice as much as a car, and is moving at twice the speed of the car. Which statement is true about the truck's kinetic energy compared to that of the car?

A) All that can be said is that the truck has more kinetic energy.

B) The truck has twice the kinetic energy of the car.

C) The truck has 4 times the kinetic energy of the car.

D) The truck has 8 times the kinetic energy of the car.

Answer: D
Diff: 1 *Page Ref: Sec. 6.3*

16) Car J moves twice as fast as car K, and car J has half the mass of car K. The kinetic energy of car J, compared to car K is

A) the same.

B) 2 to 1.

C) 4 to 1.

D) 1 to 2.

Answer: B
Diff: 2 *Page Ref: Sec. 6.3*

17) An object hits a wall and bounces back with half of its original speed. What is the ratio of the final kinetic energy to the initial kinetic energy?

A) 1/2

B) 1/4

C) 2

D) 4

Answer: B
Diff: 2 *Page Ref: Sec. 6.3*

18) A brick is moving at a speed of 3 m/s and a pebble is moving at a speed of 5 m/s. If both objects have the same kinetic energy, what is the ratio of the brick's mass to the rock's mass?

A) 25 to 9

B) 5 to 3

C) 12.5 to 4.5

D) 3 to 5

Answer: A
Diff: 2 *Page Ref: Sec. 6.3*

19) A 4.0-kg mass is moving with speed 2.0 m/s. A 1.0-kg mass is moving with speed 4.0 m/s. Both objects encounter the same constant braking force, and are brought to rest. Which object travels the greater distance before stopping?

A) the 4.0-kg mass

B) the 1.0-kg mass

C) Both travel the same distance.

D) cannot be determined from the information given

Answer: C
Diff: 2 *Page Ref: Sec. 6.3*

20) You slam on the brakes of your car in a panic, and skid a certain distance on a straight, level road. If you had been traveling twice as fast, what distance would the car have skidded, under the same conditions?

A) It would have skidded 4 times farther.

B) It would have skidded twice as far.

C) It would have skidded 1.4 times farther.

D) It is impossible to tell from the information given.

Answer: A
Diff: 2 *Page Ref: Sec. 6.3*

21) A planet of constant mass orbits the Sun in an elliptical orbit. Neglecting any friction effects, what happens to the planet's kinetic energy?

A) It remains constant.

B) It increases continually.

C) It decreases continually.

D) It increases when the planet approaches the Sun, and decreases when it moves farther away.

Answer: D
Diff: 2 *Page Ref: Sec. 6.3*

22) State the work-energy principle.

Answer: The net work done on an object is equal to the change in the object's kinetic energy.
Diff: 1 *Page Ref: Sec. 6.3*

23) The quantity mgy is

A) the kinetic energy of the object.

B) the gravitational potential energy of the object.

C) the work done on the object by the force.

D) the power supplied to the object by the force.

Answer: B
Diff: 1 *Page Ref: Sec. 6.4-6.5*

24) The quantity $1/2\ kx^2$ is

A) the kinetic energy of the object.

B) the elastic potential energy of the object.

C) the work done on the object by the force.

D) the power supplied to the object by the force.

Answer: B
Diff: 1 *Page Ref: Sec. 6.4–6.5*

25) Is it possible for a system to have negative potential energy?

A) Yes, as long as the total energy is positive.

B) Yes, since the choice of the zero of potential energy is arbitrary.

C) No, because the kinetic energy of a system must equal its potential energy.

D) No, because this would have no physical meaning.

Answer: B
Diff: 1 *Page Ref: Sec. 6.4–6.5*

26) An object is released from rest a height h above the ground. A second object with four times the mass of the first if released from the same height. The potential energy of the second object compared to the first is

A) one-fourth as much.

B) one-half as much.

C) twice as much.

D) four times as much.

Answer: D
Diff: 1 *Page Ref: Sec. 6.4–6.5*

27) A 0.200-kg mass attached to the end of a spring causes it to stretch 5.0 cm. If another 0.200-kg mass is added to the spring, the potential energy of the spring will be

A) the same.

B) twice as much.

C) 3 times as much.

D) 4 times as much.

Answer: D
Diff: 2 *Page Ref: Sec. 6.4–6.5*

28) The total mechanical energy of a system

A) is equally divided between kinetic energy and potential energy.

B) is either all kinetic energy or all potential energy, at any one instant.

C) can never be negative.

D) is constant, only if conservative forces act.

Answer: D
Diff: 1 *Page Ref: Sec. 6.6–6.7*

29) An acorn falls from a tree. Compare its kinetic energy K, to its potential energy U.

A) K increases and U decreases.

B) K decreases and U decreases.

C) K increases and U increases.

D) K decreases and U increases.

Answer: A
Diff: 1 *Page Ref: Sec. 6.6–6.7*

30) Describe the energy of a car driving up a hill.

A) entirely kinetic

B) entirely potential

C) both kinetic and potential

D) gravitational

Answer: C
Diff: 1 *Page Ref: Sec. 6.6–6.7*

31) A lightweight object and a very heavy object are sliding with equal speeds along a level frictionless surface. They both slide up the same frictionless hill. Which rises to a greater height?

A) The heavy object, because it has greater kinetic energy.

B) The lightweight object, because it weighs less.

C) They both slide to the same height.

D) cannot be determined from the information given

Answer: C
Diff: 2 *Page Ref: Sec. 6.6–6.7*

32) Consider two masses m_1 and m_2 at the top of two frictionless inclined planes. Both masses start from rest at the same height. However, the plane on which m_1 sits is at an angle of 30° with the horizontal, while the plane on which m_2 sits is at 60°. If the masses are released, which is going faster at the bottom of its plane?

A) m_1

B) m_2

C) They both are going the same speed.

D) cannot be determined without knowing the masses

Answer: C
Diff: 2 *Page Ref: Sec. 6.6–6.7*

33) State the principle of conservation of mechanical energy for conservative forces.

Answer: If only conservative forces are acting, the total mechanical energy of a system neither increases nor decreases in any process. It stays constant—it is conserved.
Diff: 1 *Page Ref: Sec. 6.6–6.7*

34) A ball falls from the top of a building, through the air (air friction is present), to the ground below. How does the kinetic energy (K) just before striking the ground compare to the potential energy (U) at the top of the building?

A) K is equal to U.

B) K is greater than U.

C) K is less than U.

D) It is impossible to tell.

Answer: C
Diff: 2 *Page Ref: Sec. 6.8–6.9*

35) A ball drops some distance and gains 30 J of kinetic energy. Do not ignore air resistance. How much gravitational potential energy did the ball lose?

A) more than 30 J

B) exactly 30 J

C) less than 30 J

D) cannot be determined from the information given

Answer: A
Diff: 2 *Page Ref: Sec. 6.8–6.9*

36) A ball drops some distance and loses 30 J of gravitational potential energy. Do not ignore air resistance. How much kinetic energy did the ball gain?

A) more than 30 J

B) exactly 30 J

C) less than 30 J

D) cannot be determined from the information given

Answer: C
Diff: 2 *Page Ref: Sec. 6.8–6.9*

37) State the law of conservation of energy.

Answer: The total energy is neither increased nor decreased in any process. Energy can be transformed from one form to another, and transferred from one object to another, but the total amount remains constant.
Diff: 1 *Page Ref: Sec. 6.8–6.9*

38) The quantity Fd/t is

A) the kinetic energy of the object.

B) the potential energy of the object.

C) the work done on the object by the force.

D) the power supplied to the object by the force.

Answer: D
Diff: 1 *Page Ref: Sec. 6.10*

39) What is the correct unit of power expressed in SI units?

A) kg m / s^2

B) kg m^2 / s^2

C) kg m^2 / s^3

D) kg^2 m / s^2

Answer: C
Diff: 1 *Page Ref: Sec. 6.10*

40) Of the following, which is not a unit of power?

A) watt / second

B) newton–meter / second

C) joule / second

D) watt

Answer: A
Diff: 2 *Page Ref: Sec. 6.10*

41) Compared to yesterday, you did 3 times the work in one–third the time. To do so, your power output must have been

A) the same as yesterday's power output.

B) one–third of yesterday's power output.

C) 3 times yesterday's power output.

D) 9 times yesterday's power output.

Answer: D
Diff: 1 *Page Ref: Sec. 6.10*

42) To accelerate your car at a constant acceleration, the car's engine must

A) maintain a constant power output.

B) develop ever–decreasing power.

C) develop ever–increasing power.

D) maintain a constant turning speed.

Answer: C
Diff: 2 *Page Ref: Sec. 6.10*

Quantitative Problems

1) An object is lifted vertically 2.0 m and held there. If the object weighs 90 N, how much work was done in lifting it?

A) 360 J

B) 180 J

C) 90 J

D) 0 J

Answer: B
Diff: 1 *Page Ref: Sec. 6.1*

2) You lift a 10-N physics book up in the air a distance of 1.0 m, at a constant velocity of 0.50 m/s. What is the work done by the weight of the book?

A) +10 J

B) -10 J

C) +5.0 J

D) -5.0 J

Answer: B
Diff: 1 *Page Ref: Sec. 6.1*

3) A 500-kg elevator is pulled upward with a constant force of 5500 N for a distance of 50.0 m. What is the work done by the 5500 N force?

A) 2.75×10^5 J

B) -2.45×10^5 J

C) 3.00×10^4 J

D) -5.20×10^5 J

Answer: A
Diff: 1 *Page Ref: Sec. 6.1*

4) A 500-kg elevator is pulled upward with a constant force of 5500 N for a distance of 50.0 m. What is the work done by the weight of the elevator?

A) 2.75×10^5 J

B) -2.45×10^5 J

C) 3.00×10^4 J

D) -5.20×10^5 J

Answer: B
Diff: 1 *Page Ref: Sec. 6.1*

5) A 500-kg elevator is pulled upward with a constant force of 5500 N for a distance of 50.0 m. What is the net work done on the elevator?

A) 2.75×10^5 J

B) -2.45×10^5 J

C) 3.00×10^4 J

D) -5.20×10^5 J

Answer: C
Diff: 2 *Page Ref: Sec. 6.1*

6) A 30-N box is pulled 6.0 m up along a 37° inclined plane. What is the work done by the weight (gravitational force) of the box?

A) −11 J

B) -1.1×10^2J

C) -1.4×10^2 J

D) -1.8×10^2 J

Answer: B
Diff: 2 *Page Ref: Sec. 6.1*

7) A 4.00-kg box of fruit slides 8.0 m down a ramp, inclined at 30.0° from the horizontal. If the box slides at a constant velocity of 5.00 m/s, what is the work done by the weight of the box?

A) 157 J

B) −157 J + 78.4 J

C) 78.4 J

D) −78.4 J

Answer: A
Diff: 2 *Page Ref: Sec. 6.1*

8) Matthew pulls his little sister Sarah in a sled on an icy surface (assume no friction), with a force of 60.0 N at an angle of 37.0° upward from the horizontal. If he pulls her a distance of 12.0 m, what is the work done by Matthew?

A) 185 J

B) 433 J

C) 575 J

D) 720 J

Answer: C
Diff: 2 *Page Ref: Sec. 6.1*

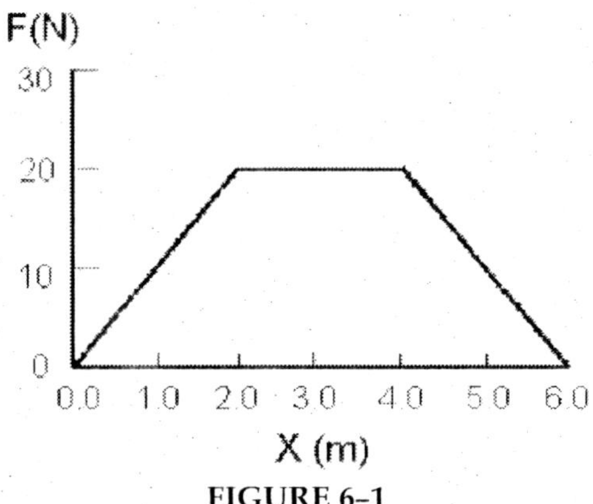

FIGURE 6-1

9) A force moves an object in the direction of the force. The graph in Fig. 6-1 shows the force versus the object's position. Find the work done when the object moves from 0 to 2.0 m.

A) 20 J

B) 40 J

C) 60 J

D) 80 J

Answer: A

Diff: 2 *Page Ref: Sec. 6.2*

10) A force moves an object in the direction of the force. The graph in Fig. 6-1 shows the force versus the object's position. Find the work done when the object moves from 2.0 to 4.0 m.

A) 20 J

B) 40 J

C) 60 J

D) 80 J

Answer: B

Diff: 2 *Page Ref: Sec. 6.2*

11) A force moves an object in the direction of the force. The graph in Fig. 6-1 shows the force versus the object's position. Find the work done when the object moves from 4.0 to 6.0 m.

A) 20 J

B) 40 J

C) 60 J

D) 80 J

Answer: A

Diff: 2 *Page Ref: Sec. 6.2*

12) A force moves an object in the direction of the force. The graph in Fig. 6-1 shows the force versus the object's position. Find the work done when the object moves from 0 to 6.0 m.

A) 20 J

B) 40 J

C) 60 J

D) 80 J

Answer: D
Diff: 2 *Page Ref: Sec. 6.2*

13) A horizontal force of 200 N is applied to move a 55-kg cart (initially at rest) across a 10 m level surface. What is the final kinetic energy of the cart?

A) 1.0×10^3 J

B) 2.0×10^3 J

C) 2.7×10^3 J

D) 4.0×10^3 J

Answer: B
Diff: 1 *Page Ref: Sec. 6.3*

14) A horizontal force of 200 N is applied to move a 55-kg cart (initially at rest) across a 10 m level surface. What is the final speed of the cart?

A) 73 m/s

B) 36 m/s

C) 8.5 m/s

D) 6.0 m/s

Answer: C
Diff: 1 *Page Ref: Sec. 6.3*

15) A 10-kg mass is moving with a speed of 5.0 m/s. How much work is required to stop the mass?

A) 50 J

B) 75 J

C) 100 J

D) 125 J

Answer: D
Diff: 1 *Page Ref: Sec. 6.3*

16) If it takes 50 m to stop a car initially moving at 25 m/s, what distance is required to stop a car moving at 50 m/s under the same condition?

A) 50 m

B) 100 m

C) 200 m

D) 400 m

Answer: C
Diff: 2 *Page Ref: Sec. 6.3*

17) A spring-driven dart gun propels a 10-g dart. It is cocked by exerting a force of 20 N over a distance of 5.0 cm. With what speed will the dart leave the gun, assuming the spring has negligible mass?

A) 10 m/s

B) 14 m/s

C) 17 m/s

D) 20 m/s

Answer: B
Diff: 2 *Page Ref: Sec. 6.3*

18) A 100-N force has a horizontal component of 80 N and a vertical component of 60 N. The force is applied to a box which rests on a level frictionless floor. The cart starts from rest, and moves 2.0 m horizontally along the floor. What is the cart's final kinetic energy?

A) 200 J

B) 160 J

C) 120 J

D) zero

Answer: B
Diff: 2 *Page Ref: Sec. 6.3*

19) An arrow of mass 20 g is shot horizontally into a bale of hay, striking the hay with a velocity of 60 m/s. It penetrates a depth of 20 cm before stopping. What is the average stopping force acting on the arrow?

A) 45 N

B) 90 N

C) 180 N

D) 360 N

Answer: C
Diff: 2 *Page Ref: Sec. 6.3*

20) A 15.0-kg object is moved from a height of 7.00 m above a floor to a height of 13.0 m above the floor. What is the change in gravitational potential energy?

A) zero

B) 1030 J

C) 1176 J

D) 1910 J

Answer: C
Diff: 2 *Page Ref: Sec. 6.4-6.5*

21) A 400-N box is pushed up an inclined plane. The plane is 4.0 m long and rises 2.0 m. If the plane is frictionless, how much work was done by the push?

A) 1600 J

B) 800 J

C) 400 J

D) 100 J

Answer: B
Diff: 2 *Page Ref: Sec. 6.4-6.5*

22) A 10-kg mass, hung onto a spring, causes the spring to stretch 2.0 cm. What is the spring constant?

A) 4.9×10^3 N/m

B) 5.0×10^3 N/m

C) 20 N/m

D) 2.0 N/m

Answer: A
Diff: 1 *Page Ref: Sec. 6.4-6.5*

23) A spring is characterized by a spring constant of 60 N/m. How much potential energy does it store, when stretched by 1.0 cm?

A) 3.0×10^{-3} J

B) 0.30 J

C) 60 J

D) 600 J

Answer: A
Diff: 1 *Page Ref: Sec. 6.4-6.5*

24) Calculate the work required to compress an initially uncompressed spring with a spring constant of 25 N/m by 10 cm.

A) 0.10 J

B) 0.13 J

C) 0.17 J

D) 0.25 J

Answer: B
Diff: 1 *Page Ref: Sec. 6.4-6.5*

25) What work is required to stretch a spring of spring constant 40 N/m from x = 0.20 m to 0.25 m? (Assume the unstretched position is at x = 0.)

A) 0.45 J

B) 0.80 J

C) 1.3 J

D) 0.050 J

Answer: A
Diff: 2 *Page Ref: Sec. 6.4-6.5*

26) A spring with a spring constant of 15 N/m is initially compressed by 3.0 cm. How much work is required to compress the spring an additional 4.0 cm?

A) 0.0068 J

B) 0.012 J

C) 0.024 J

D) 0.030 J

Answer: D
Diff: 2 *Page Ref: Sec. 6.4-6.5*

27) A 60-kg skier starts from rest from the top of a 50-m high slope. What is the speed of the slier on reaching the bottom of the slope? (Neglect friction.)

A) 22 m/s

B) 31 m/s

C) 9.8 m/s

D) 41 m/s

Answer: B
Diff: 1 *Page Ref: Sec. 6.6-6.7*

28) A skier, of mass 40 kg, pushes off the top of a hill with an initial speed of 4.0 m/s. Neglecting friction, how fast will she be moving after dropping 10 m in elevation?

A) 7.3 m/s

B) 15 m/s

C) 49 m/s

D) 196 m/s

Answer: B
Diff: 2 *Page Ref: Sec. 6.6-6.7*

29) An object slides down a frictionless inclined plane. At the bottom, it has a speed of 9.80 m/s. What is the vertical height of the plane?

A) 19.6 m

B) 9.80 m

C) 4.90 m

D) 2.45 m

Answer: C
Diff: 2 *Page Ref: Sec. 6.6-6.7*

30) A 1.0-kg ball falls to the floor. When it is 0.70 m above the floor, its potential energy exactly equals its kinetic energy. How fast is it moving?

A) 3.7 m/s

B) 6.9 m/s

C) 14 m/s

D) 45 m/s

Answer: A
Diff: 2 *Page Ref: Sec. 6.6-6.7*

31) A toy rocket, weighing 10 N, blasts straight up from ground level with a kinetic energy of 40 J. At the exact top of its trajectory, its total mechanical energy is 140 J. To what vertical height does it rise?

A) 1.0 m

B) 10 m

C) 14 m

D) 24 m

Answer: B
Diff: 2 *Page Ref: Sec. 6.6-6.7*

32) A projectile of mass m leaves the ground with a kinetic energy of 220 J. At the highest point in its trajectory, its kinetic energy is 120 J. To what vertical height, relative to its launch point, did it rise?

A) 220/(mg) meters

B) 120/(mg) meters

C) 100/(mg) meters

D) Impossible to determine without knowing the angle of launch

Answer: C
Diff: 2 *Page Ref: Sec. 6.6-6.7*

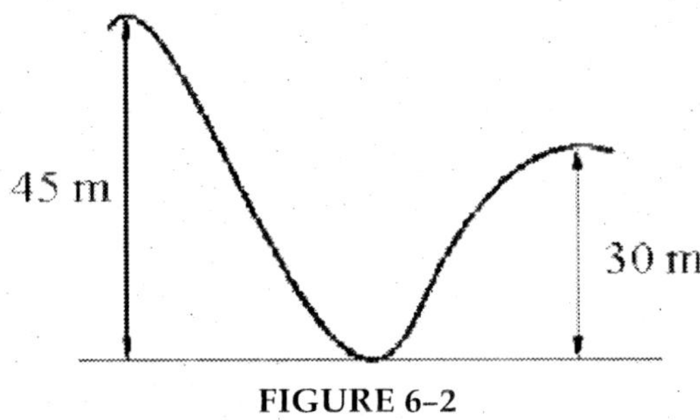

FIGURE 6-2

33) A roller coaster starts from rest at a point 45 m above the bottom of a dip (See Fig. 6-2). Neglect friction, what will be the speed of the roller coaster at the top of the next slope, which is 30 m above the bottom of the dip?

A) 14 m/s

B) 17 m/s

C) 24 m/s

D) 30 m/s

Answer: B
Diff: 2 *Page Ref: Sec. 6.6-6.7*

34) A roller coaster starts with a speed of 5.0 m/s at a point 45 m above the bottom of a dip (See Fig. 6-2). Neglect friction, what will be the speed of the roller coaster at the top of the next slope, which is 30 m above the bottom of the dip?

A) 12 m/s

B) 14 m/s

C) 16 m/s

D) 18 m/s

Answer: D
Diff: 2 *Page Ref: Sec. 6.6-6.7*

35) A roller coaster starts at a point 30 m above the bottom of a dip with a speed of 25 m/s (See Fig. 6-2). Neglect friction, what will be the speed of the roller coaster at the top of the next slope, which is 45 m above the bottom of the dip?

A) 14 m/s

B) 16 m/s

C) 18 m/s

D) 20 m/s

Answer: C
Diff: 2 *Page Ref:* Sec. 6.6-6.7

36) What is the minimum speed of the ball at the bottom of its swing (point B) in order for it to reach point A, which is 1.0-m above the bottom of the swing?

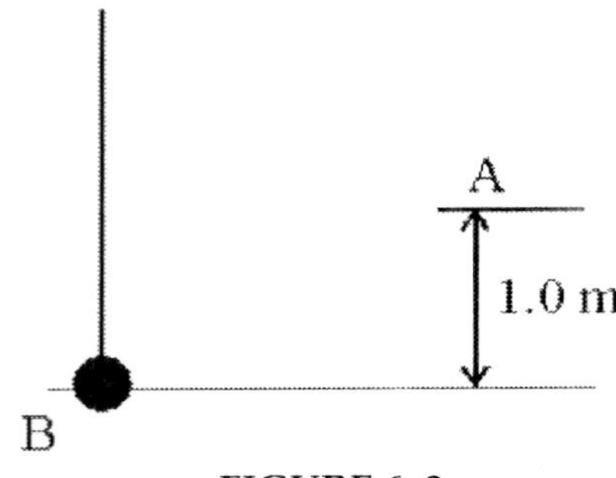

FIGURE 6-3

A) 2.2 m/s

B) 3.1 m/s

C) 4.4 m/s

D) 4.9 m/s

Answer: C
Diff: 2 *Page Ref:* Sec. 6.6-6.7

37) A pendulum of length 50 cm is pulled 30 cm away from the vertical axis and released from rest. What will be its speed at the bottom of its swing?

A) 0.50 m/s

B) 0.79 m/s

C) 1.2 m/s

D) 1.4 m/s

Answer: D
Diff: 2 *Page Ref:* Sec. 6.6-6.7

38) A 1500-kg car moving at 25 m/s hits an initially uncompressed horizontal spring with spring constant of 2.0×10^6 N/m. What is the maximum compression of the spring? (Neglect the mass of the spring.)

A) 0.17 m

B) 0.34 m

C) 0.51 m

D) 0.68 m

Answer: D
Diff: 2 *Page Ref: Sec. 6.6-6.7*

39) A driver, traveling at 22 m/s, slows down her 2000 kg car to stop for a red light. What work is done by the friction force against the wheels?

A) -2.2×10^4 J

B) -4.4×10^4 J

C) -4.84×10^5 J

D) -9.68×10^5 J

Answer: C
Diff: 1 *Page Ref: Sec. 6.8-6.9*

40) The kinetic friction force between a 60.0-kg object and a horizontal surface is 50.0 N. If the initial speed of the object is 25.0 m/s, what distance will it slide before coming to a stop?

A) 15.0 m

B) 30.0 m

C) 375 m

D) 750 m

Answer: C
Diff: 2 *Page Ref: Sec. 6.8-6.9*

41) A 12-kg object is moving on a rough, level surface. It has 24 J of kinetic energy. The friction force on it is a constant 0.50 N. How far will it slide?

A) 2.0 m

B) 12 m

C) 24 m

D) 48 m

Answer: D
Diff: 2 *Page Ref: Sec. 6.8-6.9*

42) A force of 10 N is applied horizontally to a 2.0-kg mass on a level surface. The coefficient of kinetic friction between the mass and the surface is 0.20. If the mass is moved a distance of 10 m, what is the change in its kinetic energy?

A) 20 J

B) 39 J

C) 46 J

D) 61 J

Answer: D
Diff: 2 *Page Ref: Sec. 6.8-6.9*

43) A 60-kg skier starts from rest from the top of a 50-m high slope. If the work done by friction is -6.0×10^3 J, what is the speed of the skier on reaching the bottom of the slope?

A) 17 m/s

B) 24 m/s

C) 34 m/s

D) 31 m/s

Answer: C
Diff: 2 *Page Ref: Sec. 6.8-6.9*

44) An 800-N box is pushed up an inclined plane. The plane is 4.0 m long and rises 2.0 m. It requires 3200 J of work to get the box to the top of the plane. What was the magnitude of the average friction force on the box?

A) 0 N

B) non-zero, but less than 400 N

C) 400 N

D) greater than 400 N

Answer: C
Diff: 2 *Page Ref: Sec 6.8-6.9*

45) A 2.0-kg mass is released from rest at the top of a plane inclined at 20° above horizontal. The coefficient of kinetic friction between the mass and the plane is 0.20. What will be the speed of the mass after sliding 4.0 m along the plane?

A) 2.2 m/s

B) 3.0 m/s

C) 3.5 m/s

D) 5.2 m/s

Answer: C
Diff: 3 *Page Ref: Sec. 6.8-6.9*

46) A 30.0-N stone is dropped from a height of 10.0 m, and strikes the ground with a velocity of 7.00 m/s. What average force of air friction acts on it as it falls?

A) 22.5 N

B) 75.0 N

C) 225 N

D) 293 N

Answer: A
Diff: 3 *Page Ref: Sec. 6.8-6.9*

47) At what rate is a 60.0-kg boy using energy when he runs up a flight of stairs 10.0-m high, in 8.00 s?

A) 75.0 W

B) 735 W

C) 4.80 kW

D) 48 W

Answer: B
Diff: 1 *Page Ref: Sec. 6.10*

48) A 10-N force is needed to move an object with a constant velocity of 5.0 m/s. What power must be delivered to the object by the force?

A) 0.50 W

B) 1.0 W

C) 50 W

D) 100 W

Answer: C
Diff: 1 *Page Ref: Sec. 6.10*

49) How many joules of energy are used by a 1.0 hp motor that runs for 1.0 hr? (1 hp = 746 W)

A) 3.6×10^3 J

B) 2.7×10^6 J

C) 4.5×10^4 J

D) 4.8 J

Answer: B
Diff: 1 *Page Ref: Sec. 6.10*

50) A cyclist does work at the rate of 500 W while riding. How much force does her foot push with when she is traveling at 8.0 m/s?

A) 31 N

B) 63 N

C) 80 N

D) 4000 N

Answer: B
Diff: 1 *Page Ref: Sec. 6.10*

51) A 1500-kg car accelerates from 0 to 25 m/s in 7.0 s. What is the average power delivered by the engine? (1 hp = 746 W)

A) 60 hp

B) 70 hp

C) 80 hp

D) 90 hp

Answer: D
Diff: 2 *Page Ref: Sec. 6.10*

Chapter 7 Linear Momentum

Conceptual Questions

1) What is the SI unit of momentum?

A) N•m

B) N/s

C) N•s

D) N/m

Answer: C
Diff: 1 *Page Ref: Sec. 7.1–7.2*

2) When a cannon fires a cannonball, the cannon will recoil backward because the

A) energy of the cannonball and cannon is conserved.

B) momentum of the cannonball and cannon is conserved.

C) energy of the cannon is greater than the energy of the cannonball.

D) momentum of the cannon is greater than the energy of the cannonball.

Answer: B
Diff: 1 *Page Ref: Sec. 7.1–7.2*

3) A freight car moves along a frictionless level railroad track at constant speed. The car is open on top. A large load of coal is suddenly dumped into the car. What happens to the velocity of the car?

A) It increases.

B) It remains the same.

C) It decreases.

D) cannot be determined from the information given

Answer: C
Diff: 1 *Page Ref: Sec. 7.1–7.2*

4) A child falls sideways off a sled while sledding on frictionless ice. What happens to the velocity of the sled?

A) It increases.

B) It remains the same.

C) It decreases.

D) cannot be determined from the information given

Answer: B
Diff: 1 *Page Ref: Sec. 7.1–7.2*

5) A rubber ball and a lump of putty have equal mass. They are thrown with equal speed against a wall. The ball bounces back with nearly the same speed with which it hit. The putty sticks to the wall. Which objects experiences the greater momentum change?

A) the ball

B) the putty

C) Both experience the same momentum change.

D) cannot be determined from the information given

Answer: A
Diff: 2 *Page Ref: Sec. 7.1-7.2*

6) A sailboat of mass m is moving with a momentum p. How would you represent its kinetic energy in terms of these two quantities?

A) $p^2/(2m)$

B) $1/2\ mp^2$

C) mp

D) mp/2

Answer: A
Diff: 1 *Page Ref: Sec. 7.1-7.2*

7) If you pitch a baseball with twice the kinetic energy you gave it in the previous pitch, the magnitude of its momentum is

A) the same.

B) 1.41 times as much.

C) doubled.

D) 4 times as much.

Answer: B
Diff: 1 *Page Ref: Sec. 7.1-7.2*

8) State Newton's second law in terms of momentum.

Answer: The rate of change of momentum of an object is equal to the net force applied to it.
Diff: 1 *Page Ref: Sec. 7.1-7.2*

9) State the law of conservation of momentum.

Answer: The total momentum of an isolated system of objects remains constant.
Diff: 1 *Page Ref: Sec. 7.1-7.2*

10) The area under the curve on a Force versus time (F vs. t) graph represents
   A) impulse.
   B) momentum.
   C) work.
   D) kinetic energy.

Answer: A
Diff: 1 Page Ref: Sec. 7.3

11) Which of the following is an accurate statement?
   A) The momentum of a projectile is constant.
   B) The momentum of a moving object is constant.
   C) If an object is acted on by a non-zero net external force, its momentum will not remain constant.
   D) If the kinetic energy of an object is doubled, its momentum will also double.

Answer: C
Diff: 1 Page Ref: Sec. 7.3

12) A small car meshes with a large truck in a head-on collision. Which of the following statements concerning the magnitude of the average collision force is correct?
   A) The truck experiences the greater average force.
   B) The small car experiences the greater average force.
   C) The small car and the truck experience the same average force.
   D) It is impossible to tell since the masses and velocities are not given.

Answer: C
Diff: 1 Page Ref: Sec. 7.3

13) Two equal mass balls (one red and the other blue) are dropped from the same height, and rebound off the floor. The red ball rebounds to a higher position. Which ball is subjected to the greater magnitude of impulse during its collision with the floor?
   A) It's impossible to tell since the time intervals and forces are unknown.
   B) Both balls were subjected to the same magnitude impulse.
   C) the blue ball
   D) the red ball

Answer: D
Diff: 2 Page Ref: Sec. 7.3

14) A Ping-Pong ball moving east at a speed of 4 m/s, collides with a stationary bowling ball. The Ping-Pong ball bounces back to the west, and the bowling ball moves very slowly to the east. Which object experiences the greater magnitude impulse during the collision?

   A) Neither; both experienced the same magnitude impulse.

   B) the Ping-Pong ball

   C) the bowling ball

   D) It's impossible to tell since the velocities after the collision are unknown.

Answer: A
Diff: 2 *Page Ref: Sec. 7.3*

15) Two objects collide and bounce off each other. Linear momentum

   A) is definitely conserved.

   B) is definitely not conserved.

   C) is conserved only if the collision is elastic.

   D) is conserved only if the environment is frictionless.

Answer: D
Diff: 1 *Page Ref: Sec. 7.4*

16) A 3.0-kg object moves to the right at 4.0 m/s. It collides head-on with a 6.0-kg object moving to the left at 2.0 m/s. Which statement is correct?

   A) The total momentum both before and after the collision is 24 kg• m/s.

   B) The total momentum before the collision is 24 kg•m/s, and after the collision is 0 kg•m/s.

   C) The total momentum both before and after the collision is zero.

   D) None of the above is true.

Answer: C
Diff: 2 *Page Ref: Sec. 7.4*

17) A 100-kg football linebacker moving at 2.0 m/s tackles head-on an 80-kg halfback running 3.0 m/s. Neglecting the effects due to digging in of cleats,

   A) the linebacker will drive the halfback backward.

   B) the halfback will drive the linebacker backward.

   C) neither player will drive the other backward.

   D) this is a simple example of an elastic collision.

Answer: B
Diff: 2 *Page Ref: Sec. 7.4*

18) In an elastic collision, if the momentum is conserved, then which of the following statements is true about kinetic energy?

A) Kinetic energy is also conserved.

B) Kinetic energy is gained.

C) Kinetic energy is lost.

D) none of the above

Answer: A
Diff: 1 *Page Ref: Sec. 7.5*

19) When is kinetic energy conserved?

A) in elastic collisions

B) in inelastic collisions

C) in any collision in which the objects do not stick together

D) in all collisions

Answer: A
Diff: 1 *Page Ref: Sec. 7.5*

20) In a game of pool, the white cue ball hits the #5 ball and stops, while the #5 ball moves away with the same velocity as the cue ball had originally. The type of collision is

A) elastic.

B) inelastic.

C) completely inelastic.

D) any of the above, depending on the mass of the balls.

Answer: A
Diff: 2 *Page Ref: Sec. 7.5*

21) When a light beach ball rolling with a speed of 6.0 m/s collides with a heavy exercise ball at rest, the beach ball's speed after the collision will be, approximately,

A) 0.

B) 3.0 m/s.

C) 6.0 m/s.

D) 12 m/s.

Answer: C
Diff: 2 *Page Ref: Sec. 7.5*

22) A golf ball traveling 3.0 m/s to the right collides in a head-on collision with a stationary bowling ball in a friction-free environment. If the collision is almost perfectly elastic, the speed of the golf ball immediately after the collision is

A) slightly less than 3.0 m/s.

B) slightly greater than 3.0 m/s.

C) equal to 3.0 m/s.

D) much less than 3.0 m/s.

Answer: A
Diff: 2 Page Ref: Sec. 7.5

23) A rubber ball with a speed of 5.0 m/s collides head-on elastically with an identical ball at rest. What is the speed of the initially stopped ball after the collision?

A) zero

B) 1.0 m/s

C) 2.5 m/s

D) 5.0 m/s

Answer: D
Diff: 2 Page Ref: Sec. 7.5

24) A very heavy object moving with speed v collides head-on with a very light object at rest. The collision is elastic, and there is no friction. The heavy object barely slows down. What is the speed of the light object after the collision?

A) nearly v

B) nearly 2v

C) nearly 3v

D) nearly infinite

Answer: B
Diff: 2 Page Ref: Sec. 7.5

25) A very light object moving with speed v collides head-on with a very heavy object at rest, in a frictionless environment. The collision is almost perfectly elastic. The speed of the heavy object after the collision is

A) slightly greater than v.

B) equal to v.

C) slightly less than v.

D) much less than v.

Answer: D
Diff: 2 Page Ref: Sec. 7.5

26) A red ball with a velocity of +3.0 m/s collides head-on with a yellow ball of equal mass moving with a velocity of -2.0 m/s. What is the velocity of the yellow ball after the collision?

A) zero

B) +3.0 m/s

C) -2.0 m/s

D) +5.0 m/s

Answer: B
Diff: 2 *Page Ref: Sec. 7.5*

27) A very heavy object moving with velocity v collides head-on with a very light object moving with velocity -v. The collision is elastic, and there is no friction. The heavy object barely slows down. What is the speed of the light object after the collision?

A) nearly v

B) nearly 2v

C) nearly 3v

D) nearly infinite

Answer: C
Diff: 3 *Page Ref: Sec. 7.5*

28) In an inelastic collision, if the momentum is conserved, then which of the following statements is true about kinetic energy?

A) Kinetic energy is also conserved.

B) Kinetic energy is gained.

C) Kinetic energy is lost.

D) none of the above

Answer: C
Diff: 1 *Page Ref: Sec. 7.6*

29) Two objects collide and stick together. Kinetic energy

A) is definitely conserved.

B) is definitely not conserved.

C) is conserved only if the collision is elastic.

D) is conserved only if the environment is frictionless.

Answer: B
Diff: 1 *Page Ref: Sec. 7.6*

30) A 3.0-kg object moves to the right at 4.0 m/s. It collides in a perfectly inelastic collision with a 6.0 kg object moving to the left at 2.0 m/s. What is the total kinetic energy after the collision?

A) 72 J

B) 36 J

C) 24 J

D) 0 J

Answer: D
Diff: 2 *Page Ref: Sec. 7.6*

31) A small object collides with a large object and sticks. Which object experiences the larger magnitude of momentum change?

A) the large object

B) the small object

C) Both objects experience the same magnitude of momentum change.

D) cannot be determined from the information given

Answer: C
Diff: 2 *Page Ref: Sec. 7.6*

32) In a game of pool, the white cue ball hits the #9 ball and is deflected at a 35° angle to the original line of motion. What is the angle of deflection below the original line of motion for the #9 ball?

A) 35°

B) 55°

C) 75°

D) 90°

Answer: B
Diff: 2 *Page Ref: Sec. 7.7*

33) Consider two unequal masses, M and m. Which of the following statements is false?

A) The center of mass lies on the line joining the centers of each mass.

B) The center of mass is closer to the larger mass.

C) It is possible for the center of mass to lie within one of the objects.

D) If a uniform rod of mass m were to join the two masses, this would not alter the position of the center of mass of the system without the rod present.

Answer: D
Diff: 1 *Page Ref: Sec. 7.8*

34) Which of the following is a false statement?

A) For a uniform symmetric object, the center of mass is at the center of symmetry.

B) For an object on the surface of the Earth, the center of gravity and the center of mass are the same point.

C) The center of mass of an object must lie within the object.

D) The center of gravity of an object may be thought of as the "balance point."

Answer: C
Diff: 2 *Page Ref: Sec. 7.8*

35) Tightrope walkers walk with a long flexible rod in order to

A) increase their total weight.

B) allow both hands to hold onto something.

C) lower their center of mass.

D) move faster along the rope.

Answer: C
Diff: 2 *Page Ref: Sec. 7.8*

36) A plane, flying horizontally, releases a bomb, which explodes before hitting the ground. Neglecting air resistance, the center of mass of the bomb fragments, just after the explosion

A) is zero.

B) moves horizontally.

C) moves vertically.

D) moves along a parabolic path.

Answer: D
Diff: 2 *Page Ref: Sec. 7.10*

37) Two cars collide head-on on a level friction-free road. The collision was completely inelastic and both cars quickly came to rest during the collision. What is true about the velocity of this system's center of mass?

A) It was always zero.

B) It was never zero.

C) It was not zero, but ended up zero.

D) none of the above

Answer: A
Diff: 2 *Page Ref: Sec. 7.10*

38) State Newton's second law for a system of particles.

Answer: The sum of all forces acting on the system is equal to the total mass of the system times the acceleration of its center of mass.
Diff: 1 *Page Ref: Sec. 7.10*

Quantitative Problems

1) What is the momentum of a 2000-kg truck traveling at 35 m/s?

A) 57 kg•m/s

B) 3.5×10^4 kg•m/s

C) 7.0×10^4 kg•m/s

D) 7.0×10^5 kg•m/s

Answer: C
Diff: 1 Page Ref: Sec. 7.1-7.2

2) A 1200-kg ferryboat is moving south at 20 m/s. What is the magnitude of its momentum?

A) 1.7×10^{-3} kg•m/s

B) 6.0×10^2 kg•m/s

C) 2.4×10^3 kg•m/s

D) 2.4×10^4 kg•m/s

Answer: D
Diff: 1 Page Ref: Sec. 7.1-7.2

3) A ball of mass 0.10 kg is dropped from a height of 12 m. Its momentum when it strikes the ground is

A) 1.5 kg•m/s.

B) 1.8 kg•m/s.

C) 2.4 kg•m/s.

D) 4.8 kg•m/s.

Answer: A
Diff: 2 Page Ref: Sec. 7.1-7.2

4) Two identical 1500-kg cars are moving perpendicular to each other. One moves with a speed of 25 m/s due north and the other moves at 15 m/s due east. What is the total momentum of the system?

A) 4.4×10^4 kg•m/s at 31° N of E

B) 4.4×10^4 kg•m/s at 59° N of E

C) 6.0×10^4 kg•m/s at 31° N of E

D) 6.0×10^4 kg•m/s at 59° N of E

Answer: B
Diff: 2 Page Ref: Sec. 7.1-7.2

5) A handball of mass 0.10 kg, traveling horizontally at 30 m/s, strikes a wall and rebounds at 24 m/s. What is the change in the momentum of the ball?

A) 0.60 kg•m/s

B) 1.2 kg•m/s

C) 5.4 kg•m/s

D) 72 kg•m/s

Answer: C
Diff: 2 *Page Ref: Sec. 7.1–7.2*

6) A 0.060–kg tennis ball, initially moving at a speed of 12 m/s, is struck by a racket causing it to rebound in the opposite direction at a speed of 18 m/s. What is the change in momentum of the ball?

A) 0.36 kg•m/s

B) 0.72 kg•m/s

C) 1.1 kg•m/s

D) 1.8 kg•m/s

Answer: D
Diff: 2 *Page Ref: Sec. 7.1–7.2*

7) A 50–kg pitching machine (excluding the baseball) is placed on a frozen pond. The machine fires a 0.40–kg baseball with a speed of 35 m/s in the horizontal direction. What is the recoil speed of the pitching machine? (Assume negligible friction.)

A) 0.14 m/s

B) 0.28 m/s

C) 0.70 m/s

D) 4.4×10^3 m/s

Answer: B
Diff: 1 *Page Ref: Sec. 7.1–7.2*

8) A 70–kg astronaut is space–walking outside the space capsule and is stationary when the tether line breaks. As a means of returning to the capsule he throws his 2.0–kg space hammer at a speed of 14 m/s away from the capsule. At what speed does the astronaut move toward the capsule?

A) 0.40 m/s

B) 1.5 m/s

C) 3.5 m/s

D) 5.0 m/s

Answer: A
Diff: 1 *Page Ref: Sec. 7.1–7.2*

9) A small object with momentum 5.0 kg•m/s approaches head-on a large object at rest. The small object bounces straight back with a momentum of magnitude 4.0 kg•m/s. What is the magnitude of the large object's momentum change?

A) 9.0 kg•m/s

B) 5.0 kg•m/s

C) 4.0 kg•m/s

D) 1.0 kg•m/s

Answer: A
Diff: 2 *Page Ref: Sec. 7.1-7.2*

10) You (50-kg mass) skate on ice at 4.0 m/s to greet your friend (40-kg mass), who is standing still, with open arms. As you collide, while holding each other, with what speed do you both move off together?

A) zero

B) 2.2 m/s

C) 5.0 m/s

D) 23 m/s

Answer: B
Diff: 2 *Page Ref: Sec. 7.1-7.2*

11) A car of mass 1000 kg moves to the right along a level, straight road at a speed of 6.0 m/s. It collides directly with a stopped motorcycle of mass 200 kg. What is the total momentum after the collision?

A) zero

B) 6000 kg•m/s to the right

C) 2000 kg•m/s to the right

D) 10,000 kg•m/s to the right

Answer: B
Diff: 2 *Page Ref: Sec. 7.1-7.2*

12) A 1000-kg car traveling at 25 m/s runs into the rear of a stopped car that has a mass of 1500 kg and they stick together. What is the speed of the cars after the collision?

A) 5.0 m/s

B) 10 m/s

C) 15 m/s

D) 20 m/s

Answer: B
Diff: 2 *Page Ref: Sec. 7.1-7.2*

13) A railroad freight car, mass 15,000 kg, is allowed to coast along a level track at a speed of 2.0 m/s. It collides and couples with a 50,000-kg second car, initially at rest and with brakes released. What is the speed of the two cars after coupling?

A) 0.46 m/s

B) 0.60 m/s

C) 1.2 m/s

D) 1.8 m/s

Answer: A
Diff: 2 *Page Ref: Sec. 7.1-7.2*

14) A railroad car, of mass 200 kg, rolls with negligible friction on a horizontal track with a speed of 10 m/s. A 70-kg stunt man drops straight down a distance of 4.0 m, and lands in the car. How fast will the car be moving after this happens?

A) 2.8 m/s

B) 4.7 m/s

C) 7.4 m/s

D) 10 m/s

Answer: C
Diff: 2 *Page Ref: Sec. 7.1-7.2*

15) A 60-kg person walks on a 100-kg log at the rate of 0.80 m/s (with respect to the log). With what speed does the log move, with respect to the shore?

A) 0.24 m/s

B) 0.30 m/s

C) 0.48 m/s

D) 0.60 m/s

Answer: B
Diff: 3 *Page Ref: Sec. 7.1-7.2*

16) A 4.0-N force acts for 3.0 s on an object. The force suddenly increases to 15 N and acts for one more second. What impulse was imparted by these forces to the object?

A) 12 N•s

B) 15 N•s

C) 19 N•s

D) 27 N•s

Answer: D
Diff: 2 *Page Ref: Sec. 7.3*

17) A constant 9.0-N net force acts for 2.0 s on a 6.0-kg object. What is the object's change of velocity?

A) 3.0 m/s

B) 9.0 m/s

C) 27 m/s

D) 110 m/s

Answer: A
Diff: 1 *Page Ref: Sec. 7.3*

18) A 2000-kg car, traveling to the right at 30 m/s, collides with a brick wall and comes to rest in 0.20 s. What is the average force the car exerts on the wall?

A) 12,000 N to the right

B) 300,000 N to the right

C) 60,000 N to the right

D) none of the above

Answer: B
Diff: 1 *Page Ref: Sec. 7.3*

19) A 2.0--kg softball is pitched to you at 20 m/s. You hit the ball back along the same path, and at the same speed. If the bat was in contact with the ball for 0.10 s, what is the magnitude of the average force the bat exerted?

A) zero

B) 40 N

C) 400 N

D) 800 N

Answer: D
Diff: 2 *Page Ref: Sec. 7.3*

20) A 0.10-kg ball is dropped onto a table top. The speeds of the ball right before and right after hitting the table top are 5.0 m/s and 4.0 m/s, respectively. If the collision between the ball and the table top lasts 0.15 s, what is the magnitude of the average force exerted on the ball by the table top?

A) 0.67 N

B) 1.3 N

C) 3.0 N

D) 6.0 N

Answer: D
Diff: 2 *Page Ref: Sec. 7.3*

21) A machine gun, of mass 35.0 kg, fires 50.0-gram bullets, with a muzzle velocity of 750 m/s, at the rate of 300 rounds per minute. What is the average force exerted on the machine gun mount?

A) 94.0 N

B) 188 N

C) 219 N

D) 438 N

Answer: B
Diff: 2 *Page Ref: Sec. 7.3*

22) A fire hose is turned on the door of a burning building in order to knock the door down. This requires a force of 1000 N. If the hose delivers 40 kg per second, what is the minimum velocity of the stream needed, assuming the water doesn't bounce back?

A) 15 m/s

B) 20 m/s

C) 25 m/s

D) 30 m/s

Answer: C
Diff: 2 *Page Ref: Sec. 7.3*

23) Water runs out of a horizontal drainpipe at the rate of 120 kg per minute. It falls 3.20 m to the ground. Assuming the water doesn't splash up, what average force does it exert on the ground?

A) 6.20 N

B) 12.0 N

C) 15.8 N

D) 19.6 N

Answer: C
Diff: 3 *Page Ref: Sec. 7.3*

24) A toy rocket, of mass 0.12 kg, achieves a velocity of 40 m/s after 3.0 s, when fired straight up. What average thrust force does the rocket engine exert?

A) 1.2 N

B) 1.6 N

C) 2.8 N

D) 4.4 N

Answer: C
Diff: 3 *Page Ref: Sec. 7.3*

25) Two astronauts, of masses 60 kg and 80 kg, are initially at rest in outer space. They push each other apart. What is their separation after the lighter astronaut has moved 12 m?

A) 15 m

B) 18 m

C) 21 m

D) 24 m

Answer: C
Diff: 2 *Page Ref: Sec. 7.4-7.5*

26) A 3.0-kg object moves to the right with a speed of 2.0 m/s. It collides in a perfectly elastic collision with a 6.0-kg object moving to the left at 1.0 m/s. What is the total kinetic energy after the collision?

A) 9.0 J

B) 6.0 J

C) 3.0 J

D) 0 J

Answer: A
Diff: 2 *Page Ref: Sec. 7.4-7.5*

27) A 0.10-kg object with a velocity of 0.20 m/s in the +x direction makes a head-on elastic collision with a 0.15 kg object initially at rest. What is the final velocity of the 0.10-kg object after collision?

A) -0.16 m/s

B) +0.16 m/s

C) -0.040 m/s

D) +0.040 m/s

Answer: C
Diff: 2 *Page Ref: Sec. 7.4-7.5*

28) A 10.0-g bullet moving at 300 m/s is fired into a 1.00-kg block at rest. The bullet emerges (the bullet does not get embedded in the block) with half of its original speed. What is the velocity of the block right after the collision?

A) 1.50 m/s

B) 2.97 m/s

C) 3.00 m/s

D) 273 m/s

Answer: A
Diff: 2 *Page Ref: Sec. 7.4-7.5*

29) A proton, of mass m, at rest, is struck head-on by an alpha-particle (which consists of 2 protons and 2 neutrons) moving at speed v. If the collision is completely elastic, what speed will the alpha-particle have after the collision? (Assume the neutron's mass equals the proton's mass.)

A) zero

B) 2v/3

C) 3v/5

D) 5v/3

Answer: C
Diff: 3 *Page Ref: Sec. 7.4-7.5*

30) A 50-gram ball moving +10 m/s collides head-on with a stationary ball of mass 100 g. The collision is elastic. What is the speed of each ball immediately after the collision?

A) -3.3 m/s and +6.7 m/s

B) +3.3 m/s and -6.7 m/s

C) -6.7 m/s and +3.3 m/s

D) +6.7 m/s and -3.3 m/s

Answer: A
Diff: 3 *Page Ref: Sec. 7.4-7.5*

31) A ball of mass 400 g moving toward the east with a speed of 3.70 m/s collides head-on with a 200 g ball sitting at rest. The collision is perfectly elastic.
(a) Determine the velocity of the first ball after the collision.
(b) Determine the velocity of the second ball after the collision.
(c) Is kinetic energy conserved in this collision?

Answer: (a) 1.2 m/s toward the east
(b) 4.9 m/s toward the east
(c) Yes, it is an elastic collision.
Diff: 2 *Page Ref: Sec. 7.4-7.5*

32) A 2.0-kg mass moves with a speed of 5.0 m/s. It collides head-on with a 3.0 kg mass at rest. If the collision is perfectly inelastic, what is the speed of the masses after the collision?

A) 10 m/s

B) 2.5 m/s

C) 2.0 m/s

D) 0, since the collision is inelastic

Answer: C
Diff: 1 *Page Ref: Sec. 7.6*

33) A 2.0-kg mass moving to the east at a speed of 4.0 m/s collides head-on in a perfectly inelastic collision with a stationary 2.0-kg mass. How much kinetic energy is lost during this collision?

A) 16 J

B) 4.0 J

C) 8.0 J

D) zero

Answer: C

Diff: 2 *Page Ref: Sec. 7.6*

34) A car of mass m, traveling with a velocity v, strikes a parked station wagon, who's mass is 2m. The bumpers lock together in this head-on inelastic collision. What fraction of the initial kinetic energy is lost in this collision?

A) 1/2

B) 1/3

C) 1/4

D) 2/3

Answer: D

Diff: 2 *Page Ref: Sec. 7.6*

35) A 15-g bullet traveling 213 m/s in a vertical direction buries itself in a 2.4-kg block of wood a rest directly above it. As a result, the bullet/block combination moves vertically upward.
(a) Determine the velocity of the bullet/block combination at the point of impact.
(b) Determine the maximum height reached by the bullet/block combination.
(c) Is kinetic energy conserved in this collision?

Answer: (a) 1.3 m/s
(b) 0.089 m
(c) No, this is an inelastic collision.

Diff: 2 *Page Ref: Sec. 7.6*

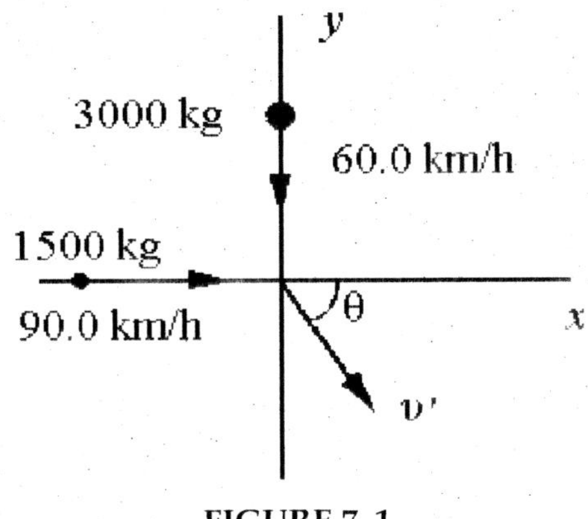

FIGURE 7-1

36) A 1500-kg car traveling at 90.0 km/h east collides with a 3000-kg car traveling at 60.0 km/h south. The two cars stick together after the collision. (See Fig. 7-1.) What is the speed of the cars after collision?

A) 8.33 m/s

B) 13.9 m/s

C) 17.4 m/s

D) 21.7 m/s

Answer: B
Diff: 2 *Page Ref: Sec. 7.7*

37) A 1500-kg car traveling at 90.0 km/h east collides with a 3000-kg car traveling at 60.0 km/h south. The two cars stick together after the collision. (See Fig. 7-1.) What is the direction of motion of the cars after collision?

A) 36.9° S of E

B) 36.9° E of S

C) 53.1° S of E

D) 53.1° E of S

Answer: C
Diff: 2 *Page Ref: Sec. 7.7*

38) Two objects move on a level frictionless surface. Object A moves east with a momentum of 24 kg•m/s. Object B moves north with momentum 10 kg•m/s. They make a perfectly inelastic collision. What is the magnitude of their combined momentum after the collision?

A) 14 kg•m/s

B) 26 kg•m/s

C) 34 kg•m/s

D) cannot be determined without knowing masses and velocities

Answer: B
Diff: 2 *Page Ref: Sec. 7.7*

39) A small bomb, of mass 10 kg, is moving toward the North with a velocity of 4.0 m/s. It explodes into three fragments: a 5.0-kg fragment moving west with a speed of 8.0 m/s; a 4.0-kg fragment moving east with a speed of 10 m/s; and a third fragment with a mass of 1.0 kg. What is the velocity of the third fragment? (Neglect air friction.)

A) zero

B) 40 m/s north

C) 40 m/s south

D) none of the above

Answer: B

Diff: 2 *Page Ref: Sec. 7.7*

40) A 4.00-kg mass sits at the origin, and a 10.0-kg mass sits at x = + 21.0 m. Where is the center of mass on the x-axis?

A) +7.00 m

B) +10.5 m

C) +14.0 m

D) +15.0 m

Answer: D

Diff: 1 *Page Ref: Sec. 7.8*

41) The center of mass of a two-particle system is at the origin. One particle is located at (3.0 m, 0) and has a mass of 2.0 kg. What is the location of the second mass of 3.0 kg?

A) (-3.0 m, 0)

B) (-2.0 m, 0)

C) (2.0 m, 0)

D) (3.0 m, 0)

Answer: B

Diff: 2 *Page Ref: Sec. 7.8*

42) Three masses are positioned as follows: 2.0 kg at (0, 0), 2.0 kg at (2.0, 0), and 4.0 kg at (2.0, 1.0). Determine the coordinates of the center of mass.

A) (0.50, 1.5)

B) (1.5, 0.50)

C) (2.5, 1.5)

D) (2.5, 0.50)

Answer: B

Diff: 1 *Page Ref: Sec. 7.8*

43) Three masses, 1.0 kg, 2.0 kg, and 3.0 kg, are located at (0, 0), (1.0 m, 1.0 m), and (2.0 m, -2.0 m), respectively. What is the location of the center of mass of the system?

A) (1.3 m, 0.67 m)

B) (1.3 m, -0.67 m)

C) (-1.3 m, 0.67 m)

D) (-1.3 m, -0.67 m)

Answer: B
Diff: 2 *Page Ref: Sec. 7.8*

44) A 3.0-kg mass is positioned at (0, 8.0), and a 1.0-kg mass is positioned at (12, 0). What are the coordinates of a 4.0-kg mass which will result in the center of mass of the system of three masses being located at the origin, (0, 0)?

A) (-3.0, -6.0)

B) (-12, -8.0)

C) (3.0, 6.0)

D) (-6.0, -3.0)

Answer: A
Diff: 2 *Page Ref: Sec. 7.8*

TABLE 7-1 Center of Mass of Parts of Typical Human Body
(full height and mass = 100 units)

Distance Above Floor of Hinge Points (%)	Hinge Points (•) (Joints)		Center of Mass (×) (% Height Above Floor)		Percent Mass
91.2	Base of skull		Head	93.5	6.9
81.2	Shoulder joint		Trunk and neck	71.1	46.1
			Upper arms	71.7	6.6
		elbow 62.2	Lower arms	55.3	4.2
52.1	Hip joint	wrist 46.2	Hands	43.1	1.7
			Upper legs (thighs)	42.5	21.5
28.5	Knee joint				
			Lower legs	18.2	9.6
4.0	Ankle joint		Feet	1.8	3.4
			Body CM =	58.0	100.0

45) Use Table 7-1 to calculate the position of the CM of a whole leg including the foot when the leg is stretched straight out. Assume the person is 1.60 m tall.

A) 0.20 m above the bottom of the foot

B) 0.32 m above the bottom of the foot

C) 0.51 m above the bottom of the foot

D) 0.54 m above the bottom of the foot

Answer: C
Diff: 2 *Page Ref: Sec. 7.9*

Chapter 8 Rotational Motion

Conceptual Questions

1) Angular displacement is usually express in units of

A) meters.

B) radians.

C) revolutions.

D) arcs.

Answer: B
Diff: 1 *Page Ref: Sec. 8.1*

2) Angular velocity is expressed in units of

A) meters per second.

B) radians per second.

C) omegas per second.

D) arcs per second.

Answer: B
Diff: 1 *Page Ref: Sec. 8.1*

3) Angular acceleration is expressed in units of

A) meters per second squared.

B) radians per second squared.

C) alphas per second squared.

D) arcs per second squared.

Answer: B
Diff: 1 *Page Ref: Sec. 8.1*

4) A boy and a girl are riding on a merry-go-round which is turning at a constant rate. The boy is near the outer edge, and the girl is closer to the center. Who has the greater angular displacement?

A) the boy

B) the girl

C) Both have the same non-zero angular displacement.

D) Both have zero angular displacement.

Answer: C
Diff: 1 *Page Ref: Sec. 8.1*

5) A boy and a girl are riding on a merry-go-round which is turning at a constant rate. The boy is near the outer edge, and the girl is closer to the center. Who has the greater angular speed?

   A) the boy

   B) the girl

   C) Both have the same non-zero angular velocity.

   D) Both have zero angular velocity.

   Answer: C
   Diff: 1 *Page Ref: Sec. 8.1*

6) A boy and a girl are riding on a merry-go-round which is turning at a constant rate. The boy is near the outer edge, and the girl is closer to the center. Who has the greater linear speed?

   A) the boy

   B) the girl

   C) Both have the same non-zero translational velocity.

   D) Both have zero translational velocity.

   Answer: A
   Diff: 1 *Page Ref: Sec. 8.1*

7) A boy and a girl are riding a merry-go-round which is turning at a constant rate. The boy is near the outer edge, while the girl is closer to the center. Who has the greater centripetal acceleration?

   A) the boy

   B) the girl

   C) Both have the same non-zero centripetal acceleration.

   D) Both have zero centripetal acceleration.

   Answer: A
   Diff: 1 *Page Ref: Sec. 8.1*

8) A boy and a girl are riding a merry-go-round which is turning at a constant rate. The boy is near the outer edge, while the girl is closer to the center. Who has the greater tangential acceleration?

   A) the boy

   B) the girl

   C) Both have the same non-zero tangential acceleration.

   D) Both have zero tangential acceleration.

   Answer: D
   Diff: 1 *Page Ref: Sec. 8.1*

9) Consider a rigid body that is rotating. Which of the following is an accurate statement?

A) Its center of rotation is its center of gravity.

B) All points on the body are moving with the same angular velocity.

C) All points on the body are moving with the same linear velocity.

D) Its center of rotation is at rest, i.e., not moving.

Answer: B
Diff: 2 *Page Ref: Sec. 8.1*

10) Rolling without slipping depends on

A) kinetic friction between the rolling object and the ground.

B) static friction between the rolling object and the ground.

C) tension between the rolling object and the ground.

D) the force of gravity between the rolling object and the Earth.

Answer: B
Diff: 2 *Page Ref: Sec. 8.2-8.3*

11) Two equal forces are applied to a door. The first force is applied at the midpoint of the door; the second force is applied at the doorknob. Both forces are applied perpendicular to the door. Which force exerts the greater torque?

A) the first at the midpoint

B) the second at the doorknob

C) both exert equal non-zero torques

D) both exert zero torques

Answer: B
Diff: 2 *Page Ref: Sec. 8.4*

12) Two equal forces are applied to a door at the doorknob. The first force is applied perpendicular to the door; the second force is applied at 30° to the plane of the door. Which force exerts the greater torque?

A) the first applied perpendicular to the door

B) the second applied at an angle

C) both exert equal non-zero torques

D) both exert zero torques

Answer: A
Diff: 2 *Page Ref: Sec. 8.4*

13) Two forces are applied to a doorknob, perpendicular to the door. The first force is twice as large as the second force. The ratio of the torque of the first to the torque of the second is

A) 1/4.

B) 1/2.

C) 2.

D) 4.

Answer: C
Diff: 2 *Page Ref: Sec. 8.4*

14) What is the quantity used to measure an object's resistance to changes in rotation?

A) mass

B) moment of inertia

C) torque

D) angular velocity

Answer: B
Diff: 1 *Page Ref: Sec. 8.5-8.6*

15) Consider two uniform solid spheres where both have the same diameter, but one has twice the mass of the other. The ratio of the larger moment of inertia to that of the smaller moment of inertia is

A) 2.

B) 8.

C) 10.

D) 4.

E) 6.

Answer: A
Diff: 2 *Page Ref: Sec. 8.5-8.6*

16) Two uniform solid spheres have the same mass, but one has twice the radius of the other. The ratio of the larger sphere's moment of inertia to that of the smaller sphere is

A) 4/5.

B) 8/5.

C) 2.

D) 4.

Answer: D
Diff: 2 *Page Ref: Sec. 8.5-8.6*

17) Consider two uniform solid spheres where one has twice the mass and twice the diameter of the other. The ratio of the larger moment of inertia to that of the smaller moment of inertia is

A) 2.

B) 8.

C) 4.

D) 10.

E) 6.

Answer: B
Diff: 2 *Page Ref: Sec. 8.5–8.6*

18) A uniform solid sphere has mass M and radius R. If these are increased to 2M and 3R, what happens to the sphere's moment of inertia about a central axis?

A) increases by a factor of 6

B) increases by a factor of 12

C) increases by a factor of 18

D) increases by a factor of 54

Answer: C
Diff: 2 *Page Ref: Sec. 8.5–8.6*

19) If a constant net torque is applied to an object, that object will

A) rotate with constant angular velocity.

B) rotate with constant angular acceleration.

C) having an increasing moment of inertia.

D) having a decreasing moment of inertia.

Answer: B
Diff: 1 *Page Ref: Sec. 8.5–8.6*

20) The moment of inertia of a solid cylinder about its axis is given by $0.5 MR^2$. If this cylinder rolls without slipping, the ratio of its rotational kinetic energy to its translational kinetic energy is

A) 1:1.

B) 1:2.

C) 2:1.

D) 1:3.

Answer: B
Diff: 2 *Page Ref: Sec. 8.7*

21) Consider a motorcycle of mass 150 kg, one wheel of which has a mass of 10 kg and a radius of 30 cm. What is the ratio of the rotational kinetic energy of the wheels to the total translational kinetic energy of the bike? Assume the wheels are uniform disks.

A) 0.033:1

B) 0.067:1

C) 0.33:1

D) 0.67:1

Answer: B
Diff: 3 *Page Ref: Sec. 8.7*

22) Suppose a solid sphere of mass M and radius R rolls without slipping down an inclined plane starting from rest. The linear velocity of the sphere at the bottom of the incline depends on

A) the mass of the sphere.

B) the radius of the sphere.

C) both the mass and the radius of the sphere.

D) neither the mass nor the radius of the sphere.

Answer: D
Diff: 2 *Page Ref: Sec. 8.7*

23) Suppose a solid sphere of mass M and radius R rolls without slipping down an inclined plane starting from rest. The angular velocity of the sphere at the bottom of the incline depends on

A) the mass of the sphere.

B) the radius of the sphere.

C) both the mass and the radius of the sphere.

D) neither the mass nor the radius of the sphere.

Answer: B
Diff: 2 *Page Ref: Sec. 8.7*

24) "The total angular momentum of a system of particles changes when a net external force acts on the system." This statement is

A) always true.

B) never true.

C) sometimes true. It depends on the force's magnitude.

D) sometimes true. It depends on the force's point of application.

Answer: D
Diff: 2 *Page Ref: Sec. 8.8*

25) In what circumstances can the angular velocity of system of particles change without any change in the system's angular momentum?

A) This cannot happen under any circumstances.

B) This can happen if a net external force acts on the system's center of mass.

C) This can happen if the only forces acting are internal to the system.

D) This can happen if an external net torque is applied properly to the system.

Answer: C
Diff: 2 *Page Ref: Sec. 8.8*

26) The Earth orbits the Sun in an elliptical orbit. Ignore any friction which may be present. What happens over time to the Earth's angular momentum about the Sun?

A) It continually increases.

B) It continually decreases.

C) It remains constant.

D) It increases during some parts of the orbit, and decreases during others.

Answer: C
Diff: 2 *Page Ref: Sec. 8.8*

27) The Earth moves about the Sun in an elliptical orbit. As the Earth moves close to the Sun, then which of the following best describes the orbiting speed of the Earth about the Sun?

A) increases

B) decreases

C) remains constant

D) none of the above

Answer: A
Diff: 2 *Page Ref: Sec. 8.8*

28) An ice skater performs a pirouette (a fast spin) by pulling in his outstretched arms close to his body. What happens to his angular momentum about the axis of rotation?

A) It does not change.

B) It increases.

C) It decreases.

D) It changes, but it is impossible to tell which way.

Answer: A
Diff: 1 *Page Ref: Sec. 8.8*

29) An ice skater performs a pirouette (a fast spin) by pulling in his outstretched arms close to his body. What happens to his rotational kinetic energy about the axis of rotation?

A) It does not change.

B) It increases.

C) It decreases.

D) It changes, but it is impossible to tell which way.

Answer: B
Diff: 2 *Page Ref: Sec. 8.8*

30) An ice skater performs a pirouette (a fast spin) by pulling in his outstretched arms close to his body. What happens to his moment of inertia about the axis of rotation?

A) It does not change.

B) It increases.

C) It decreases.

D) It changes, but it is impossible to tell which way.

Answer: C
Diff: 1 *Page Ref: Sec. 8.8*

31) State the law of conservation of angular momentum.

Answer: The total angular momentum of a rotating object remains constant if the net torque acting on it is zero.
Diff: 1 *Page Ref: Sec. 8.8*

Quantitative Problems

1) What arc length does the Earth travel in a three month period in its nearly circular orbit about the Sun with a radius of 1.5×10^{11} m?

A) 1.2×10^{11} m

B) 1.8×10^{11} m

C) 2.4×10^{11} m

D) 3.0×10^{11} m

Answer: C
Diff: 1 *Page Ref: Sec. 8.1*

2) The second hand of a clock has a length of 0.30 m. What distance does the tip of the second hand sweep through in 3 minutes and 45 seconds?

A) 1.1 m

B) 1.8 m

C) 7.1 m

D) 13 m

Answer: C
Diff: 2 *Page Ref: Sec. 8.1*

3) How many rad/s is 25 revolutions per minute equivalent to?

A) 0.42 rad/s

B) 2.6 rad/s

C) 160 rad/s

D) 240 rad/s

Answer: B
Diff: 1 *Page Ref: Sec. 8.1*

4) A bicycle wheel rotates uniformly through 2.0 revolutions in 4.0 s. What is the frequency of the wheel's rotation?

A) 0.50 Hz

B) 1.0 Hz

C) 2.0 Hz

D) 4.0 Hz

Answer: A
Diff: 1 *Page Ref: Sec. 8.1*

5) A pulsar (a rotating neutron star) emits pulses at a frequency of 0.40 kHz. The period of its rotation is

A) 2.5 ms.

B) 2.5 s.

C) 0.025 s.

D) 25 ms.

Answer: A
Diff: 1 *Page Ref: Sec. 8.1*

6) A phonograph record rotates at 45 rpm. Through what angle does it turn in 0.20 s?

A) 9.0°

B) 15°

C) 54°

D) 96°

Answer: C
Diff: 2 *Page Ref: Sec. 8.1*

7) A wheel of diameter 26 cm turns at 1500 rpm. How far will a point on the outer rim move in 2.0 s?

A) 3.1 m

B) 41 m

C) 90 m

D) 180 m

Answer: B
Diff: 2 *Page Ref: Sec. 8.1*

8) A bicycle wheel rotates uniformly through 2.0 revolutions in 4.0 s. What is the average angular speed of the wheel?

A) 0.79 rad/s

B) 1.6 rad/s

C) 3.1 rad/s

D) 6.3 rad/s

Answer: C
Diff: 1 *Page Ref: Sec. 8.1*

9) A bicycle wheel rotates uniformly through 2.0 revolutions in 4.0 s. What is the linear speed of a point 0.10 m from the center of the wheel?

A) 0.63 rad/s

B) 0.31 rad/s

C) 0.16 rad/s

D) 0.079 rad/s

Answer: B
Diff: 1 *Page Ref: Sec. 8.1*

10) A cable car at a ski resort carries skiers a distance of 6.8 km. The cable which moves the car is driven by a pulley with diameter 3.0 m. Assuming no slippage, how fast must the pulley rotate for the cable car to make the trip in 12 minutes?

A) 9.4 rpm

B) 30 rpm

C) 60 rpm

D) 720 rpm

Answer: C
Diff: 2 *Page Ref: Sec. 8.1*

11) A wheel of radius 1.0 m is rotating with a constant angular speed of 2.0 rad/s. What is the linear speed of a point on the wheel's rim?

A) 0.50 m/s

B) 1.0 m/s

C) 2.0 m/s

D) 4.0 m/s

Answer: C
Diff: 1 *Page Ref: Sec. 8.1*

12) The cutting cord on a gas-powered weed cutter is 0.16 m in length. If the motor rotates at the rate of 20 rev/s, what is the approximate linear speed of the end of the cord?

A) 20 m/s

B) 25 m/s

C) 35 m/s

D) 65 m/s

Answer: A
Diff: 2 *Page Ref: Sec. 8.1*

13) A wheel of radius 1.0 m is rotating with a constant angular speed of 2.0 rad/s. What is the centripetal acceleration of a point on the wheel's rim?

A) 0.50 m/s^2

B) 1.0 m/s^2

C) 2.0 m/s^2

D) 4.0 m/s^2

Answer: D
Diff: 1 *Page Ref: Sec. 8.1*

14) What is the centripetal acceleration of a point on the perimeter of a bicycle wheel of diameter 70.0 cm when the bike is moving 8.00 m/s?

A) 91.0 m/s^2

B) 183 m/s^2

C) 206 m/s^2

D) 266 m/s^2

Answer: B
Diff: 2 *Page Ref: Sec. 8.1*

15) How many revolutions per minute (rpm) must a circular, rotating space station (r = 1000 m) rotate to produce an artificial gravity of 9.80 m/s^2?

A) 0.95 rpm

B) 0.83 rpm

C) 0.075 rpm

D) 0.094 rpm

Answer: A
Diff: 2 *Page Ref: Sec. 8.1*

16) A car is negotiating a flat circular curve of radius 50 m with a speed of 20 m/s. The maximum centripetal force (provided by static friction) is 1.2×10^4 N. What is the centripetal acceleration of the car?

A) 0.40 m/s^2

B) 0.80 m/s^2

C) 4.0 m/s^2

D) 8.0 m/s^2

Answer: D
Diff: 1 *Page Ref: Sec. 8.1*

17) A car is negotiating a flat circular curve of radius 50 m with a speed of 20 m/s. The maximum centripetal force (provided by static friction) is 1.2×10^4 N. What is the mass of the car?

A) 0.50×10^3 kg

B) 1.0×10^3 kg

C) 1.5×10^3 kg

D) 2.0×10^3 kg

Answer: C
Diff: 2 *Page Ref: Sec. 8.1*

18) A 0.300-kg mass, attached to the end of a 0.750-m string, is whirled around in a smooth level table. If the maximum tension that the string can withstand is 250 N, then what maximum linear speed can the mass have if the string is not to break?

A) 19.4 m/s

B) 22.4 m/s

C) 25.0 m/s

D) 32.7 m/s

Answer: C
Diff: 2 *Page Ref: Sec. 8.1*

19) A bowling ball of mass 7.5 kg and radius 9.0 cm rolls without slipping 10 m down a lane at 4.3 m/s.
(a) Calculate the angular displacement of the bowling ball.
(b) Calculate the angular velocity of the bowling ball.
(c) Calculate the radial acceleration of the bowling ball.
(d) Calculate the tangential acceleration of the bowling ball.

Answer: (a) 110 rad
(b) 48 rad/s
(c) 210 m/s^2
(d) 0 m/s^2
Diff: 1 *Page Ref: Sec. 8.1*

20) A wheel accelerates with a constant angular acceleration of 4.5 rad/s^2. If the initial angular velocity is 1.0 rad/s, what is the angle the wheel rotates through in 2.0 s?

A) 11 rad

B) 9.0 rad

C) 7.0 rad

D) 4.5 rad

Answer: A
Diff: 1 *Page Ref: Sec. 8.2-8.3*

21) A wheel accelerates with a constant angular acceleration of 4.5 rad/s^2. If the initial angular velocity is 1.0 rad/s, what is the angular velocity at t = 2.0 s?

A) 1.0 rad/s

B) 7.0 rad/s

C) 9.0 rad/s

D) 10 rad/s

Answer: D
Diff: 1 *Page Ref: Sec. 8.2-8.3*

22) How many radians does a 0.300-m radius automobile tire rotate after starting from rest and accelerating at a constant angular acceleration of 2.00 rad/s^2 over a 5.00-s interval?

A) 1.00 rad

B) 2.00 rad

C) 12.5 rad

D) 25.0 rad

Answer: D
Diff: 1 *Page Ref: Sec. 8.2-8.3*

23) A wheel starts at rest, and has an angular acceleration of 4 rad/s^2. Through what angle does it turn in 3.0 s?

A) 36 rad

B) 18 rad

C) 12 rad

D) 9.0 rad

Answer: B
Diff: 1 *Page Ref: Sec. 8.2-8.3*

24) A Ferris wheel rotating at 20 rad/s decelerates with a constant angular acceleration of -5.0 rad/s^2. How many revolutions does it rotate before coming to rest?

A) 40

B) 20

C) 6.4

D) 3.2

Answer: C
Diff: 2 *Page Ref: Sec. 8.2-8.3*

25) A wheel starts from rest and reaches an angular speed of 6.0 rad/s while turning through 2.0 revolutions. What is the average angular acceleration of the wheel?

A) 0.24 rad/s^2

B) 1.4 rad/s^2

C) 3.0 rad/s^2

D) 9.0 rad/s^2

Answer: B
Diff: 2 *Page Ref: Sec. 8.2-8.3*

26) A wheel of diameter of 68.0 cm slows down uniformly from 8.40 m/s to rest over a distance of 115 m. What is the total number of revolutions the wheel rotates in coming to rest?

A) 53.8 rev

B) 26.9 rev

C) 338 rev

D) 169 rev

Answer: A
Diff: 1 *Page Ref: Sec. 8.2-8.3*

27) A wheel of diameter of 68.0 cm slows down uniformly from 8.40 m/s to rest over a distance of 115 m. What is the angular acceleration?

A) -1.80 rad/s^2

B) -0.90 rad/s^2

C) -5.65 rad/s^2

D) -11.3 rad/s^2

Answer: B
Diff: 2 *Page Ref: Sec. 8.2-8.3*

28) A wheel of diameter of 68.0 cm slows down uniformly from 8.40 m/s to rest over a distance of 115 m. How long does it take for the wheel to come to the stop?

A) 24.7 s

B) 27.4 s

C) 42.7 s

D) 47.2 s

Answer: B
Diff: 2 *Page Ref: Sec. 8.2–8.3*

29) A centrifuge in a medical laboratory rotates at a rotational speed of 3600 rev/min. When switched off, it rotates 50.0 times at a constant angular acceleration before coming to rest.
(a) Determine the initial angular speed of the centrifuge.
(b) Determine the angle (in radians) through which the centrifuge rotates before coming to rest.
(c) Calculate the constant angular acceleration of the centrifuge.
(d) Calculate the time necessary for the centrifuge to come to rest.

Answer: (a) 377 rad/s
(b) 314 rad
(c) –226 rad/s^2
(d) 1.67 s
Diff: 2 *Page Ref: Sec. 8.2–8.3*

30) The bolts on a car wheel require tightening to a torque of 90 N•m. If a 30 cm long wrench is used, what is the magnitude of the force required when the force is perpendicular to the wrench?

A) 300 N

B) 150 N

C) 30 N

D) 15 N

Answer: A
Diff: 1 *Page Ref: Sec. 8.4*

31) The bolts on a car wheel require tightening to a torque of 90 N•m. If a 30 cm long wrench is used, what is the magnitude of the force required when the force applied at 53° to the wrench?

A) 190 N

B) 380 N

C) 19 N

D) 38 N

Answer: B
Diff: 2 *Page Ref: Sec. 8.4*

32) A wheel with moment of inertia 3.00 kg•m^2 has a net torque of 3.50 N•m applied to it. What angular acceleration does it experience?

A) 0.857 rad/s^2

B) 1.17 rad/s^2

C) 3.00 rad/s^2

D) 3.50 rad/s^2

Answer: B

Diff: 1 *Page Ref: Sec. 8.5–8.6*

33) A triatomic molecule is modeled as follows: mass m is at the origin, mass 2m is at x = a, and, mass 3m is at x = 2a. What is the moment of inertia about the origin?

A) 2 ma^2

B) 3 ma^2

C) 12 ma^2

D) 14 ma^2

Answer: D

Diff: 2 *Page Ref: Sec. 8.5–8.6*

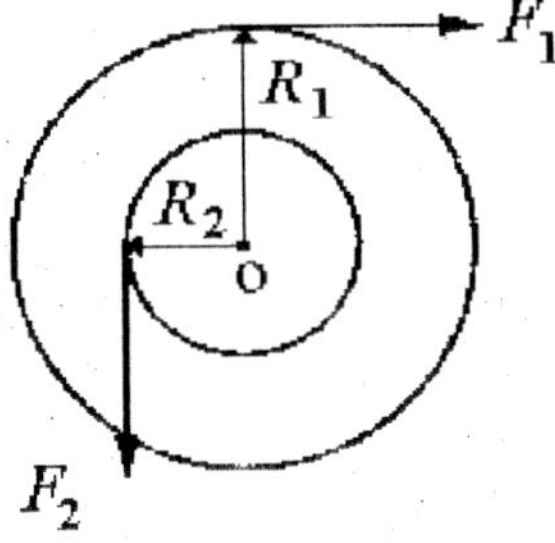

FIGURE 8-1

34) A solid cylinder of mass 10 kg is pivoted about a frictionless axis thought the center O. A rope wrapped around the outer radius R_1 = 1.0 m, exerts a force F_1 = 5.0 N to the right. A second rope wrapped around another section of radius R_2 = 0.50 m exerts a force F_2 = 6.0 N downward. (See Fig. 8-1.) What is the angular acceleration of the cylinder?

A) 1.0 rad/s^2

B) 0.60 rad/s^2

C) 0.40 rad/s^2

D) 0.80 rad/s^2

Answer: C

Diff: 2 *Page Ref: Sec. 8.5–8.6*

35) A solid cylinder of mass 10 kg is pivoted about a frictionless axis thought the center O. A rope wrapped around the outer radius $R_1 = 1.0$ m, exerts a force $F_1 = 5.0$ N to the right. A second rope wrapped around another section of radius $R_2 = 0.50$ m exerts a force $F_2 = 6.0$ N downward. How many radians does the cylinder rotate through in the first 5.0 seconds, if it starts from rest?

A) 13 rad

B) 7.5 rad

C) 5.0 rad

D) 10 rad

Answer: C
Diff: 2 *Page Ref: Sec. 8.5–8.6*

36) A 4.00-m long rod is hinged at one end. The rod is initially held in the horizontal position, and then released as the free end is allowed to fall. What is the angular acceleration as it is released? (The moment of inertia of a rod about one end is $ML^2/3$.)

A) 2.45 rad/s^2

B) 3.68 rad/s^2

C) 4.90 rad/s^2

D) 6.75 rad/s^2

Answer: B
Diff: 2 *Page Ref: Sec. 8.5–8.6*

37) Consider a bicycle wheel to be a ring of radius 30 cm and mass 1.5 kg. Neglect the mass of the axle and sprocket. If a force of 20 N is applied tangentially to a sprocket of radius 4.0 cm for 4.0 s, what linear speed does the wheel achieve, assuming it rolls without slipping?

A) 3.0 m/s

B) 5.9 m/s

C) 7.1 m/s

D) 24 m/s

Answer: C
Diff: 3 *Page Ref: Sec. 8.5–8.6*

38) A 1.53-kg mass hangs on a rope wrapped around a frictionless disk pulley of mass 7.07 kg and radius 66.0 cm. What is the angular acceleration of the pulley?

A) 4.49 rad/s^2

B) 7.98 rad/s^2

C) 9.87 rad/s^2

D) zero

Answer: A
Diff: 3 *Page Ref: Sec. 8.5–8.6*

39) A 1.53-kg mass hangs on a rope wrapped around a frictionless disk pulley of mass 7.07 kg and radius 66.0 cm. What is the acceleration of the mass?

A) 9.26 m/s^2

B) 2.96 m/s^2

C) 6.29 m/s^2

D) zero

Answer: B
Diff: 3 *Page Ref: Sec. 8.5-8.6*

40) A rotating flywheel can be used to store energy. If it is required to store 1.00×10^6 J of energy when rotating at 400 rad/s, what is the moment of inertial of the wheel in $kg \cdot m^2$?

A) 6.25

B) 12.5

C) 25.0

D) 50.0

Answer: B
Diff: 2 *Page Ref: Sec. 8.7*

41) A wheel of moment of inertia of 5.00 $kg \cdot m^2$ starts from rest and accelerates under a constant torque of 3.00 N•m for 8.00 s. What is the wheel's rotational kinetic energy at the end of 8.00 s?

A) 57.6 J

B) 64.0 J

C) 78.8 J

D) 122 J

Answer: A
Diff: 2 *Page Ref: Sec. 8.7*

42) A solid sphere of mass 1.0 kg and radius 0.010 m starts from rest and rolls without slipping down a 1.0-m high inclined plane. What is the speed of the sphere when it reaches the bottom of the inclined plane?

A) 3.7 m/s

B) 4.4 m/s

C) 5.6 m/s

D) 6.3 m/s

Answer: A
Diff: 2 *Page Ref: Sec. 8.7*

43) A solid sphere of mass 1.0 kg and radius 0.010 m rolls with a speed of 10 m/s. How high up an inclined plane can it climb before coming to rest?

A) 0.071 m

B) 0.71 m

C) 7.1 m

D) 71 m

Answer: C

Diff: 2 *Page Ref: Sec. 8.7*

44) A hoop of radius 0.50 m and a mass of 0.20 kg is released from rest and allowed to roll down an inclined plane. How fast is it moving after dropping a vertical distance of 3.0 m?

A) 2.2 m/s

B) 3.8 m/s

C) 5.4 m/s

D) 7.7 m/s

Answer: C

Diff: 2 *Page Ref: Sec. 8.7*

45) A solid sphere of mass 1.5 kg and radius 15 cm rolls without slipping down a 35° incline that is 7.0 m long. Assume it started from rest. The moment of inertia of a sphere is given by $I = (2/5)MR^2$.

(a) Calculate the linear speed of the sphere when it reaches the bottom of the incline.

(b) Determine the angular speed of the sphere at the bottom of the incline.

(c) Does the linear speed depend on the radius or mass of the sphere? Does the angular speed depend on the radius or mass of the sphere?

Answer: (a) 7.5 m/s

(b) 50 rad/s

(c) The linear speed depends on neither the radius or the mass of the sphere. The angular speed depends on the radius of the sphere.

Diff: 2 *Page Ref: Sec. 8.7*

46) An object's angular momentum changes by 20 kg•m^2/s in 4.0 s. What magnitude average torque acted on this object?

A) 2.5 N•m

B) 5.0 N•m

C) 40 N•m

D) 80 N•m

Answer: B

Diff: 1 *Page Ref: Sec. 8.8*

47) A proton of mass 1.67×10^{-27} kg rotates with an angular speed of 2×10^6 rad/s in a circle of radius 0.80 m in a cyclotron. What is the orbital angular momentum of the proton?

A) 1.28×10^{-21} kg•m^2/s

B) 1.76×10^{-21} kg•m^2/s

C) 2.14×10^{-21} kg•m^2/s

D) 3.20×10^{-21} kg•m^2/s

Answer: C
Diff: 2 *Page Ref: Sec. 8.8*

48) An ice skater has a moment of inertia of 5.0 kg•m^2 when her arms are outstretched. At this time she is spinning at 3.0 revolutions per second (rps). If she pulls in her arms and decreases her moment of inertia to 2.0 kg•m^2, how fast will she be spinning?

A) 2.0 rps

B) 3.3 rps

C) 7.5 rps

D) 10 rps

Answer: C
Diff: 1 *Page Ref: Sec. 8.8*

49) A figure skater rotating at 5.00 rad/s with arms extended has a moment of inertia of 2.25 kg•m^2. If the arms are pulled in so the moment of inertia decreases to 1.80 kg•m^2, what is the final angular speed?

A) 2.25 rad/s

B) 4.60 rad/s

C) 6.25 rad/s

D) 0.81 rad/s

Answer: C
Diff: 2 *Page Ref: Sec. 8.8*

Chapter 9 Static Equilibrium; Elasticity and Fracture

Conceptual Questions

1) What condition or conditions are necessary for rotational equilibrium?

A) $\Sigma F_x = 0$

B) $\Sigma F_x = 0$, $\Sigma T = 0$

C) $\Sigma T = 0$

D) $\Sigma F_x = 0$, $\Sigma F_y = 0$

Answer: C
Diff: 1 *Page Ref: Sec. 9.1-9.2*

2) What condition or conditions are necessary for static equilibrium?

A) $\Sigma F_x = 0$

B) $\Sigma F_x = 0$, $\Sigma F_y = 0$, $\Sigma T = 0$

C) $\Sigma T = 0$

D) $\Sigma F_x = 0$, $\Sigma F_y = 0$

Answer: B
Diff: 1 *Page Ref: Sec. 9.1-9.2*

3) A book weighs 6 N. When held at rest above your head the net force on the book is

A) 0 N.

B) 6 N.

C) 9.8 N.

D) -6 N.

Answer: A
Diff: 1 *Page Ref: Sec. 9.1-9.2*

4) A rocket moves through outer space with a constant velocity of 9.8 m/s. What net force acts on it?

A) a force equal to its weight on Earth, mg

B) a force equal to the gravity acting on it

C) The net force is zero.

D) cannot be determined without more information

Answer: C
Diff: 1 *Page Ref: Sec. 9.1-9.2*

5) A person weighing 800 N stands with one foot on each of two bathroom scales. Which statement is definitely true?

A) Each scale will read 800 N.

B) Each scale will read 400 N.

C) If one scale reads 500 N, the other will read 300 N.

D) None of the above is definitely true.

Answer: C
Diff: 2 *Page Ref: Sec. 9.1–9.2*

6) A heavy boy and a light girl are balanced on a massless seesaw. If they both move forward so that they are one-half their original distance from the pivot point, what will happen to the seesaw?

A) The side the boy is sitting on will tilt downward.

B) The side the girl is sitting on will tilt downward.

C) Nothing, the seesaw will still be balanced.

D) It is impossible to say without knowing the masses and the distances.

Answer: C
Diff: 2 *Page Ref: Sec. 9.1–9.2*

7) Muscles that tend to bring two limbs closer together are called

A) tendons.

B) flexors.

C) extensors.

D) insertions.

Answer: B
Diff: 1 *Page Ref: Sec. 9.3*

8) Muscles that act to extend a limb outward are called

A) tendons.

B) flexors.

C) extensors.

D) insertions.

Answer: C
Diff: 1 *Page Ref: Sec. 9.3*

9) A sphere hanging freely from a cord is in

A) stable equilibrium.

B) unstable equilibrium.

C) neutral equilibrium.

D) positive equilibrium.

Answer: A
Diff: 1 *Page Ref: Sec. 9.4*

10) A cone balanced on its small end is in
    A) stable equilibrium.
    B) unstable equilibrium.
    C) neutral equilibrium.
    D) positive equilibrium.

Answer: B
Diff: 1 *Page Ref: Sec. 9.4*

11) A cube resting on a horizontal tabletop is in
    A) stable equilibrium.
    B) unstable equilibrium.
    C) neutral equilibrium.
    D) positive equilibrium.

Answer: C
Diff: 1 *Page Ref: Sec. 9.4*

12) Consider two identical bricks, each of dimensions 20.0 cm × 10.0 cm × 6.0 cm. One is stacked on the other, and the combination is then placed so that they project out over the edge of a table. What is the maximum distance that the end of the top brick can extend beyond the table edge without toppling?
    A) 7.5 cm
    B) 10 cm
    C) 12.5 cm
    D) 15 cm

Answer: D
Diff: 2 *Page Ref: Sec. 9.4*

13) A 36-kg round table is supported by three legs placed equal distances apart on the edge. What minimum mass, placed in the middle between two supports on the table's edge, will cause the table to overturn?
    A) 12 kg
    B) 24 kg
    C) 36 kg
    D) 48 kg

Answer: C
Diff: 3 *Page Ref: Sec. 9.4*

14) Stress is

A) the strain per unit length.

B) the same as force.

C) the ratio of the change in length.

D) applied force per cross-sectional area.

Answer: D
Diff: 1 *Page Ref: Sec. 9.5*

15) Strain is

A) the ratio of the change in length to the original length.

B) the stress per unit area.

C) the applied force per unit area.

D) the ratio of stress to elastic modulus.

Answer: A
Diff: 1 *Page Ref: Sec. 9.5*

16) A mass is hung from identical wires made of aluminum, brass, copper, and steel. Which wire will stretch the least?

A) aluminum

B) brass

C) copper

D) steel

E) all the same

Answer: D
Diff: 2 *Page Ref: Sec. 9.5*

17) A copper wire is found to break when subjected to minimum tension of 36 N. If the wire diameter were half as great, we would expect the wire to break when subjected to a minimum tension of

A) 9.0 N.

B) 18 N.

C) 36 N.

D) 108 N.

Answer: A
Diff: 1 *Page Ref: Sec. 9.6*

18) The horizontal component of the buttressing force at the base of a pointed arch is

A) less than that of a rounded arch.

B) equal to that of a rounded arch.

C) greater than that of a rounded arch.

D) zero in magnitude.

Answer: A
Diff: 1 *Page Ref: Sec. 9.7*

Quantitative Problems

1) A lever is 5.0 m long. The distance from the fulcrum to the weight to be lifted is 1.0 m. If a worker pushes on the opposite end with 400 N, what is the maximum weight that can be lifted?

A) 80 N

B) 100 N

C) 1600 N

D) 2000 N

Answer: C
Diff: 1 *Page Ref: Sec. 9.1–9.2*

2) A lever is 5.0 m long. The distance from the fulcrum to the weight to be lifted is 1.0 m. If a 3000 N rock is to be lifted, how much force must be exerted on the lever?

A) 600 N

B) 750 N

C) 3000 N

D) 12000 N

Answer: B
Diff: 1 *Page Ref: Sec. 9.1–9.2*

3) A boy and a girl are balanced on a massless seesaw. The boy has a mass of 75 kg and the girl's mass is 50 kg. If the boy sits 2.0 m from the pivot point on one side of the seesaw, where must the girl sit on the other side?

A) 1.3 m

B) 2.3 m

C) 2.5 m

D) 3.0 m

Answer: D
Diff: 1 *Page Ref: Sec. 9.1–9.2*

4) Two children sit on opposite ends of a uniform seesaw which pivots in the center. Child A has mass 60 kg and sits 2.0 m from the center. Child B has mass 40 kg. How far from the center must child B sit for the seesaw to balance?

A) 1.3 m

B) 2.5 m

C) 3.0 m

D) cannot be determined without knowing the seesaw's mass

Answer: C
Diff: 1 *Page Ref: Sec. 9.1–9.2*

5) A uniform board of weight 40 N supports two children weighing 500 N and 350 N, respectively. If the support is at the center of the board and the 500–N child is 1.5 m from the center, what is the position of the 350–N child?

A) 1.1 m

B) 1.5 m

C) 2.1 m

D) 2.7 m

Answer: C
Diff: 1 *Page Ref: Sec. 9.1–9.2*

6) A 10–m uniform beam of weight 100 N is supported by two ropes at the ends. If a 400–N person sits at 2.0 m from the left end of the beam, what is the tension in the left rope?

A) 130 N

B) 250 N

C) 370 N

D) 500 N

Answer: C
Diff: 2 *Page Ref: Sec. 9.1–9.2*

7) A 10–m uniform beam of weight 100 N is supported by two ropes at the ends. If a 400–N person sits at 2.0 m from the left end of the beam, what is the tension in the right rope?

A) 130 N

B) 250 N

C) 370 N

D) 500 N

Answer: A
Diff: 2 *Page Ref: Sec. 9.1–9.2*

8) A massless scaffold is held up by a wire at each end. The scaffold is 12 m long. A 300-N box sits 4.0 m from the left end. What is the tension in each wire?

A) left wire = 100 N; right wire = 200 N

B) left wire = 200 N; right wire = 100 N

C) left wire = 900 N; right wire = 2700 N

D) left wire = 2700 N; right wire = 900 N

Answer: B
Diff: 2 *Page Ref: Sec. 9.1-9.2*

9) A 200-N scaffold is held up by a wire at each end. The scaffold is 18 m long. A 650-N box sits 3.0 m from the left end. What is the tension in each wire?

A) left wire = 520 N; right wire = 130 N

B) left wire = 640 N; right wire = 210 N

C) left wire = 195 N; right wire = 975 N

D) left wire = 295 N; right wire = 1000 N

Answer: B
Diff: 2 *Page Ref: Sec. 9.1-9.2*

10) A uniform meter stick is supported by a knife edge at the 50-cm mark and has masses of 0.40 kg and 0.60 kg hanging at the 20-cm and 80-cm marks, respectively. Where (at what mark) should a third mass of 0.30 kg be hung to keep the stick in balance?

A) 20 cm

B) 25 cm

C) 30 cm

D) 70 cm

Answer: C
Diff: 2 *Page Ref: Sec. 9.1-9.2*

11) A 500-N person stands on a uniform board of weight 100 N and length 8.0 m. The board is supported at each end. If the support force at the right end is three times that at the left end, how far from the right end is the person?

A) 4.0 m

B) 2.0 m

C) 1.6 m

D) 6.4 m

Answer: C
Diff: 2 *Page Ref: Sec. 9.1-9.2*

12) Two scales are separated by 2.00 m, and a plank of mass 4.00 kg is placed between them. Each scale is observed to read 2.00 kg. A person now lies on the plank, after which the right scale reads 30.0 kg and the left scale reads 50.0 kg. How far from the right scale is the person's center of gravity located?

A) 1.20 m

B) 1.23 m

C) 1.26 m

D) 1.30 m

Answer: C
Diff: 2 *Page Ref: Sec. 9.1-9.2*

13) Two telephone poles are separated by 40 m and connected by a wire. A bird of mass 0.50 kg lands on the wire midway between the poles, causing the wire to sag 2.0 m below horizontal. Assuming the wire has negligible mass, what is the tension in the wire?

A) 6.2 N

B) 12 N

C) 25 N

D) 50 N

Answer: C
Diff: 3 *Page Ref: Sec. 9.1-9.2*

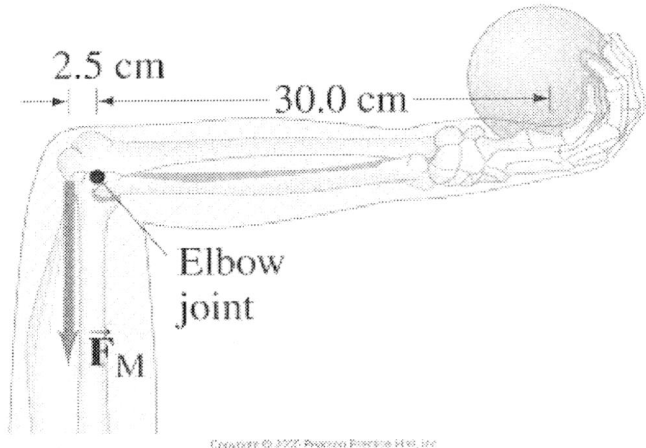

FIGURE 9-1

14) Assuming the lower arm has a mass of 2.8 kg and its CG is 12 cm from the elbow-joint pivot, how much force must the extensor muscle in the upper arm exert on the lower arm to hold a 7.5 kg shot put (Fig. 9-1)?

A) 100 N

B) 500 N

C) 1000 N

D) 1500 N

Answer: C
Diff: 2 *Page Ref: Sec. 9.3*

15) A passenger van has an outer wheel base width of 2.00 m. Its center of gravity is equidistant from the sides, and positioned 1.20 m above the ground. What is the maximum sideways angle at which it can be inclined without tipping over?

A) 32.6°

B) 39.8°

C) 50.2°

D) 57.3°

Answer: B
Diff: 2 *Page Ref: Sec. 9.4*

16) The Leaning Tower of Pisa is 55 m tall and about 7.0 m in diameter. The top is 4.5 m off center. How much farther can it lean before it becomes unstable?

A) 0.5 m

B) 1.5 m

C) 2.5 m

D) 3.5 m

Answer: C
Diff: 2 *Page Ref: Sec. 9.4*

17) A 5000-N force compresses a steel block by 0.0025 cm. How much force would be needed to compress the block by 0.0125 cm?

A) 1000 N

B) 2500 N

C) 5000 N

D) 25000 N

Answer: D
Diff: 2 *Page Ref: Sec. 9.5*

18) A cable is 100-m long and has a cross-sectional area of 1 mm^2. A 1000-N force is applied to stretch the cable. The elastic modulus for the cable is 1.0×10^{11} N/m^2. How far does it stretch?

A) 0.01 m

B) 0.10 m

C) 1.0 m

D) 10 m

Answer: C
Diff: 2 *Page Ref: Sec. 9.5*

19) A steel lift column in a service station is 4.0 m long and 0.20 m in diameter. Young's modulus for steel is 20×10^{10} N/m^2. By how much does the column shrink when a 5000-kg truck is on it?

A) 8.0×10^{-7} m

B) 3.2×10^{-6} m

C) 7.8×10^{-6} m

D) 3.1×10^{-5} m

Answer: D
Diff: 2 *Page Ref: Sec. 9.5*

20) A wire of diameter 0.20 mm stretches by 0.20% when a 6.28-N force is applied. What is the elastic modulus of the wire?

A) 2.5×10^{10} N/m^2

B) 1.0×10^{11} N/m^2

C) 2.5×10^{12} N/m^2

D) 1.0×10^{12} N/m^2

Answer: B
Diff: 2 *Page Ref: Sec. 9.5*

21) A mass of 50 kg is suspended from a steel wire of diameter 1.0 mm and length 11.2 m. How much will the wire stretch? The Young's modulus for steel is 20×10^{10} N/m^2.

A) 1.5 cm

B) 2.5 cm

C) 3.5 cm

D) 4.5 cm

Answer: C
Diff: 2 *Page Ref: Sec. 9.5*

22) Suppose that an 80-kg person walking on crutches supports all his weight on the two crutch tips, each of which is circular with a diameter of 4.0 cm. What pressure is exerted on the floor?

A) 78 kPa

B) 156 kPa

C) 312 kPa

D) 624 kPa

Answer: C
Diff: 2 *Page Ref: Sec. 9.5*

23) A bridge piling has an area of 1.250 m^2. It supports 1875 N. Find the stress on the column.

A) 1875 N

B) 1875 N/m^2

C) 1500 N/m^2

D) 2344 N/m^2

Answer: C
Diff: 1 *Page Ref: Sec. 9.5*

24) An aluminum wire 2.0 m in length and 2.0 mm in diameter supports a 10.0-kg mass. What is the stress in the wire? (The Young's modulus for aluminum is 7.0×10^{10} N/m^2)

A) 3.1×10^7 N/m^2

B) 6.2×10^7 N/m^2

C) 9.3×10^7 N/m^2

D) 1.2×10^8 N/m^2

Answer: A
Diff: 1 *Page Ref: Sec. 9.5*

25) An aluminum wire 2.0 m in length and 2.0 mm in diameter supports a 10.0-kg mass. What is the elongation of the wire? (The Young's modulus for an aluminum is 7.0×10^{10} N/m^2)

A) 0.11 mm

B) 0.22 mm

C) 0.33 mm

D) 0.89 mm

Answer: D
Diff: 2 *Page Ref: Sec. 9.5*

26) A shear force of 400 N is applied to one face of an aluminum cube with sides of 30 cm. What is the resulting relative displacement? (The shear modulus for aluminum is 2.5×10^{10} N/m^2)

A) 1.9×10^{-8} m

B) 4.4×10^{-8} m

C) 5.3×10^{-8} m

D) 8.2×10^{-8} m

Answer: C
Diff: 2 *Page Ref: Sec. 9.5*

27) At a depth of about 1030 m in the sea the pressure has increased by 100 atmospheres (to about 10^7 N/m^2). By how much has 1.0 m^3 of water been compressed by this pressure? The bulk modulus of water is 2.3×10^9 N/m^2.

A) 2.3×10^{-3} m^3

B) 3.3×10^{-3} m^3

C) 4.3×10^{-3} m^3

D) 5.3×10^{-3} m^3

Answer: C
Diff: 2 *Page Ref: Sec. 9.5*

28) A 55-cm brass rod has a diameter of 30 cm. The compressive strength of steel is 250×10^6 N/m^2. What is the compression force that would break the rod?

A) 1.8×10^7 N

B) 1.4×10^8 N

C) 2.4×10^8 N

D) 4.5×10^8 N

Answer: A
Diff: 1 *Page Ref: Sec. 9.6*

Chapter 10 Fluids

Conceptual Questions

1) The three common phases of matter are

A) solid, liquid, and gas.

B) solid, liquid, and vapor.

C) solid, plasma, and gas.

D) condensate, plasma, and gas.

Answer: A
Diff: 1 *Page Ref: Sec. 10.1*

2) Density is

A) proportional to both mass and volume.

B) proportional to mass and inversely proportional to volume.

C) inversely proportional to mass and proportional to volume.

D) inversely proportional to both mass and volume.

Answer: B
Diff: 1 *Page Ref: Sec. 10.2*

3) Substance A has a density of 3.0 g/cm^3 and substance B has a density of 4.0 g/cm^3. In order to obtain equal masses of these two substances, the ratio of the volume of A to the volume of B will be equal to

A) 1:3.

B) 4:3.

C) 3:4.

D) 1:4.

Answer: B
Diff: 1 *Page Ref: Sec. 10.2*

4) Pressure is

A) proportional to both force and area.

B) proportional to force and inversely proportional to area.

C) inversely proportional to force and proportional to area.

D) inversely proportional to both force and area.

Answer: B
Diff: 1 *Page Ref: Sec. 10.3*

5) Which of the following is not a unit of pressure?

A) atmosphere

B) N/m

C) Pascal

D) mm of mercury

Answer: B
Diff: 1 *Page Ref: Sec. 10.3*

6) Consider three drinking glasses. All three have the same area base, and all three are filled to the same depth with water. Glass A is cylindrical. Glass B is wider at the top than at the bottom, and so holds more water than A. Glass C is narrower at the top than at the bottom, and so holds less water than A. Which glass has the greatest liquid pressure at the bottom?

A) Glass A

B) Glass B

C) Glass C

D) All three have equal pressure.

Answer: D
Diff: 2 *Page Ref: Sec. 10.3*

7) What is the difference between the pressures inside and outside a tire called?

A) absolute pressure

B) atmospheric pressure

C) gauge pressure

D) N/m^2

Answer: C
Diff: 1 *Page Ref: Sec. 10.4*

8) When atmospheric pressure changes, what happens to the absolute pressure at the bottom of a pool?

A) It does not change.

B) It increases by a lesser amount.

C) It increases by the same amount.

D) It increases by a greater amount.

Answer: C
Diff: 2 *Page Ref: Sec. 10.4*

9) You are originally 1.0 m beneath the surface of a pool. If you dive to 2.0 m beneath the surface, what happens to the absolute pressure on you?

A) It quadruples.

B) It more than doubles.

C) It doubles.

D) It less than doubles.

Answer: D
Diff: 2 *Page Ref: Sec. 10.4*

10) State Pascal's principle.

Answer: If an external pressure is applied to a confined fluid, the pressure at every point within the fluid increases by that amount.
Diff: 1 *Page Ref: Sec. 10.5*

11) State Archimedes' principle.

Answer: The buoyant force on an object immersed in a fluid is equal to the weight of the fluid displaced by that object.
Diff: 1 *Page Ref: Sec. 10.7*

12) 50 cm^3 of wood is floating on water, and 50 cm^3 of iron is totally submerged. Which has the greater buoyant force on it?

A) the wood

B) the iron

C) Both have the same buoyant force.

D) cannot be determined without knowing their densities

Answer: B
Diff: 2 *Page Ref: Sec. 10.7*

13) As a rock sinks deeper and deeper into water of constant density, what happens to the buoyant force on it?

A) It increases.

B) It remains constant.

C) It decreases.

D) It may increase or decrease, depending on the shape of the rock.

Answer: B
Diff: 2 *Page Ref: Sec. 10.7*

14) Salt water has greater density than fresh water. A boat floats in both fresh water and in salt water. Where is the buoyant force greater on the boat?

A) salt water

B) fresh water

C) Buoyant force is the same in both.

D) impossible to determine from the information given

Answer: C
Diff: 2 *Page Ref: Sec. 10.7*

15) Salt water is more dense than fresh water. A ship floats in both fresh water and salt water. Compared to the fresh water, the volume of water displaced in the salt water is

A) more.

B) less.

C) the same.

D) cannot be determined from the information given

Answer: B
Diff: 2 *Page Ref: Sec. 10.7*

16) A steel ball sinks in water but floats in a pool of mercury. Where is the buoyant force on the ball greater?

A) floating on the mercury

B) submerged in the water

C) It is the same in both cases.

D) cannot be determined from the information given

Answer: A
Diff: 2 *Page Ref: Sec. 10.7*

17) A 10-kg piece of aluminum sits at the bottom of a lake, right next to a 10-kg piece of lead. Which has the greater buoyant force on it?

A) the aluminum

B) the lead

C) Both have the same buoyant force.

D) cannot be determined without knowing their volumes

Answer: A
Diff: 2 *Page Ref: Sec. 10.7*

18) A piece of iron rests on top of a piece of wood floating in a bathtub. If the iron is removed from the wood, what happens to the water level in the tub?

A) It goes up.

B) It goes down.

C) It does not change.

D) impossible to determine from the information given

Answer: B
Diff: 2 *Page Ref: Sec. 10.7*

19) A piece of wood is floating in a bathtub. A second piece of wood sits on top of the first piece, and does not touch the water. If the top piece is taken off and placed in the water, what happens to the water level in the tub?

A) It goes up.

B) It goes down.

C) It does not change.

D) cannot be determined from the information given

Answer: C
Diff: 3 *Page Ref: Sec. 10.7*

20) Water flows through a pipe. The diameter of the pipe at point B is larger than at point A. Where is the speed of the water greater?

A) point A

B) point B

C) same at both A and B

D) cannot be determined from the information given

Answer: A
Diff: 1 *Page Ref: Sec. 10.8*

21) An ideal fluid flows at 12 m/s in a horizontal pipe. If the pipe widens to twice its original radius, what is the flow speed in the wider section?

A) 12 m/s

B) 6.0 m/s

C) 4.0 m/s

D) 3.0 m/s

Answer: D
Diff: 1 *Page Ref: Sec. 10.8*

22) An ideal fluid flows at 12 m/s in a horizontal pipe. If the pipe narrows to half its original radius, what is the flow speed in the narrower section?

A) 12 m/s

B) 24 m/s

C) 36 m/s

D) 48 m/s

Answer: D
Diff: 1 *Page Ref: Sec. 10.8*

23) State Bernoulli's principle.

Answer: Where the velocity of fluid is high, the pressure is low; and where the velocity is low, the pressure is high.
Diff: 1 *Page Ref: Sec. 10.9–10.10*

24) Which one of the following is associated with the law of conservation of energy in fluids?

A) Archimedes' principle

B) Bernoulli's principle

C) Pascal's principle

D) equation of continuity

Answer: B
Diff: 2 *Page Ref: Sec. 10.9–10.10*

25) As the speed of a moving fluid increases, the pressure in the fluid

A) increases.

B) remains constant.

C) decreases.

D) may increase or decrease, depending on the viscosity.

Answer: C
Diff: 1 *Page Ref: Sec. 10.9–10.10*

26) Water flows through a pipe. The diameter of the pipe at point B is larger than at point A. Where is the water pressure greatest?

A) point A

B) point B

C) same at both A and B

D) cannot be determined from the information given

Answer: B
Diff: 2 *Page Ref: Sec. 10.9–10.10*

27) When you blow some air above a paper strip, the paper rises. This is because

A) the air above the paper moves faster and the pressure is higher.

B) the air above the paper moves faster and the pressure is lower.

C) the air above the paper moves slower and the pressure is higher.

D) the air above the paper moves slower and the pressure is lower.

Answer: B
Diff: 1 *Page Ref: Sec. 10.9–10.10*

28) A sky diver falls through the air at terminal velocity. The force of air resistance on him is

A) half his weight.

B) equal to his weight.

C) twice his weight.

D) cannot be determined from the information given

Answer: B
Diff: 1 *Page Ref: Sec. 10.11*

29) Two Styrofoam balls, of radii R and 2R, are released simultaneously from a tall tower. Which will reach the ground first?

A) Both will reach the ground simultaneously.

B) the larger one

C) the smaller one

D) The result will depend on the atmospheric pressure.

Answer: B
Diff: 2 *Page Ref: Sec. 10.11*

30) When a small spherical rock of radius r falls through water, it experiences a drag force arv, where "v" is its velocity and "a" is a constant proportional to the viscosity of water. From this, one can deduce that if a rock of diameter 2.0 mm falls with terminal velocity, "v", then a rock of diameter 4.0 mm will fall with terminal velocity ________.

A) v

B) 1.4v

C) 2.0v

D) 4.0v

Answer: D
Diff: 3 *Page Ref: Sec. 10.11*

31) Which has the greatest effect on the flow of fluid through a narrow pipe? That is, if you made a 10% change in each of the quantities below, which would cause the greatest change in the flow rate?

A) the fluid viscosity

B) the pressure difference

C) the length of the pipe

D) the radius of the pipe

Answer: D
Diff: 2 *Page Ref: Sec. 10.12*

32) Two horizontal pipes are the same length, but pipe B has twice the diameter of pipe A. Water undergoes viscous flow in both pipes, subject to the same pressure difference across the lengths of the pipes. If the flow rate in pipe A is Q, what is the flow rate in pipe B?

A) 2Q

B) 4Q

C) 8Q

D) 16Q

Answer: D
Diff: 2 *Page Ref: Sec. 10.12*

33) Two horizontal pipes have the same diameter, but pipe B is twice as long as pipe A. Water undergoes viscous flow in both pipes, subject to the same pressure difference across the lengths of the pipes. If the flow rate in pipe B is Q, what is the flow rate in pipe A?

A) Q

B) 2Q

C) 4Q

D) 8Q

Answer: B
Diff: 2 *Page Ref: Sec. 10.12*

34) When soup gets cold, it often tastes greasy. This "greasy" taste seems to be associated with oil spreading out all over the surface of the soup, instead of staying in little globules. To us "physikers", this is readily explained in terms of

A) the Bernoulli effect.

B) Archimedes Principle.

C) the decrease in the surface tension of water with increasing temperature.

D) the increase in the surface tension of water with increasing temperature.

Answer: D
Diff: 2 *Page Ref: Sec. 10.13*

35) When a tube of diameter d is placed in water, the water rises to a height h. If the diameter were half as great, how high would the water rise?

A) h/2

B) h

C) 2h

D) 4h

Answer: C
Diff: 1 *Page Ref: Sec. 10.13*

36) Certain insects, such as the water bug, are sufficiently lightweight that they can run on top of water without breaking the surface tension. Water bug A has weight W. Water bug B is twice as big as bug A, in all dimensions. That is, bug B is twice as long, twice as wide, etc. What is the weight of bug B?

A) 1.3W

B) 2.0W

C) 4.0W

D) 8.0W

Answer: D
Diff: 2 *Page Ref: Sec. 10.13*

37) Certain insects, such as the water bug, are sufficiently lightweight that they can run on top of water without breaking the surface tension. This is possible because the water, due to surface tension, exerts an upward force on the bottom of the bug's feet. Suppose that the maximum possible upward force on the feet of water bug A is F. Now suppose that water bug B is twice as big as bug A in every dimension. That is, bug B is twice as long, twice as wide, etc. What is the maximum upward force on the feet of bug B?

A) 1.4F

B) 2.0F

C) 4.0F

D) 8.0F

Answer: C
Diff: 2 *Page Ref: Sec. 10.13*

Quantitative Problems

1) A plastic block of dimensions 2.00 cm × 3.00 cm × 4.00 cm has a mass of 30.0 g. What is its density?

A) 0.80 g/cm^3

B) 1.20 g/cm^3

C) 1.25 g/cm^3

D) 1.60 g/cm^3

Answer: C
Diff: 1 *Page Ref: Sec. 10.2*

2) A liquid has a specific gravity of 0.357. What is its density?

A) 357 kg/m^3

B) 643 kg/m^3

C) 1000 kg/m^3

D) 3570 kg/m^3

Answer: A

Diff: 1 *Page Ref: Sec. 10.2*

3) A brick weighs 50.0 N, and measures 30.0 cm × 10.0 cm × 4.00 cm. What is the maximum pressure it can exert on a horizontal surface?

A) 1.25 Pa

B) 12.5 Pa

C) 1.25 kPa

D) 12.5 kPa

Answer: D

Diff: 1 *Page Ref: Sec. 10.3*

4) A person weighing 900 N is standing on snowshoes. Each snowshoe has area 2500 cm^2. What is the pressure on the snow?

A) 0.18 N/m^2

B) 0.36 N/m^2

C) 1800 N/m^2

D) 3600 N/m^2

Answer: C

Diff: 1 *Page Ref: Sec. 10.3*

5) How much pressure (absolute) must a submarine withstand at a depth of 120.0 m in the ocean?

A) 1200 N/m^2

B) 1310 N/m^2

C) 1200 kPa

D) 1310 kPa

Answer: D

Diff: 1 *Page Ref: Sec. 10.3*

6) A circular window of 30 cm diameter in a submarine can withstand a maximum force of 5.20×10^5 N. What is the maximum depth in a lake to which the submarine can go without damaging the window?

A) 680 m

B) 750 m

C) 1200 m

D) 1327 m

Answer: B
Diff: 2 *Page Ref: Sec. 10.3*

7) What is the gauge pressure if the absolute pressure is 300 kPa?

A) 97 kPa

B) 101 kPa

C) 199 kPa

D) 300 kPa

Answer: C
Diff: 1 *Page Ref: Sec. 10.4*

8) What is the gauge pressure at a location 15.0 m below the surface of sea? (The density of seawater is 1.03×10^3 kg/m^3.)

A) 1.01×10^5 N/m^2

B) 1.51×10^5 N/m^2

C) 1.47×10^5 N/m^2

D) 2.52×10^5 N/m^2

Answer: B
Diff: 1 *Page Ref: Sec. 10.4*

9) What is the absolute pressure at a location 15.0 m below the surface of sea? (The density of seawater is 1.03×10^3 kg/m^3.)

A) 1.01×10^5 N/m^2

B) 1.51×10^5 N/m^2

C) 2.48×10^5 N/m^2

D) 2.52×10^5 N/m^2

Answer: D
Diff: 1 *Page Ref: Sec. 10.4*

10) A 500-N weight sits on the small piston of a hydraulic machine. The small piston has area 2.0 cm^2. If the large piston has area 40 cm^2, how much weight can the large piston support?

A) 25 N

B) 500 N

C) 10000 N

D) 40000 N

Answer: C
Diff: 1 *Page Ref: Sec. 10.5*

11) In a hydraulic garage lift, the small piston has a radius of 5.0 cm and the large piston has a radius of 15 cm. What force must be applied on the small piston in order to lift a car weighing 20,000 N on the large piston?

A) 6.7×10^3 N

B) 5.0×10^3 N

C) 2.9×10^3 N

D) 2.2×10^3 N

Answer: D
Diff: 2 *Page Ref: Sec. 10.5*

12) A 13,000 N vehicle is to be lifted by a 25 cm diameter hydraulic piston. What force needs to be applied to a 5.0 cm diameter piston to accomplish this?

A) 260 N

B) 520 N

C) 2600 N

D) 5200 N

Answer: B
Diff: 2 *Page Ref: Sec. 10.5*

13) The small piston of a hydraulic lift has a diameter of 8.0 cm, and its large piston has a diameter of 40 cm. The lift raises a load of 15,000 N.
(a) Determine the force that must be applied to the small piston.
(b) Determine the pressure applied to the fluid in the lift.

Answer: (a) 600 N
(b) 1.2×10^5 Pa
Diff: 2 *Page Ref: Sec. 10.5*

14) A block of metal weighs 40 N in air and 30 N in water. What is the buoyant force of the water?

A) 10 N

B) 30 N

C) 40 N

D) 70 N

Answer: A
Diff: 1 *Page Ref: Sec. 10.7*

15) An object has a volume of 4.0 m^3 and weighs 40,000 N. What will its weight be in water?

A) 40,000 N

B) 39,200 N

C) 9,800 N

D) 800 N

Answer: D
Diff: 1 *Page Ref: Sec. 10.7*

16) A 4.00-kg cylinder of solid iron is supported by a string while submerged in water. What is the tension in the string? (The specific gravity of iron is 7.86.)

A) 2.50 N

B) 19.6 N

C) 23.7 N

D) 34.2 N

Answer: D
Diff: 2 *Page Ref: Sec. 10.7*

17) If the density of gold is 19.3×10^3 kg/m^3, what buoyant force does a 0.60-kg gold crown experience when it is immersed in water?

A) 3.0×10^{-5} N

B) 3.0×10^{-4} N

C) 3.0×10^{-2} N

D) 0.30 N

Answer: D
Diff: 2 *Page Ref: Sec. 10.7*

18) A crane lifts a steel submarine (density = 7.8×10^3 kg/m^3) of mass 20,000 kg. What is the tension in the lifting cable (1) when the submarine is submerged, and (2) when it is entirely out of the water?

A) (1) 2.0×10^5 N (2) 1.7×10^5 N

B) (1) 1.7×10^5 N (2) 2.0×10^5 N

C) (1) 2.6×10^3 N (2) 2.0×10^5 N

D) (1) 2.0×10^5 N (2) 2.6×10^3 N

Answer: B
Diff: 2 *Page Ref: Sec. 10.7*

19) An object weighs 7.84 N when it is in air and 6.86 N when it is immersed in water. What is the specific gravity of the object?

A) 6.0

B) 7.0

C) 8.0

D) 9.0

Answer: C
Diff: 2 *Page Ref: Sec. 10.7*

20) A container of water is placed on a scale, and the scale reads 120 g. Now a 20-g piece of copper (specific gravity = 8.9) is suspended from a thread and lowered into the water, not touching the bottom of the container. What will the scale now read?

A) 120 g

B) 122 g

C) 138 g

D) 140 g

Answer: B
Diff: 3 *Page Ref: Sec. 10.7*

21) A piece of aluminum with a mass of 1.0 kg and density of 2700 kg/m^3 is suspended from a string and then completely immersed in a container of water. The density of water is 1000 kg/m^3.
(a) Determine the volume of the piece of aluminum.
(b) Determine the tension in the string after the metal is immersed in the container of water.

Answer: (a) 3.7×10^{-4} m^3
(b) 6.2 N
Diff: 2 *Page Ref: Sec. 10.7*

22) A cylindrical rod of length 12 cm and diameter 2.0 cm will just barely float in water. What is its mass?

A) 38 g

B) 75 g

C) 150 g

D) 300 g

Answer: A
Diff: 1 *Page Ref: Sec. 10.7*

23) A rectangular box of negligible mass measures 5.0 m long, 1.0 m wide, and 0.50 m high. How many kilograms of mass can be loaded onto the box before it sinks in a lake?

A) 0.5×10^3 kg

B) 1.5×10^3 kg

C) 2.5×10^3 kg

D) 3.5×10^3 kg

Answer: C

Diff: 1 *Page Ref: Sec. 10.7*

24) A 1.0-m^3 object floats in water with 20% of it above the waterline. What does the object weigh out of the water?

A) 1,960 N

B) 7,840 N

C) 9,800 N

D) 11,800 N

Answer: B

Diff: 2 *Page Ref: Sec. 10.7*

25) An object floats with half its volume beneath the surface of the water. The weight of the displaced water is 2000 N. What is the weight of the object?

A) 1000 N

B) 2000 N

C) 4000 N

D) cannot be determined from the information given

Answer: B

Diff: 2 *Page Ref: Sec. 10.7*

26) A solid object floats in water with three-fourths of its volume beneath the surface. What is the object's density?

A) 1333 kg/m^3

B) 1000 kg/m^3

C) 750 kg/m^3

D) 250 kg/m^3

Answer: C

Diff: 2 *Page Ref: Sec. 10.7*

27) A 200-N object floats with three-fourths of its volume beneath the surface of the water. What is the buoyant force on the object?

A) 50 N

B) 150 N

C) 200 N

D) 267 N

Answer: C
Diff: 2 *Page Ref: Sec. 10.7*

28) A polar bear of mass 200 kg stands on an ice floe 100 cm thick. What is the minimum area of the floe that will just support the bear in saltwater of specific gravity 1.03? The specific gravity of ice is 0.98.

A) 1.0 m^2

B) 2.0 m^2

C) 3.0 m^2

D) 4.0 m^2

Answer: D
Diff: 3 *Page Ref: Sec. 10.7*

29) Liquid flows through a pipe of diameter 3.0 cm at 2.0 m/s. Find the flow rate.

A) 1.4×10^{-3} m^3/s

B) 5.7×10^{-3} m^3/s

C) 14 m^3/s

D) 57 m^3/s

Answer: A
Diff: 2 *Page Ref: Sec. 10.8-10.10*

30) Liquid flows through a 4.0 cm diameter pipe at 1.0 m/s. There is a 2.0 cm diameter restriction in the line. What is the velocity in this restriction?

A) 0.25 m/s

B) 0.50 m/s

C) 2.0 m/s

D) 4.0 m/s

Answer: D
Diff: 2 *Page Ref: Sec. 10.8-10.10*

31) Water flows at 12 m/s in a horizontal pipe with a pressure of 3.0×10^4 N/m^2. If the pipe widens to twice its original radius, what is the pressure in the wider section?

A) 3.0×10^4 N/m^2

B) 4.9×10^4 N/m^2

C) 7.4×10^4 N/m^2

D) 9.8×10^4 N/m^2

Answer: D
Diff: 2 *Page Ref: Sec. 10.8–10.10*

32) How much pressure does it take for a pump to supply a drinking fountain with 300 kPa, if the fountain is 30.0 m above the pump?

A) 294 kPa

B) 300 kPa

C) 594 kPa

D) 675 kPa

Answer: C
Diff: 2 *Page Ref: Sec. 10.8–10.10*

33) A hole of radius 1.0 mm occurs in the bottom of a water storage tank that holds water at a depth of 15 m. At what rate will water flow out of the hole?

A) 5.4×10^{-4} m^3/s

B) 5.4×10^{-5} m^3/s

C) 5.4×10^{-6} m^3/s

D) 5.4×10^{-7} m^3/s

Answer: B
Diff: 3 *Page Ref: Sec. 10.8–10.10*

34) Water flows through a horizontal pipe of cross-sectional area 10.0 cm^2 at a pressure of 0.250 atm. The flow rate is 1.00×10^{-3} m^3/s. At a valve, the effective cross-sectional area of the pipe is reduced to 5.00 cm^2. What is the pressure at the valve?

A) 0.112 atm

B) 0.157 atm

C) 0.200 atm

D) 0.235 atm

Answer: D
Diff: 3 *Page Ref: Sec. 10.8–10.10*

35) SAE No. 10 oil has a viscosity of 0.20 Pa-s. How long would it take to pour 4.0 L of oil through a funnel with a neck 15 cm long and 2.0 cm in diameter? Assume the surface of the oil is kept 6 cm above the top of the neck, and neglect any drag effects due to the upper part of the funnel.

A) 46 s

B) 52 s

C) 84 s

D) 105 s

Answer: B
Diff: 3 *Page Ref: Sec. 10.11*

36) Suppose that the build-up of fatty tissue on the wall of an artery decreased the radius by 10%. By how much would the pressure provided by the heart have to be increased to maintain a constant blood flow?

A) 48%

B) 52%

C) 46%

D) 54%

Answer: B
Diff: 2 *Page Ref: Sec. 10.12*

37) Two narrow tubes are placed in a pan of water. Tube A has twice the diameter of tube B. If water rises 24 cm in tube A, how high will it rise in tube B?

A) 12 cm

B) 24 cm

C) 48 cm

D) 96 cm

Answer: C
Diff: 1 *Page Ref: Sec. 10.13*

38) The surface tension of water is 0.073 N/m. How high will water rise in a capillary tube of diameter 1.2 mm?

A) 1.2 cm

B) 1.5 cm

C) 2.2 cm

D) 2.5 cm

Answer: D
Diff: 2 *Page Ref: Sec. 10.13*

39) To what height would water at 0 degree Celsius rise in a glass capillary tube with a diameter of 0.50 mm?

A) zero

B) 3.1 cm

C) 6.2 cm

D) 9.3 cm

Answer: C
Diff: 2 *Page Ref: Sec. 10.13*

40) A narrow tube is placed vertically in a pan of water, and the water rises in the tube to 4.0 cm above the level of the pan. The surface tension in the liquid is lowered to one–half its original value by the addition of some soap. What happens to the height of the liquid column in the tube?

A) It drops to 2.0 cm.

B) It drops to 1.0 cm.

C) It drops or rises, but the height cannot be calculated from the information given.

D) It remains at the same height.

Answer: A
Diff: 2 *Page Ref: Sec. 10.13*

41) Consider a rectangular frame of length 0.120 m and width 0.600 m with a soap film formed within its confined area. If the surface tension of soapy water is 0.0260 N/m, how much force does the soap film exert on the 0.600 m side?

A) 6.24×10^{-3} N

B) 1.56×10^{-3} N

C) 3.12×10^{-3} N

D) none of the above

Answer: C
Diff: 2 *Page Ref: Sec. 10.13*

42) An adjustable rectangular frame has length 12 cm and width 5 cm, and is built in such a way that one of the longer sides can be moved without bursting the soap film contained in the frame. Soapy water has surface tension 0.026 N/m. How much work is required to move the adjustable long side so that the frame is 12 cm square?

A) 2.2×10^{-4} J

B) 4.4×10^{-4} J

C) 2.2 J

D) 4.4 J

Answer: B
Diff: 2 *Page Ref: Sec. 10.13*

Chapter 11 Vibrations and Waves

Conceptual Questions

1) The time for one cycle of a periodic process is called the

A) amplitude.

B) wavelength.

C) frequency.

D) period.

Answer: D
Diff: 1 *Page Ref: Sec. 11.1–11.3*

2) For a periodic process, the number of cycles per unit time is called the

A) amplitude.

B) wavelength.

C) frequency.

D) period.

Answer: C
Diff: 1 *Page Ref: Sec. 11.1–11.3*

3) For vibrational motion, the maximum displacement from the equilibrium point is called the

A) amplitude.

B) wavelength.

C) frequency.

D) period.

Answer: A
Diff: 1 *Page Ref: Sec. 11.1–11.3*

4) A mass on a spring undergoes SHM. When the mass is at its maximum displacement from equilibrium, its instantaneous velocity

A) is maximum.

B) is less than maximum, but not zero.

C) is zero.

D) cannot be determined from the information given.

Answer: C
Diff: 1 *Page Ref: Sec. 11.1–11.3*

5) A mass on a spring undergoes SHM. When the mass passes through the equilibrium position, its instantaneous velocity

A) is maximum.

B) is less than maximum, but not zero.

C) is zero.

D) cannot be determined from the information given.

Answer: A
Diff: 1 *Page Ref: Sec. 11.1–11.3*

6) A mass on a spring undergoes SHM. When the mass is at maximum displacement from equilibrium, its instantaneous acceleration

A) is a maximum.

B) is less than maximum, but not zero.

C) is zero.

D) cannot be determined from the information given

Answer: A
Diff: 1 *Page Ref: Sec. 11.1–11.3*

7) A mass is attached to a vertical spring and bobs up and down between points A and B. Where is the mass located when its kinetic energy is a minimum?

A) at either A or B

B) midway between A and B

C) one-fourth of the way between A and B

D) none of the above

Answer: A
Diff: 2 *Page Ref: Sec. 11.1–11.3*

8) A mass is attached to a vertical spring and bobs up and down between points A and B. Where is the mass located when its kinetic energy is a maximum?

A) at either A or B

B) midway between A and B

C) one-fourth of the way between A and B

D) none of the above

Answer: B
Diff: 2 *Page Ref: Sec. 11.1–11.3*

9) A mass is attached to a vertical spring and bobs up and down between points A and B. Where is the mass located when its potential energy is a minimum?

A) at either A or B

B) midway between A and B

C) one-fourth of the way between A and B

D) none of the above

Answer: B
Diff: 2 *Page Ref: Sec. 11.1–11.3*

10) A mass is attached to a vertical spring and bobs up and down between points A and B. Where is the mass located when its potential energy is a maximum?

A) at either A or B

B) midway between A and B

C) one-fourth of the way between A and B

D) none of the above

Answer: A
Diff: 2 *Page Ref: Sec. 11.1–11.3*

11) Doubling only the amplitude of a vibrating mass-and-spring system produces what effect on the system's mechanical energy?

A) increases the energy by a factor of two

B) increases the energy by a factor of three

C) increases the energy by a factor of four

D) produces no change

Answer: C
Diff: 1 *Page Ref: Sec. 11.1–11.3*

12) Doubling only the mass of a vibrating mass-and-spring system produces what effect on the system's mechanical energy?

A) increases the energy by a factor of two

B) increases the energy by a factor of three

C) increases the energy by a factor of four

D) produces no change

Answer: D
Diff: 1 *Page Ref: Sec. 11.1–11.3*

13) Doubling only the spring constant of a vibrating mass-and-spring system produces what effect on the system's mechanical energy?

A) increases the energy by a factor of two

B) increases the energy by a factor of three

C) increases he energy by a factor of four

D) produces no change

Answer: A
Diff: 1 *Page Ref: Sec. 11.1-11.3*

14) A mass oscillates on the end of a spring, both on Earth and on the Moon. Where is the period the greatest?

A) Earth

B) the Moon

C) same on both Earth and the Moon

D) cannot be determined from the information given

Answer: C
Diff: 2 *Page Ref: Sec. 11.1-11.3*

15) Increasing the spring constant k of a mass-and-spring system causes what kind of change in the resonant frequency of the system? (Assume no change in the system's mass m.)

A) The frequency increases.

B) The frequency decreases.

C) There is no change in the frequency.

D) The frequency increases if the ratio k/m is greater than or equal to 1 and decreases if the ratio k/m is less than 1.

Answer: A
Diff: 1 *Page Ref: Sec. 11.1-11.3*

16) Increasing the mass M of a mass-and-spring system causes what kind of change in the resonant frequency of the system? (Assume no change in the system's spring constant k.)

A) The frequency increases.

B) The frequency decreases.

C) There is no change in the frequency.

D) The frequency increases if the ratio k/m is greater than or equal to 1 and decreases if the ratio k/m is less than 1.

Answer: B
Diff: 1 *Page Ref: Sec. 11.1-11.3*

17) Increasing the amplitude of a mass-and-spring system causes what kind of change in the resonant frequency of the system? (Assume no other changes in the system.)

A) The frequency increases.

B) The frequency decreases.

C) There is no change in the frequency.

D) The frequency depends on the displacement, not the amplitude.

Answer: C
Diff: 1 *Page Ref: Sec. 11.1-11.3*

18) A mass m hanging on a spring has a natural frequency f. If the mass is increased to 4m, what is the new natural frequency?

A) 4f

B) 2f

C) 0.5f

D) 0.25f

Answer: C
Diff: 1 *Page Ref: Sec. 11.1-11.3*

19) A simple pendulum consists of a mass M attached to a weightless string of length L. For this system, when undergoing small oscillations

A) the frequency is proportional to the amplitude.

B) the period is proportional to the amplitude.

C) the frequency is independent of the mass M.

D) the frequency is independent of the length L.

Answer: C
Diff: 2 *Page Ref: Sec. 11.4*

20) When the mass of a simple pendulum is tripled, the time required for one complete vibration

A) increases by a factor of 3.

B) does not change.

C) decreases to one-third of its original value.

D) decreases to $1/\sqrt{3}$ of its original value.

Answer: B
Diff: 1 *Page Ref: Sec. 11.4*

21) Both pendulum A and B are 3.0 m long. The period of A is T. Pendulum A is twice as heavy as pendulum B. What is the period of B?

A) 0.71T

B) T

C) 1.4T

D) 2T

Answer: B
Diff: 1 *Page Ref: Sec. 11.4*

22) When the length of a simple pendulum is tripled, the time for one complete vibration increases by a factor of

A) 3.

B) 2.

C) 1.7.

D) 1.4.

Answer: C
Diff: 1 *Page Ref: Sec. 11.4*

23) What happens to a simple pendulum's frequency if both its length and mass are increased?

A) It increases.

B) It decreases.

C) It remains constant.

D) It could remain constant, increase, or decrease; it depends on the length to mass ratio.

Answer: B
Diff: 1 *Page Ref: Sec. 11.4*

24) Simple pendulum A swings back and forth at twice the frequency of simple pendulum B. Which statement is correct?

A) Pendulum B is twice as long as A.

B) Pendulum B is twice as massive as A.

C) The length of B is four times the length of A.

D) The mass of B is four times the mass of A.

Answer: C
Diff: 2 *Page Ref: Sec. 11.4*

25) If you take a given pendulum to the Moon, where the acceleration of gravity is less than on Earth, the resonant frequency of the pendulum will

A) increase.

B) decrease.

C) not change.

D) either increase or decrease; it depends on its length to mass ratio.

Answer: B
Diff: 1 *Page Ref: Sec. 11.4*

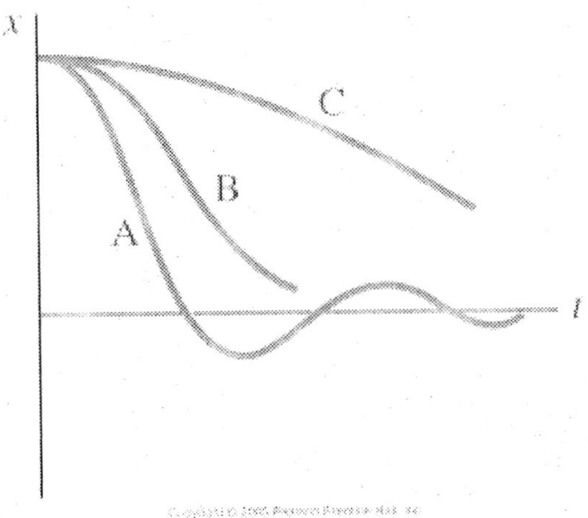

FIGURE 11-1

26) Curve A in Fig. 11-1 represents

A) an underdamped situation.

B) an overdamped situation.

C) a moderately damped situation.

D) critical damping.

Answer: A
Diff: 1 *Page Ref: Sec. 11.5*

27) Curve B in Fig. 11-1 represents

A) an underdamped situation.

B) an overdamped situation.

C) a moderately damped situation.

D) critical damping.

Answer: D
Diff: 1 *Page Ref: Sec. 11.5*

28) Curve C in Fig. 11-1 represents

A) an underdamped situation.

B) an overdamped situation.

C) a moderately damped situation.

D) critical damping.

Answer: B

Diff: 1 *Page Ref: Sec. 11.5*

29) For a forced vibration, the amplitude of vibration is found to depend on the

A) sum of the external frequency and the natural frequency.

B) difference of the external frequency and the natural frequency.

C) product of the external frequency and the natural frequency.

D) ratio of the external frequency and the natural frequency.

Answer: B

Diff: 1 *Page Ref: Sec. 11.6*

30) In a wave, the maximum displacement of points of the wave from equilibrium is called the wave's

A) speed.

B) frequency.

C) wavelength.

D) amplitude.

Answer: D

Diff: 1 *Page Ref: Sec. 11.7-11.8*

31) The distance between successive crests on a wave is called the wave's

A) speed.

B) frequency.

C) wavelength.

D) amplitude.

Answer: C

Diff: 1 *Page Ref: Sec. 11.7-11.8*

32) The number of crests of a wave passing a point per unit time is called the wave's

A) speed.

B) frequency.

C) wavelength.

D) amplitude.

Answer: B

Diff: 1 *Page Ref: Sec. 11.7-11.8*

33) For a wave, the frequency times the wavelength is the wave's

A) speed.

B) amplitude.

C) intensity.

D) power.

Answer: A
Diff: 1 *Page Ref: Sec. 11.7–11.8*

34) The frequency of a wave increases. What happens to the distance between successive crests if the speed remains constant?

A) It increases.

B) It remains the same.

C) It decreases.

D) It cannot be determined from the information given.

Answer: C
Diff: 1 *Page Ref: Sec. 11.7–11.8*

35) A wave moves on a string with wavelength λ and frequency f. A second wave on the same string has wavelength 2λ and travels with the same velocity. What is the frequency of the second wave?

A) 0.5f

B) f

C) 2f

D) It cannot be determined from the information given.

Answer: A
Diff: 1 *Page Ref: Sec. 11.7–11.8*

36) Consider a traveling wave on a string of length L, mass M, and tension T. A standing wave is set up. Which of the following is true?

A) The wave velocity depends on M, L, T.

B) The wavelength of the wave is proportional to the frequency.

C) The particle velocity is equal to the wave velocity.

D) The wavelength is proportional to T.

Answer: A
Diff: 2 *Page Ref: Sec. 11.7–11.8*

37) A string of mass m and length L is under tension T. The speed of a wave in the string is v. What will be the speed of a wave in the string if the mass of the string is increased to 2m, with no change in length?

A) 0.5v

B) 0.71v

C) 1.4v

D) 2v

Answer: B
Diff: 1 *Page Ref: Sec. 11.7–11.8*

38) A string of mass m and length L is under tension T. The speed of a wave in the string is v. What will be the speed of a wave in the string if the length is increased to 2L, with no change in mass?

A) 0.5v

B) 0.71v

C) 1.4v

D) 2v

Answer: C
Diff: 1 *Page Ref: Sec. 11-7–11.8*

39) A string of mass m and length L is under tension T. The speed of a wave in the string is v. What will be the speed of a wave in the string if the tension is increased to 2T?

A) 0.5v

B) 0.71Tv

C) 1.4v

D) 2 v

Answer: C
Diff: 2 *Page Ref: Sec. 11.7–11.8*

40) In seismology, the S wave is a transverse wave. As an S wave travels through the Earth, the relative motion between the S wave and the particles is

A) parallel.

B) perpendicular.

C) first parallel, then perpendicular.

D) first perpendicular, then parallel.

Answer: B
Diff: 1 *Page Ref: Sec. 11.7–11.8*

41) In seismology, the P wave is a longitudinal wave. As a P wave travels through the Earth, the relative motion between the P wave and the particles is

A) parallel.

B) perpendicular.

C) first parallel, then perpendicular.

D) first perpendicular, then parallel.

Answer: A
Diff: 1 *Page Ref: Sec. 11.7–11.8*

42) The intensity of a wave is

A) proportional to both the amplitude squared and the frequency squared

B) proportional to the amplitude squared and inversely proportional to the frequency squared.

C) inversely proportional to the amplitude squared and proportional to the frequency squared.

D) inversely proportional to both the amplitude squared and the frequency squared.

Answer: A
Diff: 1 *Page Ref: Sec. 11.9–11.10*

43) A wave pulse traveling to the right along a thin cord reaches a discontinuity where the rope becomes thicker and heavier. What is the orientation of the reflected and transmitted pulses?

A) Both are right side up.

B) The reflected pulse returns right side up while the transmitted pulse is inverted.

C) The reflected pulse returns inverted while the transmitted pulse is right side up.

D) Both are inverted.

Answer: C
Diff: 1 *Page Ref: Sec. 11.11*

44) Two wave pulses with equal positive amplitudes pass each other on a string, one is traveling toward the right and the other toward the left. At the point that they occupy the same region of space at the same time

A) constructive interference occurs.

B) destructive interference occurs.

C) a standing wave is produced.

D) a traveling wave is produced.

Answer: A
Diff: 1 *Page Ref: Sec. 11–12*

45) Two wave pulses pass each other on a string. The one traveling toward the right has a positive amplitude, while the one traveling toward the left has an equal amplitude in the negative direction. At the point that they occupy the same region of space at the same time

A) constructive interference occurs.

B) destructive interference occurs.

C) a standing wave is produced.

D) a traveling wave is produced.

Answer: B
Diff: 1 *Page Ref: Sec. 11.12*

46) Resonance in a system, such as a string fixed at both ends, occurs when

A) it is oscillating in simple harmonic motion.

B) its frequency is the same as the frequency of an external source.

C) its frequency is greater than the frequency of an external source.

D) its frequency is smaller than the frequency of an external source.

Answer: B
Diff: 2 *Page Ref: Sec. 11.13*

47) If one doubles the tension in a violin string, the fundamental frequency of that string will increase by a factor of

A) 2.

B) 4.

C) 1.4.

D) 1.7.

Answer: C
Diff: 2 *Page Ref: Sec. 11.13*

Quantitative Problems

1) What is the spring constant of a spring that stretches 2.00 cm when a mass of 0.600 kg is suspended from it?

A) 0.300 N/m

B) 30.0 N/m

C) 2.94 N/m

D) 294 N/m

Answer: D
Diff: 1 *Page Ref: Sec. 11.1–11.3*

2) A mass is attached to a spring of spring constant 60 N/m along a horizontal, frictionless surface. The spring is initially stretched by a force of 5.0 N on the mass and let go. It takes the mass 0.50 s to go back to its equilibrium position when it is oscillating. What is the amplitude?

A) 0.030 m

B) 0.083 m

C) 0.30 m

D) 0.83 m

Answer: B
Diff: 1 *Page Ref: Sec. 11.1-11.3*

3) A mass is attached to a spring of spring constant 60 N/m along a horizontal, frictionless surface. The spring is initially stretched by a force of 5.0 N on the mass and let go. It takes the mass 0.50 s to go back to its equilibrium position when it is oscillating. What is the period of oscillation?

A) 0.50 s

B) 1.0 s

C) 1.5 s

D) 2.0 s

Answer: D
Diff: 1 *Page Ref: Sec. 11.1-11.3*

4) A mass is attached to a spring of spring constant 60 N/m along a horizontal, frictionless surface. The spring is initially stretched by a force of 5.0 N on the mass and let go. It takes the mass 0.50 s to go back to its equilibrium position when it is oscillating. What is the frequency of oscillation?

A) 0.50 Hz

B) 1.0 Hz

C) 1.5 Hz

D) 2.0 Hz

Answer: A
Diff: 1 *Page Ref: Sec. 11.1-11.3*

5) A mass on a spring undergoes SHM. It goes through 10 complete oscillations in 5.0 s. What is the period?

A) 0.020 s

B) 0.50 s

C) 2.0 s

D) 50 s

Answer: B
Diff: 1 *Page Ref: Sec. 11.1-11.3*

6) A mass vibrates back and forth from the free end of an ideal spring of spring constant 20 N/m with an amplitude of 0.30 m. What is the kinetic energy of this vibrating mass when it is 0.30 m from its equilibrium position?

A) zero

B) 0.90 J

C) 0.45 J

D) It is impossible to give an answer without knowing the object's mass.

Answer: A
Diff: 1 *Page Ref: Sec. 11.1-11.3*

7) A 0.50-kg mass is attached to a spring of spring constant 20 N/m along a horizontal, frictionless surface. The object oscillates in simple harmonic motion and has a speed of 1.5 m/s at the equilibrium position. What is the total energy of the system?

A) 0.27 J

B) 0.56 J

C) 0.65 J

D) 1.1 J

Answer: B
Diff: 1 *Page Ref: Sec. 11.1-11.3*

8) A mass undergoes SHM with amplitude of 4 cm. The energy is 8.0 J at this time. The mass is cut in half, and the system is again set in motion with amplitude 4.0 cm. What is the energy of the system now?

A) 2.0 J

B) 4.0 J

C) 8.0 J

D) 16 J

Answer: C
Diff: 2 *Page Ref: Sec. 11.1-11.3*

9) A 0.50-kg mass is attached to a spring of spring constant 20 N/m along a horizontal, frictionless surface. The object oscillates in simple harmonic motion and has a speed of 1.5 m/s at the equilibrium position. What is the amplitude of vibration?

A) 0.024 m

B) 0.058 m

C) 0.24 m

D) 0.58 m

Answer: C
Diff: 2 *Page Ref: Sec. 11.1-11.3*

10) A 0.50-kg mass is attached to a spring of spring constant 20 N/m along a horizontal, frictionless surface. The object oscillates in simple harmonic motion and has a speed of 1.5 m/s at the equilibrium position. At what location are the kinetic energy and the potential energy the same?

A) 0.017 m

B) 0.029 m

C) 0.12 m

D) 0.17 m

Answer: D
Diff: 2 *Page Ref: Sec. 11.1-11.3*

11) A 2.0-kg mass is attached to the end of a horizontal spring of spring constant 50 N/m and set into simple harmonic motion with an amplitude of 0.10 m. What is the total mechanical energy of this system?

A) 0.020 J

B) 25 J

C) 0.25 J

D) 1.0 J

Answer: C
Diff: 2 *Page Ref: Sec. 11.1-11.3*

12) A 2.0-kg mass is attached to the end of a horizontal spring of spring constant 50 N/m and set into simple harmonic motion with an amplitude of 0.10 m. What is the total mechanical energy of this system?

A) 0.020 J

B) 25 J

C) 0.25 J

D) 1.0 J

Answer: C
Diff: 2 *Page Ref: Sec. 11.1-11.3*

13) A mass vibrates back and forth from the free end of an ideal spring of spring constant 20.0 N/m with an amplitude of 0.250 m. What is the maximum kinetic energy of this vibrating mass?

A) 2.50 J

B) 1.25 J

C) 0.625 J

D) It is impossible to give an answer since kinetic energy cannot be determined without knowing the object's mass.

Answer: C
Diff: 2 *Page Ref: Sec. 11.1-11.3*

14) The mass of a mass-and-spring system is displaced 10 cm from its equilibrium position and released. A frequency of 4.0 Hz is observed. What frequency would be observed if the mass had been displaced only 5.0 cm and then released?

A) 2.0 Hz

B) 4.0 Hz

C) 8.0 Hz

D) none of the above

Answer: B
Diff: 1 *Page Ref: Sec. 11.1-11.3*

15) A 4.0-kg object is attached to a spring of spring constant 10 N/m. The object is displaced by 5.0 cm from the equilibrium position and let go. What is the period of vibration?

A) 2.0 s

B) 4.0 s

C) 8.0 s

D) 16 s

Answer: B
Diff: 1 *Page Ref: Sec. 11.1-11.3*

16) A 4.0-kg object is attached to a spring of spring constant 10 N/m. The object is displaced by 5.0 cm from the equilibrium position and let go. What is the frequency of vibration?

A) 0.25 Hz

B) 0.50 Hz

C) 1.0 Hz

D) 2.0 Hz

Answer: A
Diff: 1 *Page Ref: Sec. 11.1-11.3*

17) A 2.0-kg mass is hung from a spring of spring constant 18 N/m, displaced slightly from its equilibrium position, and released. What is the frequency of its vibration?

A) 0.48 Hz

B) 0.95 Hz

C) 1.5 Hz

D) none of the above

Answer: A
Diff: 2 *Page Ref: Sec. 11.1-11.3*

18) A mass is attached to a spring. It oscillates at a frequency of 1.27 Hz when displaced a distance of 2.0 cm from equilibrium and released. What is the maximum velocity attained by the mass?

A) 0.02 m/s

B) 0.04 m/s

C) 0.08 m/s

D) 0.16 m/s

Answer: D
Diff: 2 *Page Ref: Sec. 11.1-11.3*

19) Two masses, A and B, are attached to different springs. Mass A vibrates with amplitude of 8.0 cm at a frequency of 10 Hz and mass B vibrates with amplitude of 5.0 cm at a frequency of 16 Hz. How does the maximum speed of A compare to the maximum speed of B?

A) Mass A has the greater maximum speed.

B) Mass B has the greater maximum speed.

C) They are equal.

D) There is not enough information to determine.

Answer: C
Diff: 2 *Page Ref: Sec. 11.1-11.3*

20) A 0.30-kg mass is suspended on a spring. In equilibrium the mass stretches the spring 2.0 cm downward. The mass is then pulled an additional distance of 1.0 cm down and released from rest. Calculate the period of oscillation.

A) 0.14 s

B) 0.28 s

C) 0.020 s

D) 0.078 s

Answer: B
Diff: 2 *Page Ref: Sec. 11.1-11.3*

21) A 0.30-kg mass is suspended on a spring. In equilibrium the mass stretches the spring 2.0 cm downward. The mass is then pulled an additional distance of 1.0 cm down and released from rest. Calculate the total energy of the system.

A) 0.0074 J

B) 0.015 J

C) 0.022 J

D) 0.030 J

Answer: A
Diff: 2 *Page Ref: Sec. 11.1-11.3*

22) A 0.30-kg mass is suspended on a spring. In equilibrium the mass stretches the spring 2.0 cm downward. The mass is then pulled an additional distance of 1.0 cm down and released from rest. Write down its equation of motion.

A) y = (0.01 m) cos (22.1 t)

B) y = (0.01 m) sin (22.1 t)

C) y = (0.03 m) cos (22.1 t)

D) y = (0.03 m) sin (22.1 t)

Answer: A
Diff: 2 *Page Ref: Sec. 11.1-11.3*

23) An object in simple harmonic motion obeys the following position versus time equation: y = (0.50 m) sin (π/2 t). What is the amplitude of vibration?

A) 0.25 m

B) 0.50 m

C) 0.75 m

D) 1.0 m

Answer: B
Diff: 1 *Page Ref: Sec. 11.1-11.3*

24) An object in simple harmonic motion obeys the following position versus time equation: y = (0.50 m) sin (π/2 t). What is the period of vibration?

A) 1.0 s

B) 2.0 s

C) 3.0 s

D) 4.0 s

Answer: D
Diff: 2 *Page Ref: Sec. 11.1-11.3*

25) An object in simple harmonic motion obeys the following position versus time equation: y = (0.50 m) sin (π/2 t). What is the maximum speed of the object?

A) 0.13 m/s

B) 0.26 m/s

C) 0.39 m/s

D) 0.79 m/s

Answer: D
Diff: 2 *Page Ref: Sec. 11.1-11.3*

26) A mass attached to the free end of a spring executes simple harmonic motion according to the equation y = (0.50 m) sin (18π t) where y is in meters and t is seconds. What is the period of vibration?

A) 9.0 s

B) 18 s

C) 1/9 s

D) 1/18 s

Answer: C
Diff: 2 *Page Ref: Sec. 11.1-11.3*

27) A 1.5-kg mass attached to spring with a force constant of 20.0 N/m oscillates on a horizontal, frictionless track. At t= 0, the mass is released from rest at x= 10.0 cm. (That is, the spring is stretched by 10.00 cm.)
(a) Determine the frequency of the oscillations.
(b) Determine the maximum speed of the mass. Where does the maximum speed occur?
(c) Determine the maximum acceleration of the mass. Where does the maximum acceleration occur?
(d) Determine the total energy of the oscillating system.
(e) Express the displacement as a function of time.

Answer: (a) 0.58 Hz
(b) 0.37 m/s, at the equilibrium position
(c) 1.3 m/s^2, at maximum displacement
(d) 0.10 J
(e) $x = (0.10 \text{ m}) \cos (3.7t)$
Diff: 2 *Page Ref: Sec. 11.1-11.3*

28) A pendulum makes 12 complete swings in 8.0 s. (a) What are its frequency and period on Earth?

A) 1.5 Hz, 0.67 s

B) 0.67 Hz, 1.5 s

C) 0.24 Hz, 4.2 s

D) 4.2 Hz, 0.24 s

Answer: A
Diff: 1 *Page Ref: Sec. 11.4*

29) A 3.00-kg pendulum is 28.84 m long. What is its period on Earth?

A) 10.78 s

B) 7.891 s

C) 4.897 s

D) 0.09278 s

Answer: A
Diff: 1 *Page Ref: Sec. 11.4*

30) A pendulum has a period of 2.0 s on Earth. What is its length?

A) 2.0 m

B) 1.0 m

C) 0.70 m

D) 0.50 m

Answer: B
Diff: 1 *Page Ref: Sec. 11.4*

31) The pendulum of a grandfather clock is 1.0 m long. What is its period on the Earth?

A) 1.0 s

B) 2.0 s

C) 4.0 s

D) 8.0 s

Answer: B
Diff: 1 *Page Ref: Sec. 11.4*

32) The pendulum of a grandfather clock is 1.0 m long. What is its period on the Moon where the acceleration due to gravity is only 1.7 m/s^2?

A) 1.2 s

B) 2.4 s

C) 4.8 s

D) 23 s

Answer: C
Diff: 1 *Page Ref: Sec. 11.4*

33) A simple pendulum consists of a 0.25-kg spherical mass attached to a massless string. When the mass is displaced slightly from its equilibrium position and released, the pendulum swings back and forth with a frequency of 2.0 Hz. What frequency would have resulted if a 0.50-kg mass (same diameter sphere) had been attached to the string instead?

A) 1.0 Hz

B) 2.0 Hz

C) 1.4 Hz

D) none of the above

Answer: B
Diff: 1 *Page Ref: Sec. 11.4*

34) A simple pendulum consisting of a 20-g mass has initial angular displacement of 8.0°. It oscillates with a period of 3.00 s.
(a) Determine the length of the pendulum.
(b) Does the period of the pendulum depend on the initial angular displacement?
(c) Does the period of the pendulum depend on the mass of the pendulum?
(d) Does the period of the pendulum depend on the length of the pendulum?
(e) Does the period of the pendulum depend on the acceleration due to gravity?

Answer: (a) 2.2 m
(b) No
(c) No
(d) Yes
(e) Yes
Diff: 1 *Page Ref: Sec. 11.4*

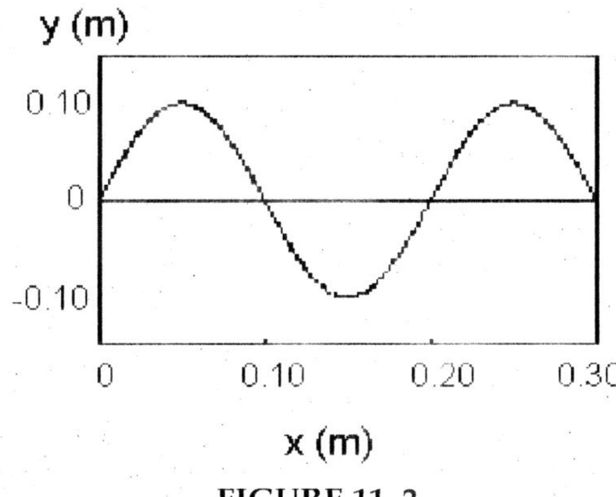

FIGURE 11-2

35) Figure 11-2 is a "snapshot" of a wave at a given time. The frequency of the wave is 120 Hz. What is the amplitude?

A) 0.05 m
B) 0.10 m
C) 0.15 m
D) 0.20 m

Answer: B
Diff: 1 *Page Ref: Sec. 11.7-11.8*

36) Figure 11-2 is a "snapshot" of a wave at a given time. The frequency of the wave is 120 Hz. What is the wavelength?

A) 0.05 m
B) 0.10 m
C) 0.20 m
D) 0.30 m

Answer: C
Diff: 1 *Page Ref: Sec. 11.7-11.8*

37) Figure 11-2 is a "snapshot" of a wave at a given time. The frequency of the wave is 120 Hz. What is the wave speed?

A) 12 m/s

B) 24 m/s

C) 36 m/s

D) 48 m/s

Answer: B
Diff: 1 *Page Ref: Sec. 11.7-11.8*

38) What is the frequency of a wave which has a period of 6.00 ms?

A) 16.7 Hz

B) 167 Hz

C) 1.67 kHz

D) 16.7 kHz

Answer: B
Diff: 1 *Page Ref: Sec. 11.7-11.8*

39) What is the period of a wave with a frequency of 1500 Hz?

A) 0.67 μs

B) 0.67 ms

C) 0.67 s

D) 6.7 s

Answer: B
Diff: 1 *Page Ref: Sec. 11.7-11.8*

40) What is the wave speed if a wave has a frequency of 12 Hz and a wavelength of 3.0 m?

A) 4.0 m/s

B) 9.0 m/s

C) 15 m/s

D) 36 m/s

Answer: D
Diff: 1 *Page Ref: Sec. 11.7-11.8*

41) What is the velocity of a wave that has a wavelength of 3.0 m and a frequency of 12 Hz?

A) 4.0 m/s

B) 9.0 m/s

C) 15 m/s

D) 36 m/s

Answer: D
Diff: 1 *Page Ref: Sec. 11.7-11.8*

42) What is the frequency of a 2.5 m wave traveling at 1400 m/s?

A) 178 Hz

B) 1.78 kHz

C) 560 Hz

D) 5.6 kHz

Answer: C
Diff: 1 *Page Ref: Sec. 11.7–11.8*

43) A piano string of linear mass density 0.0050 kg/m is under a tension of 1350 N. What is the wave speed?

A) 130 m/s

B) 260 m/s

C) 520 m/s

D) 1040 m/s

Answer: C
Diff: 1 *Page Ref: Sec. 11.7–11.8*

44) A string of linear density 6.0 g/m is under a tension of 180 N. What is the velocity of propagation of transverse waves along the string?

A) 2.9×10^4 m/s

B) 1.7×10^2 m/s

C) 13 m/s

D) 5.8×10^{-3} m/s

Answer: B
Diff: 2 *Page Ref: Sec. 11.7–11.8*

45) A wave whose wavelength is 0.500 m is traveling down a 500 m long wire whose total mass is 25.0 kg. The wire is under a tension of 2000 N.
(a) Determine the velocity of the wave on the wire.
(b) Determine the frequency of this wave.

Answer: (a) 200 m/s
(b) 400 Hz
Diff: 2 *Page Ref: Sec. 11.7–11.8*

46) The velocity of propagation of a transverse wave on a 2.0-m long string fixed at both ends is 200 m/s. Which one of the following is not a resonant frequency of this string?

A) 25 Hz

B) 50 Hz

C) 100 Hz

D) 200 Hz

Answer: A
Diff: 2 *Page Ref: Sec. 11.13*

47) If a guitar string has a fundamental frequency of 500 Hz, which one of the following frequencies can set the string into resonant vibration?

A) 250 Hz

B) 750 Hz

C) 1500 Hz

D) 1750 Hz

Answer: C
Diff: 2 *Page Ref: Sec. 11.13*

48) A stretched string is observed to have four equal segments in a standing wave driven at a frequency of 480 Hz. What driving frequency will set up a standing wave with five equal segments?

A) 600 Hz

B) 360 Hz

C) 240 Hz

D) 120 Hz

Answer: A
Diff: 2 *Page Ref: Sec. 11.13*

49) A string, fixed at both ends, vibrates at a frequency of 12 Hz with a standing transverse wave pattern containing 3 loops. What frequency is needed if the standing wave pattern is to contain 4 loops?

A) 48 Hz

B) 36 Hz

C) 16 Hz

D) 12 Hz

Answer: C
Diff: 2 *Page Ref: Sec. 11.13*

50) A string of linear density 1.5 g/m is under a tension of 20 N. What should its length be if its fundamental resonance frequency is 220 Hz?

A) 0.26 m

B) 0.96 m

C) 1.1 m

D) 1.2 m

Answer: A
Diff: 3 *Page Ref: Sec. 11.13*

51) Find the first three harmonics of a string of linear mass density 2.00 g/m and length 0.600 m when it is subjected to tension of 50.0 N.

A) 132 Hz, 264 Hz, 396 Hz

B) 66 Hz, 132 Hz, 198 Hz

C) 264 Hz, 528 Hz, 792 Hz

D) none of the above

Answer: A
Diff: 3 *Page Ref: Sec. 11.13*

52) A string of length 2.5 m is fixed at both ends. When the string vibrates at a frequency of 85 Hz, a standing wave with five loops is formed.
(a) Determine the distance between two adjacent nodes.
(b) Determine the wavelength of the waves that travel on the string.
(c) Determine the velocity of waves.
(d) Determine the fundamental frequency of this string.

Answer: (a) 0.50 m
(b) 1.0 m
(c) 85 m/s
(d) 17 Hz
Diff: 2 *Page Ref: Sec. 11.13*

Chapter 12 Sound

Conceptual Questions

1) Which of the following is a false statement?

A) Sound waves are longitudinal pressure waves.

B) Sound can travel through a vacuum.

C) Light travels very much faster than sound.

D) The transverse waves on a vibrating string are different from sound waves.

E) "Pitch" (in music) and frequency have approximately the same meaning.

Answer: B
Diff: 1 *Page Ref: Sec. 12.1*

2) In general, sound is conducted fastest through

A) gases.

B) liquids.

C) solids.

D) a vacuum.

Answer: C
Diff: 1 *Page Ref: Sec. 12.1*

3) What is the speed of sound in a steel rod?

A) 1500 m/s

B) 3000 m/s

C) 5000 m/s

D) 8000 m/s

Answer: C
Diff: 2 *Page Ref: Sec. 12.1*

4) As the temperature of the air increases, what happens to the velocity of sound? (Assume that all other factors remain constant.)

A) It increases.

B) It decreases.

C) It does not change.

D) It increases when atmospheric pressure is high and decreases when the pressure is low.

Answer: A
Diff: 1 *Page Ref: Sec. 12.1*

5) Compared to the velocity of a 400 Hz sound, the velocity of a 200 Hz sound through air is

A) twice as great.

B) the same.

C) one-half as great.

D) none of the above

Answer: B
Diff: 1 *Page Ref: Sec. 12.1*

6) Compared to the wavelength of a 400 Hz sound, the wavelength of a 200 Hz sound in air is

A) twice as long.

B) the same.

C) one-half as long.

D) none of the above

Answer: A
Diff: 1 *Page Ref: Sec. 12.1*

7) Sound vibrations with frequencies greater than 20,000 Hz are called

A) infrasonics.

B) ultrasonics.

C) supersonics.

D) none of the above

Answer: B
Diff: 1 *Page Ref: Sec. 12.1*

8) Sound vibrations with frequency less than 20 Hz are called

A) infrasonics.

B) ultrasonics.

C) supersonics.

D) none of the above

Answer: A
Diff: 1 *Page Ref: Sec. 12.1*

9) Suppose that a sound source is emitting waves uniformly in all directions. If you move to a point twice as far away from the source, the frequency of the sound will be

A) unchanged.

B) half as great.

C) one-fourth as great.

D) twice as great.

Answer: A
Diff: 1 *Page Ref: Sec. 12.2*

10) For spherically diverging waves, intensity is proportional to

A) R^2.

B) R.

C) 1/R.

D) $1/R^2$.

Answer: D
Diff: 1 *Page Ref: Sec. 12.2*

11) The intensity of a point source at a distance d from the source is I. What is the intensity at a distance 2d from the source?

A) 4I

B) 2I

C) I/2

D) I/4

Answer: D
Diff: 2 *Page Ref: Sec. 12.2*

12) You double your distance from a sound source that is radiating equally in all directions. What happens to the intensity of the sound? It reduces to

A) one-half its original value.

B) one-fourth its original value.

C) one-sixteenth its original value.

D) none of the above

Answer: B
Diff: 1 *Page Ref: Sec. 12.2*

13) You double your distance from a sound source that is radiating equally in all directions. What happens to the intensity level of the sound? It drops by

A) 2 dB.

B) 3 dB.

C) 6 dB.

D) 8 dB.

Answer: C
Diff: 2 *Page Ref: Sec. 12.2*

14) Which of the following increases as a sound becomes louder?

A) frequency

B) wavelength

C) amplitude

D) period

E) velocity

Answer: C
Diff: 1 *Page Ref: Sec. 12.3*

15) You move slowly toward a speaker emitting a pure tone. What characteristic of the sound increases?

A) frequency

B) amplitude

C) wavelength

D) period

Answer: B
Diff: 1 *Page Ref: Sec. 12.4*

16) What determines "loudness" of a musical note?

A) frequency

B) velocity

C) phase

D) amplitude

Answer: D
Diff: 1 *Page Ref: Sec. 12.4*

17) What determines the "pitch" of a musical note?

A) amplitude

B) wavelength

C) frequency

D) phase

Answer: C
Diff: 1 *Page Ref: Sec. 12.4*

18) When sound passes from air into water

A) its wavelength does not change.

B) its frequency does not change.

C) its velocity does not change.

D) all of the above

Answer: B
Diff: 1 *Page Ref: Sec. 12.4*

19) Pressure and displacement waves are

A) in phase.

B) 45° out of phase.

C) 90° out of phase.

D) 180° out of phase.

Answer: C
Diff: 2 *Page Ref: Sec. 12.4*

20) Consider the standing wave on a guitar string and the sound wave generated by the guitar as a result of this vibration. What do these two waves have in common?

A) They have the same wavelength.

B) They have the same velocity.

C) They have the same frequency.

D) More than one of the above is true.

E) None of the above is true.

Answer: C
Diff: 2 *Page Ref: Sec. 12.4*

21) In a resonating pipe which is open at both ends, there

A) are displacement nodes at each end.

B) are displacement antinodes at each end.

C) is a displacement node at one end and a displacement antinode at the other end.

D) none of the above

Answer: B
Diff: 2 *Page Ref: Sec. 12.4*

22) Consider an open pipe of length L. What are the wavelengths of the three lowest tones produced by this pipe?

A) 4L, 2L, L

B) 2L, L, L/2

C) 2L, L, 2L/3

D) 4L, 4L/3, 4L/5

Answer: C
Diff: 2 *Page Ref: Sec. 12.4*

23) The lowest tone to resonate in an open pipe of length L is 200 Hz. Which one of the following frequencies will not resonate in the same pipe?

A) 400 Hz

B) 600 Hz

C) 800 Hz

D) 900 Hz

Answer: D
Diff: 2 *Page Ref: Sec. 12.4*

24) An open pipe of length L is resonating at its fundamental frequency. Which statement is correct?

A) The wavelength is 2L and there is a displacement node at the pipe's midpoint.

B) The wavelength is 2L and there is a displacement antinode at the pipe's midpoint.

C) The wavelength is L and there is a displacement node at the pipe's midpoint.

D) The wavelength is L and there is a displacement antinode at the pipe's midpoint.

Answer: A
Diff: 2 *Page Ref: Sec. 12.4*

25) In a resonating pipe which is open at one end and closed at the other, there

A) are displacement nodes at each end.

B) are displacement antinodes at each end.

C) is a displacement node at the open end and a displacement antinode at the closed end.

D) is a displacement node at the closed end and a displacement antinode at the open end.

Answer: D
Diff: 2 *Page Ref: Sec. 12.4*

26) Consider a closed pipe of length L. What are the wavelengths of the three lowest tones produced by this pipe?

A) 4L, 2L, L

B) 2L, L, L/2

C) 2L, L, 2L/3

D) 4L, 4L/3, 4L/5

Answer: D
Diff: 2 *Page Ref: Sec. 12.4*

27) The lowest tone to resonate in a closed pipe of length L is 200 Hz. Which of the following frequencies will not resonate in that pipe?

A) 400 Hz

B) 600 Hz

C) 1000 Hz

D) 1400 Hz

Answer: A
Diff: 2 *Page Ref: Sec. 12.4*

28) A pipe of length L closed at one end is resonating at its fundamental frequency. Which statement is correct?

A) The wavelength is 4L and there is a displacement node at the pipe's open end.

B) The wavelength is 4L and there is a displacement antinode at the pipe's open end.

C) The wavelength is L and there is a displacement node at the pipe's open end.

D) The wavelength is L and there is a displacement antinode at the pipe's open end.

Answer: B
Diff: 2 *Page Ref: Sec. 12.4*

29) A person stands between two speakers driven by the same source. Each speaker produces a tone with a frequency of 200 Hz on a day when the speed of sound is 330 m/s. The person is 1.65 m from one speaker and 4.95 m from the other. What type of interference does the person sense?

A) constructive

B) destructive

C) both constructive and destructive

D) neither constructive nor destructive

Answer: A
Diff: 2 *Page Ref: Sec. 12.6*

30) In order to produce beats, the two sound waves should have

A) the same amplitude.

B) slightly different amplitudes.

C) the same frequency.

D) slightly different frequencies.

Answer: D
Diff: 1 *Page Ref: Sec. 12.6*

31) Two pure tones are sounded together and a particular beat frequency is heard. What happens to the beat frequency if the frequency of one of the tones is increased?

A) It increases.

B) It decreases.

C) It does not change.

D) It could either increase or decrease.

Answer: D
Diff: 2 *Page Ref: Sec. 12.6*

32) The Doppler shift explains

A) why the siren on a police car changes its pitch as it races past us.

B) why a sound grows quieter as we move away from the source.

C) how sonar works.

D) the phenomenon of beats.

E) why it is that our hearing is best near 3000 Hz.

Answer: A
Diff: 1 *Page Ref: Sec. 12.7*

33) A sound source approaches a stationary observer. The frequency heard by the observer is

A) higher than the source.

B) lower than the source.

C) the same as that of the source.

D) equal to zero.

Answer: A
Diff: 1 *Page Ref: Sec. 12.7*

34) A sound source departs from a stationary observer. The frequency heard by the observer is

A) higher than the source.

B) lower than the source.

C) the same as that of the source.

D) equal to zero.

Answer: B
Diff: 1 *Page Ref: Sec. 12.7*

35) If a jet plane were to double its MACH-speed, its half-angle will decrease by a factor of:

A) 1/2

B) 2

C) $\sin^{-1}(1/2)$

D) none of the above

Answer: D
Diff: 3 *Page Ref: Sec. 12.8*

Quantitative Problems

1) The speed of an ultrasonic sound of frequency 45 kHz in air is 352 m/s. What is the air temperature?

A) 33°C

B) 34°C

C) 35°C

D) 36°C

Answer: C
Diff: 1 *Page Ref: Sec. 12.1*

2) What is the ratio of the speed of sound in air at 0°C to the speed at 100°C?

A) 0.75

B) 0.85

C) 0.95

D) 1.1

Answer: B
Diff: 2 *Page Ref: Sec. 12.1*

3) On a day when the speed of sound in air is 340 m/s, a bat emits a shriek whose echo reaches it 0.0250 s later. How far away was the object that reflected back the sound?

A) 4.25 m

B) 8.50 m

C) 0.425 m

D) 0.850 m

Answer: A
Diff: 1 *Page Ref: Sec. 12.1*

4) You shout at a cliff, and hear the echo in 4.00 s. The temperature is 0°C. How far away is the cliff?

A) 662 m

B) 680 m

C) 1320 m

D) 1760 m

Answer: A
Diff: 1 *Page Ref: Sec. 12.1*

5) If you hear thunder 5.0 s after seeing a flash of lightning, the distance to the lightning strike is about

A) 600 m.

B) 1200 m.

C) 1700 m.

D) 2200 m.

Answer: C
Diff: 1 *Page Ref: Sec. 12.1*

6) An echo is heard 2.0 s from a cliff on a day the temperature is 15°C. Approximately how far is the cliff from the observer?

A) 85 m

B) 170 m

C) 340 m

D) 680 m

Answer: C
Diff: 2 *Page Ref: Sec. 12.1*

7) On a 30°C day, there is an explosion. The sound is heard 3.4 s after seeing the flash. How far away was the explosion?

A) 0.10 km

B) 0.75 km

C) 1.2 km

D) 1.5 km

Answer: C
Diff: 2 *Page Ref: Sec. 12.1*

8) You drop a stone into a deep well and hear the splash 2.5 s later. How deep is the well? (Ignore air resistance, and assume the velocity of sound is 340 m/s.)

A) 25 m

B) 27 m

C) 29 m

D) 31 m

Answer: C
Diff: 3 *Page Ref: Sec. 12.1*

9) The wavelength in air of a sound wave of frequency 500 Hz is

A) 0.69 m.

B) 0.75 m.

C) 1.5 m.

D) 1.8 m.

Answer: A
Diff: 1 *Page Ref: Sec. 12.1*

10) Sound traveling in air at 23°C enters a cold front where the air temperature is 2°C. If the sound frequency is 1500 Hz, determine the wavelength in the warmer air and in the colder air.

A) 0.230 m, 0.221 m

B) 0.221 m, 0.230 m

C) 0.321 m, 0.254 m

D) 0.254 m, 0.321 m

Answer: A
Diff: 2 *Page Ref: Sec. 12.1*

11) What is the intensity level of a sound with intensity 10^{-3} W/m^2?

A) 30 dB

B) 60 dB

C) 90 dB

D) 96 dB

Answer: C
Diff: 1 *Page Ref: Sec. 12.2*

12) What is the intensity of a 70-dB sound?

A) 10^{-4} W/m^2

B) 10^{-5} W/m^2

C) 10^{-6} W/m^2

D) 10^{-7} W/m^2

Answer: B
Diff: 1 *Page Ref: Sec. 12.2*

13) What is the ratio of the intensities of two sounds with intensity levels of 70 dB and 40 dB?

A) 10:1

B) 100:1

C) 1000:1

D) 10,000:1

Answer: C
Diff: 2 *Page Ref: Sec. 12.2*

14) The intensity level by 15 engines in a garage is 100 dB. What is the intensity level generated by one engine?

A) 67 dB

B) 13 dB

C) 44 dB

D) 88 dB

Answer: D
Diff: 2 *Page Ref: Sec. 12.2*

15) The intensity at a distance of 6.0 m from a source that is radiating equally in all directions is 6.0×10^{-10} W/m^2. What is the power emitted by the source?

A) 2.1×10^{-8} W

B) 2.7×10^{-7} W

C) 2.1×10^{-6} W

D) 2.7×10^{-5} W

Answer: B
Diff: 2 *Page Ref: Sec. 12.2*

16) The intensity at a distance of 6.0 m from a source that is radiating equally in all directions is 6.0×10^{-10} W/m^2. What is the intensity level in dB?

A) 18 dB

B) 23 dB

C) 28 dB

D) 32 dB

Answer: C
Diff: 2 *Page Ref: Sec. 12.2*

17) A barking dog delivers about 1 mW of power, which is assumed to be uniformly distributed in all directions. What is the intensity level at a distance 5.00 m from the dog?

A) 61 dB

B) 63 dB

C) 65 dB

D) 68 dB

Answer: C
Diff: 2 *Page Ref: Sec. 12.2*

18) The intensity level is 65 dB at a distance 5.00 m from a barking dog. What would be the intensity level if two identical dogs very close to each other are barking?

A) 65 dB

B) 68 dB

C) 130 dB

D) 136 dB

Answer: B
Diff: 3 *Page Ref: Sec. 12.2*

19) At a distance of 15 m from a sound source the intensity level is 60 dB. What is the intensity level (in dB) at a point 2.0 m from the source? Assume that the source radiates equally in all directions.

A) 55.7 dB

B) 57.5 dB

C) 75.5 dB

D) 77.5 dB

Answer: D
Diff: 3 *Page Ref: Sec. 12.2*

20) The sound intensity level 5.0 m from a point source is 95 dB. At what distance will it be 75 dB?

A) 25 m

B) 50 m

C) 75 m

D) 225 m

Answer: B
Diff: 3 *Page Ref: Sec. 12.2*

21) The third harmonic of a complex tone has a frequency of 1200 Hz. What is the frequency of the fourth harmonic?

A) 400 Hz

B) 900 Hz

C) 1600 Hz

D) 4800 Hz

Answer: C
Diff: 1 *Page Ref: Sec. 12.4*

22) The frequency of the third harmonic of an open pipe is 900 Hz. What is the length of the pipe?

A) 0.189 m

B) 0.283 m

C) 0.567 m

D) 1.13 m

Answer: C
Diff: 2 *Page Ref: Sec. 12.4*

23) The lowest tone to resonate in an open pipe of length L is 400 Hz. What is the frequency of the lowest tone that will resonate in an open pipe of length 2L?

A) 800 Hz

B) 200 Hz

C) 1600 Hz

D) 100 Hz

Answer: B
Diff: 2 *Page Ref: Sec. 12.4*

24) An organ pipe open at both ends has a length of 0.80 m. If the velocity of sound in air is 340 m/s, what is the frequency of the second harmonic?

A) 213 Hz

B) 425 Hz

C) 638 Hz

D) 850 Hz

Answer: B
Diff: 2 *Page Ref: Sec. 12.4*

25) A 3.00-m long pipe is in a room where the temperature is 20°C. What is the fundamental frequency if the pipe is open at both ends?

A) 57 Hz

B) 114 Hz

C) 29 Hz

D) none of the above

Answer: A
Diff: 2 *Page Ref: Sec. 12.4*

26) The fundamental frequency in a pipe closed at one end is 330 Hz. What is the frequency of the third harmonic?

A) 110 Hz

B) 220 Hz

C) 660 Hz

D) 990 Hz

Answer: D
Diff: 1 *Page Ref: Sec.12.4*

27) What is the length of the shortest pipe closed on one end that will have a fundamental frequency of 60 Hz on a day when the velocity of sound is 340 m/s?

A) 1.24 m

B) 1.42 m

C) 2.14 m

D) 4.12 m

Answer: B
Diff: 2 *Page Ref: Sec. 12.4*

28) A 3.00-m long pipe is in a room where the temperature is 20°C. What is the fundamental frequency if the pipe is closed at one end?

A) 57 Hz

B) 114 Hz

C) 29 Hz

D) none of the above

Answer: C
Diff: 2 *Page Ref: Sec. 12.4*

29) A 3.00-m long pipe is in a room where the temperature is 20°C. What is the frequency of the second harmonic if the pipe is closed at one end?

A) 57 Hz

B) 114 Hz

C) 29 Hz

D) none of the above

Answer: D
Diff: 2 *Page Ref: Sec. 12.4*

30) A closed organ pipe of length 0.75 m is played when the speed of sound in air is 340 m/s. What is the fundamental frequency?

A) 57 Hz

B) 113 Hz

C) 170 Hz

D) 227 Hz

Answer: B
Diff: 2 *Page Ref: Sec. 12.4*

31) Consider two pipes of the same length: one is open and the other is closed on one end. If the fundamental frequency of the open pipe is 300 Hz, what is the fundamental frequency of the closed pipe?

A) 150 Hz

B) 300 Hz

C) 450 Hz

D) 600 Hz

Answer: A
Diff: 2 *Page Ref: Sec. 12.4*

32) Two adjacent sources each emit a frequency of 800 Hz in air where the velocity of sound is 340 m/s. How much farther back would source 1 have to be moved so an observer in front of the sources would hear no sound?

A) 0.123 m

B) 0.321 m

C) 0.213 m

D) 0.312 m

Answer: C
Diff: 2 *Page Ref: Sec. 12.6*

33) Two speakers are placed side by side and driven by the same frequency of 500 Hz. If the distance from a person to one speaker is 5.00 m and the person detects little or no sound, which of the following is a possible the distance from the person to the other speaker? (The sound speed is 340 m/s.)

A) 7.7 m

B) 8.1 m

C) 8.4 m

D) 9.1 m

Answer: B
Diff: 2 *Page Ref: Sec. 12.6*

34) Two tunes have frequencies of 440 Hz and 444 Hz. What is the beat frequency?

A) 4 Hz

B) 442 Hz

C) 884 Hz

D) none of the above

Answer: A
Diff: 1 *Page Ref: Sec. 12.6*

35) A music tuner uses a 550–Hz tuning fork to tune the frequency of a musical instrument. If the tuner hears a beat frequency of 2 Hz, what is the frequency of the instrument?

A) It must be 552 Hz.

B) It must be 548 Hz.

C) It could be either 552 Hz or 548 Hz.

D) It is neither 552 Hz or 548 Hz.

Answer: C
Diff: 1 *Page Ref: Sec. 12.6*

36) The wavelengths of the sounds produced by two horns are 6 m and 7 m respectively. What beat frequency is heard when the horns are sounded on a day when the velocity of sound is 340 m/s?

A) 5 Hz

B) 6 Hz

C) 7 Hz

D) 8 Hz

Answer: D
Diff: 2 *Page Ref: Sec. 12.6*

37) The corresponding violin strings on two violins in an orchestra are found to produce a beat frequency of 2 Hz when a frequency of 660 Hz is played. What percentage change in the tension of one of the strings would bring them to the same frequency?

A) 0.2%

B) 0.4%

C) 0.6%

D) 0.8%

Answer: C
Diff: 3 *Page Ref: Sec. 12.6*

38) An observer approaches a stationary 1000-Hz sound source at twice the speed of sound. The observer hears a frequency of

A) 4000 Hz.

B) 2000 Hz.

C) 500 Hz.

D) none of the above

Answer: D
Diff: 2 *Page Ref: Sec. 12.7*

39) A sound source (normal frequency of 1000 Hz) approaches a stationary observer at one-half the speed of sound. The observer hears a frequency of

A) 2000 Hz.

B) 500 Hz.

C) 1500 Hz.

D) none of the above

Answer: A
Diff: 2 *Page Ref: Sec. 12.7*

40) A sound has a frequency of 1000 Hz. If a listener moves with a speed of 30 m/s away from the source, what is the frequency heard by the observer? (The sound speed is 340 m/s.)

A) 912 Hz

B) 919 Hz

C) 1000 Hz

D) 1090 Hz

Answer: A
Diff: 2 *Page Ref: Sec. 12.7*

41) A police car has an 800-Hz siren. It is traveling at 35 m/s on a day when the speed of sound through air is 340 m/s. The car approaches and passes an observer who is standing along the roadside. What change of frequency does the observer hear?

A) zero

B) 82 HZ

C) 166 Hz

D) 249 Hz

Answer: C
Diff: 2 *Page Ref: Sec.12.7*

42) What is the frequency heard by a stationary observer when a train approaches with a speed of 30 m/s. The frequency of the train horn is 600 Hz and the speed of sound is 340 m/s.

A) 551 Hz

B) 600 Hz

C) 653 Hz

D) 658 Hz

Answer: D
Diff: 2 *Page Ref: Sec. 12.7*

43) A train is traveling toward you at 120 km/h. The train blows its 400-Hz whistle. Take the speed of sound to be 340 m/s. What frequency do you hear?

A) 444 Hz

B) 439 Hz

C) 364 Hz

D) 361 Hz

Answer: A
Diff: 2 *Page Ref: Sec. 12.7*

44) You are moving at 120 km/h toward a stationary train. The train blows its 400-Hz whistle. Take the speed of sound to be 340 m/s. What frequency do you hear?

A) 444 Hz

B) 439 Hz

C) 364 Hz

D) 361 Hz

Answer: B
Diff: 2 *Page Ref: Sec. 12.7*

45) A train is traveling away from you at 120 km/h. The train blows its 400-Hz whistle. Take the speed of sound to be 340 m/s. What frequency do you hear?

A) 444 Hz

B) 439 Hz

C) 364 Hz

D) 361 Hz

Answer: C
Diff: 2 *Page Ref: Sec. 12.7*

46) A train is traveling away from you at 120 km/h. It blows its whistle, and you hear a tone of 400 Hz. Take the speed of sound to be 340 m/s. What is the actual frequency of the whistle?

A) 444 Hz

B) 439 Hz

C) 364 Hz

D) 361 Hz

Answer: B
Diff: 2 *Page Ref: Sec. 12.7*

47) The frequency of a train horn is 500 Hz. Assume the speed of sound in air is 340 m/s. What is the frequency heard by an observer if the observer is moving away from the train with a speed of 30.0 m/s?

A) 500 Hz

B) 456 Hz

C) 548 Hz

D) none of the above

Answer: B
Diff: 2 *Page Ref: Sec. 12.7*

48) The frequency of a train horn is 500 Hz. Assume the speed of sound in air is 340 m/s. What is the frequency heard by an observer if the observer is approaching the train with a speed of 30.0 m/s?

A) 456 Hz

B) 500 Hz

C) 544 Hz

D) none of the above

Answer: C
Diff: 2 *Page Ref: Sec. 12.7*

49) Sonar is used to determine the speed of an object. A 40-kHz signal is sent out, and a 42-kHz signal is returned. Assume the speed of sound is 345 m/s. How fast is the object moving?

A) 6.9 m/s

B) 8.4 m/s

C) 331 m/s

D) 347 m/s

Answer: B
Diff: 2 *Page Ref: Sec. 12.7*

50) The half angle of the conical shock wave produced by a supersonic aircraft is 60°. What is the Mach number of the aircraft?

A) 0.87

B) 1.2

C) 1.7

D) 2.0

Answer: B
Diff: 2 *Page Ref: Sec. 12.8*

51) A jet flies at a speed of Mach 1.4. What is the half-angle of the conical shock wave formed?

A) 30°

B) 36°

C) 44°

D) 46°

Answer: D
Diff: 2 *Page Ref: Sec. 12.8*

52) The Concord airplane flies from the United States to Europe with a Mach number of 1.05 where the air temperature is 5.0°C. What is the speed of the plane?

A) 334 m/s

B) 337 m/s

C) 351 m/s

D) 359 m/s

Answer: C
Diff: 2 *Page Ref: Sec. 12.8*

Chapter 13 Temperature and Kinetic Theory

Conceptual Questions

1) State the zeroth law of thermodynamics.

Answer: If two systems are in thermal equilibrium with a third system, then they are in thermal equilibrium with each other.

Diff: 1 *Page Ref: Sec. 13.3*

2) A bimetallic strip, consisting of metal G on the top and metal H on the bottom, is rigidly attached to a wall at the left. (See Fig. 13-1.) The coefficient of linear thermal expansion for metal G is greater than that of metal H. If the strip is uniformly heated, it will

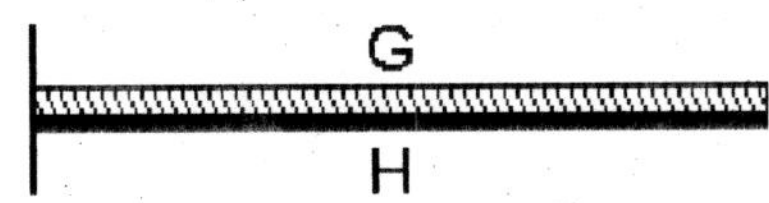

FIGURE 13-1

A) curve upward.

B) curve downward.

C) remain horizontal, but get longer.

D) bend in the middle.

Answer: B

Diff: 2 *Page Ref: Sec. 13.4*

3) When the engine of your car heats up, the spark plug gap will

A) increase.

B) decrease.

C) remain unchanged.

D) decrease at first and then increase later, so that the two effects cancel once the engine reaches operating temperature.

Answer: A

Diff: 2 *Page Ref: Sec. 13.4*

4) Consider a flat steel plate with a hole through its center as shown in Fig. 13–2. When the plate's temperature is increased, the hole will

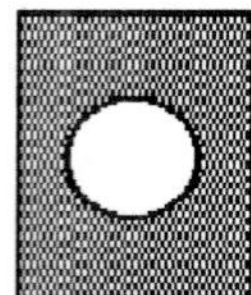

FIGURE 13–2

A) expand only if it takes up more than half the plate's surface area.

B) contract if it takes up less than half the plate's surface area.

C) always contract.

D) always expand.

Answer: D
Diff: 2 *Page Ref: Sec. 13.4*

5) The coefficient of linear expansion for aluminum is $1.8 \times 10^{-6}\ (\mathrm{C}^\circ)^{-1}$. What is its coefficient of volume expansion?

A) $9.0 \times 10^{-6}\ (\mathrm{C}^\circ)^{-1}$

B) $5.8 \times 10^{-18}\ (\mathrm{C}^\circ)^{-1}$

C) $5.4 \times 10^{-6}\ (\mathrm{C}^\circ)^{-1}$

D) $3.6 \times 10^{-6}\ (\mathrm{C}^\circ)^{-1}$

Answer: C
Diff: 2 *Page Ref: Sec. 13.4*

6) The surface water temperature on a large, deep lake is 3°C. A sensitive temperature probe is lowered several meters into the lake. What temperature will the probe record?

A) a temperature warmer than 3°C

B) a temperature less than 3°C

C) a temperature equal to 3°C

D) There is not enough information to determine.

Answer: A
Diff: 1 *Page Ref: Sec. 13.4*

7) Which temperature scale never gives negative temperatures?

A) Kelvin

B) Fahrenheit

C) Celsius

D) all of the above

Answer: A
Diff: 1 *Page Ref: Sec. 13.6*

8) Which two temperature changes are equivalent?

A) 1 K = 1 F°

B) 1 F° = 1 C°

C) 1 C° = 1 K

D) none of the above

Answer: C
Diff: 1 *Page Ref: Sec. 13.6*

9) The temperature in your classroom is approximately

A) 68 K.

B) 68°C.

C) 50°C.

D) 295 K.

Answer: D
Diff: 2 *Page Ref: Sec. 13.6*

10) State Boyle's law.

Answer: The volume of a gas is inversely proportional to the absolute pressure applied to it when the temperature is kept constant.
Diff: 1 *Page Ref: Sec. 13.6*

11) State Charles's law.

Answer: The volume of a given amount of gas is directly proportional to the absolute temperature when the pressure is kept constant.
Diff: 1 *Page Ref: Sec. 13.6*

12) State Gay-Lassac's law.

Answer: At constant volume, the absolute pressure of a gas is directly proportional to the absolute temperature.
Diff: 1 *Page Ref: Sec. 13.6*

13) A container of an ideal gas at 1 atm is compressed to one-third its volume, with the temperature held constant. What is its final pressure?

A) 1/3 atm

B) 1 atm

C) 3 atm

D) 9 atm

Answer: C
Diff: 1 *Page Ref: Sec. 13.6*

14) If the pressure acting on an ideal gas at constant temperature is tripled, its volume is

A) reduced to one-third.

B) increased by a factor of three.

C) increased by a factor of two.

D) reduced to one-half.

Answer: A
Diff: 1 *Page Ref: Sec. 13.6*

15) According to the ideal gas Law, PV = constant for a given temperature. As a result, an increase in volume corresponds to a decrease in pressure. This happens because the molecules

A) collide with each other more frequently.

B) move slower on the average.

C) strike the container wall less often.

D) transfer less energy to the walls of the container each time they strike it.

Answer: C
Diff: 2 *Page Ref: Sec. 13.7-13.9*

16) The number of molecules in one mole of a substance

A) depends on the molecular weight of the substance.

B) depends on the atomic weight of the substance.

C) depends on the density of the substance.

D) is the same for all substances.

Answer: D
Diff: 1 *Page Ref: Sec. 13.7-13.9*

17) A container holds N molecules of an ideal gas at a given temperature. If the number of molecules in the container is increased to 2N with no change in temperature or volume, the pressure in the container

A) doubles.

B) remains constant.

C) is cut in half.

D) none of the above

Answer: A
Diff: 1 *Page Ref: Sec. 13.7-13.9*

18) Both the pressure and volume of a given sample of an ideal gas double. This means that its temperature in Kelvin must

A) double.

B) quadruple.

C) reduce to one-fourth its original value.

D) remain unchanged.

Answer: B
Diff: 1 *Page Ref: Sec. 13.7-13.9*

19) The temperature of an ideal gas increases from 2°C to 4°C while remaining at constant pressure. What happens to the volume of the gas?

A) It decreases slightly.

B) It decreases to one-half its original volume.

C) It increases slightly.

D) It increases to twice as much.

Answer: C
Diff: 1 *Page Ref: Sec. 13.7-13.9*

20) A mole of diatomic oxygen molecules and a mole of diatomic nitrogen molecules at STP have

A) the same average molecular speeds.

B) the same number of molecules.

C) the same diffusion rates.

D) all of the above

Answer: B
Diff: 2 *Page Ref: Sec. 13.7-13.9*

21) Consider two equal volumes of gas at a given temperature and pressure. One gas, oxygen, has a molecular mass of 32. The other gas, nitrogen, has a molecular mass of 28. What is the ratio of the number of oxygen molecules to the number of nitrogen molecules?

A) 32:28

B) 28:32

C) 1:1

D) none of the above

Answer: C
Diff: 2 *Page Ref: Sec. 13.7-13.9*

22) The average molecular kinetic energy of a gas can be determined by knowing only

A) the number of molecules in the gas.

B) the volume of the gas.

C) the pressure of the gas.

D) the temperature of the gas.

Answer: D
Diff: 1 *Page Ref: Sec. 13.10*

23) A sample of an ideal gas is slowly compressed to one–half its original volume with no change in temperature. What happens to the average speed of the molecules in the sample?

A) It does not change.

B) It doubles.

C) It halves.

D) none of the above

Answer: A
Diff: 1 *Page Ref: Sec. 13.10*

24) A sample of an ideal gas is heated and its Kelvin temperature doubles. What happens to the average speed of the molecules in the sample?

A) It does not change.

B) It doubles.

C) It halves.

D) none of the above

Answer: D
Diff: 2 *Page Ref: Sec. 13.10*

25) The absolute temperature of an ideal gas is directly proportional to which of the following?

A) speed

B) momentum

C) kinetic energy

D) mass

Answer: C
Diff: 2 *Page Ref: Sec. 13.10*

26) In order to double the average speed of the molecules in a given sample of gas, the temperature (measured in Kelvin) must

A) quadruple.

B) double.

C) increase by a factor of square root two of its original value.

D) increase by a factor of square root three of its original value.

Answer: C
Diff: 2 *Page Ref: Sec. 13.10*

27) Oxygen molecules are 16 times more massive than hydrogen molecules. At a given temperature, the average molecular kinetic energy of oxygen, compared to hydrogen

A) is greater.

B) is less.

C) is the same.

D) cannot be determined since pressure and volume are not given

Answer: C
Diff: 2 *Page Ref: Sec. 13.10*

28) Oxygen molecules are 16 times more massive than hydrogen molecules. At a given temperature, how do their average molecular speeds compare? The oxygen molecules are moving

A) 4 times faster.

B) at 1/4 the speed.

C) 16 times faster.

D) at 1/16 the speed.

Answer: B
Diff: 2 *Page Ref: Sec. 13.10*

29) A fixed container holds oxygen and helium gases at the same temperature. Which one of the following statements is correct?

A) The oxygen molecules have the greater kinetic energy.

B) The helium molecules have the greater kinetic energy.

C) The oxygen molecules have the greater speed.

D) The helium molecules have the greater speed.

Answer: D
Diff: 2 *Page Ref: Sec. 13.10*

30) A container is filled with a mixture of helium and oxygen gases. A thermometer in the container indicates that the temperature is 22°C. Which gas molecules have the greater average kinetic energy?

A) It is the same for both because the temperatures are the same.

B) The oxygen molecules do because they are diatomic.

C) The helium molecules do because they are less massive.

D) The helium molecules do because they are monatomic.

Answer: A
Diff: 2 *Page Ref: Sec. 13.10*

31) A container is filled with a mixture of helium and oxygen gases. A thermometer in the container indicates that the temperature is 22°C. Which gas molecules have the greater average speed?

A) The helium molecules do because they are monatomic.

B) It is the same for both because the temperatures are the same.

C) The oxygen molecules do because they are more massive.

D) The helium molecules do because they are less massive.

Answer: D
Diff: 2 *Page Ref: Sec. 13.10*

32) The three phases of matter can exist together in equilibrium at the

A) critical point.

B) triple point.

C) melting point.

D) evaporation point.

Answer: B
Diff: 1 *Page Ref: Sec. 13.12*

33) Supersaturation occurs in air when the

A) relative humidity is 100% and the temperature increases.

B) relative humidity is less than 100% and the temperature increases.

C) relative humidity is less 100% and the temperature decreases.

D) relative humidity is 100% and the temperature decreases.

Answer: D
Diff: 2 *Page Ref: Sec. 13.13*

Quantitative Problems

1) Express your body temperature (98.6°F) in Celsius degrees.

A) 37.0°C

B) 45.5°C

C) 66.6°C

D) 72.6°C

Answer: A
Diff: 1 *Page Ref: Sec. 13.2*

2) Express 68°F in °C.

A) 7.0°C

B) 20°C

C) 36°C

D) 181°C

Answer: B
Diff: 1 *Page Ref: Sec. 13.2*

3) Express −40°C in °F.

A) −72°F

B) −54°F

C) 40°F

D) 4.4°F

Answer: C
Diff: 1 *Page Ref: Sec. 13.2*

4) The temperature changes from 35°F during the night to 75°F during the day. What is the temperature change on the Celsius scale?

A) 72 C°

B) 40 C°

C) 32 C°

D) 22 C°

Answer: D
Diff: 2 *Page Ref: Sec. 13.2*

5) A temperature change of 20 °C corresponds to a temperature change of

A) 68°F.

B) 11°F.

C) 36°F.

D) none of the above

Answer: C
Diff: 1 *Page Ref: Sec. 13.2*

6) At what temperature are the numerical readings on the Fahrenheit and Celsius scales the same?

A) −30°

B) −40°

C) −50°

D) −60°

Answer: B
Diff: 2 *Page Ref: Sec. 13.2*

7) A steel bridge is 1000 m long at -20°C in winter. What is the change in length when the temperature rises to 40°C in summer? (The average coefficient of linear expansion of steel is 11×10^{-6} /C°.)

A) 0.33 m

B) 0.44 m

C) 0.55 m

D) 0.66 m

Answer: D
Diff: 1 *Page Ref: Sec. 13.4*

8) An aluminum rod 17.4 cm long at 20°C is heated to 100°C. What is its new length? Aluminum has a linear expansion coefficient of 25×10^{-6} /C°.

A) 17.435 cm

B) 17.365 cm

C) 0.348 cm

D) 0.0348 cm

Answer: A
Diff: 2 *Page Ref: Sec. 13.4*

9) By how much will a slab of concrete 18 m long contract when the temperature drops from 24°C to -16°C? (The coefficient of linear thermal expansion for concrete is 10^{-5} /C°.)

A) 0.50 cm

B) 0.72 cm

C) 1.2 cm

D) 1.5 cm

Answer: B
Diff: 2 *Page Ref: Sec. 13.4*

10) A bolt hole in a brass plate has a diameter of 1.200 cm at 20°C. What is the diameter of the hole when the plate is heated to 220°C? (The coefficient of linear thermal expansion for brass is 19×10^{-6} /C°.)

A) 1.205 cm

B) 1.195 cm

C) 1.200 cm

D) 1.210 cm

Answer: A
Diff: 2 *Page Ref: Sec. 13.4*

11) 20.00 cm of space is available. How long a piece of brass at 20°C can be put there and still fit at 200°C? Brass has a linear expansion coefficient of 19×10^{-6} /C°.

A) 19.93 cm

B) 19.69 cm

C) 19.50 cm

D) 19.09 cm

Answer: A
Diff: 3 *Page Ref: Sec. 13.4*

12) A 5.0-cm diameter steel shaft has 0.10 mm clearance all around its bushing at 20°C. If the bushing temperature remains constant, at what temperature will the shaft begin to bind? Steel has a linear expansion coefficient of 12×10^{-6} /C°.

A) 353°C

B) 333°C

C) 53°C

D) 680°C

Answer: A
Diff: 3 *Page Ref: Sec. 13.4*

13) 400 cm^3 of mercury at 0°C will expand to what volume at 50°C? Mercury has a volume expansion coefficient of 180×10^{-6} /C°.

A) 450 cm^3

B) 409.7 cm^3

C) 403.6 cm^3

D) 401.8 cm^3

Answer: C
Diff: 1 *Page Ref: Sec. 13.4*

14) 1 L of water at 20°C will occupy what volume at 80°C? Water has a volume expansion coefficient of 210×10^{-6} /C°.

A) 1.6 L

B) 1.013 L

C) 0.987 L

D) 0.9987 L

Answer: B
Diff: 1 *Page Ref: Sec. 13.4*

15) The volume coefficient of thermal expansion for gasoline is 950×10^{-6} /C°. By how much does the volume of 1.0 L of gasoline change when the temperature rises from 20°C to 40°C?

A) 6.0 cm^3

B) 12 cm^3

C) 19 cm^3

D) 37 cm^3

Answer: C
Diff: 1 *Page Ref: Sec. 13.4*

16) A 500-mL glass beaker of water is filled to the rim at a temperature of 0°C. How much water will overflow if the water is heated to a temperature of 95°C? (Ignore the expansion of the glass and the coefficient of volume expansion of water is 2.1×10^{-4} /C°.)

A) 3.3 mL

B) 10 mL

C) 33 mL

D) 100 mL

Answer: B
Diff: 2 *Page Ref: Sec. 13.4*

17) For mercury to expand from 4.0 cm^3 to 4.1 cm^3, what change in temperature is necessary? Mercury has a volume expansion coefficient of 180×10^{-6} /C°.

A) 400°C

B) 139°C

C) 14°C

D) 8.2°C

Answer: B
Diff: 2 *Page Ref: Sec. 13.4*

18) A mercury thermometer has a bulb of volume 0.100 cm^3 at 10°C. The capillary tube above the bulb has a cross-sectional area of 0.012 mm^2. The volume thermal expansion coefficient of mercury is 1.8×10^{-4} $(C°)^{-1}$. How much will the mercury rise when the temperature rises by 30°C?

A) 0.45 mm

B) 4.5 mm

C) 45 mm

D) 45 cm

Answer: C
Diff: 3 *Page Ref: Sec. 13.4*

19) Convert 14°C to K.

A) 46 K

B) 100 K

C) 287 K

D) 474 K

Answer: C
Diff: 1 *Page Ref: Sec. 13.6*

20) Convert 14°F to K.

A) 263 K

B) 287 K

C) -10 K

D) 474 K

Answer: A
Diff: 2 *Page Ref: Sec. 13.6*

21) Convert 14 K to °C.

A) 46°C

B) 287°C

C) 25°C

D) -259°C

Answer: D
Diff: 1 *Page Ref: Sec. 13.6*

22) Convert 14 K to °F.

A) 287°F

B) -434°F

C) -259°F

D) 474°F

Answer: B
Diff: 2 *Page Ref: Sec. 13.6*

23) Oxygen condenses into a liquid at approximately 90 K. What temperature, in degrees Fahrenheit, does this correspond to?

A) -193°F

B) -217°F

C) -265°F

D) -297°F

Answer: D
Diff: 2 *Page Ref: Sec. 13.6*

24) An ideal gas occupies 300 L at an absolute pressure of 400 kPa. Find the absolute pressure if the volume changes to 850 L and the temperature remains constant.

A) 140 kPa

B) 640 kPa

C) 850 kPa

D) 1140 kPa

Answer: A
Diff: 1 *Page Ref: Sec. 13.6*

25) Two liters of a perfect gas are at 0°C and 1 atm. If the gas is nitrogen, N_2, determine the number of moles.

A) 0.37

B) 0.73

C) 0.089

D) 0.098

Answer: C
Diff: 1 *Page Ref: Sec. 13.7–14.9*

26) Two liters of a perfect gas are at 0°C and 1 atm. If the gas is nitrogen, N_2, determine the number of molecules.

A) 3.5×10^{22}

B) 5.3×10^{22}

C) 4.7×10^{22}

D) 7.4×10^{22}

Answer: B
Diff: 2 *Page Ref: Sec. 13.7–13.9*

27) Two liters of a perfect gas are at 0°C and 1 atm. If the gas is nitrogen, N_2, determine the mass of the gas.

A) 2.5 g

B) 2.7 g

C) 2.9 g

D) 3.1 g

Answer: A
Diff: 2 *Page Ref: Sec. 13.7–13.9*

28) How many water molecules are there in 36 g of water? Express your answer as a multiple of Avogadro's number N_A. (The molecular structure of a water molecule is H_2O.)

A) $36N_A$

B) $2N_A$

C) $18N_A$

D) none of the above

Answer: B
Diff: 1 *Page Ref: Sec. 13.7–13.9*

29) How many mol are there in 2.00 kg of copper? (The atomic weight of copper is 63.5 and its specific gravity is 8.90.)

A) 15.3

B) 31.5

C) 51.3

D) 53.1

Answer: B
Diff: 1 *Page Ref: Sec. 13.7–13.9*

30) A sample of a diatomic ideal gas occupies 33.6 L under standard conditions. How many mol of gas are in the sample?

A) 0.75

B) 3.0

C) 1.5

D) 3.25

Answer: C
Diff: 2 *Page Ref: Sec. 13.7–13.9*

31) An ideal gas has a pressure of 2.5 atm, a volume of 1.0 L at a temperature of 30°C. How many molecules are there in the gas?

A) 6.1×10^{23}

B) 6.0×10^{22}

C) 2.4×10^{22}

D) 2.3×10^{23}

Answer: B
Diff: 2 *Page Ref: Sec. 13.7–13.9*

32) An ideal gas in a container of volume 100 cm^3 at 20°C has a pressure of 100 N/m^2. Determine the number of gas molecules in the container.

A) 4.2×10^6

B) 6.0×10^{23}

C) 2.5×10^{18}

D) 5.2×10^{18}

Answer: C
Diff: 2 *Page Ref: Sec. 13.7–13.9*

33) A sample of helium (He) occupies 44.8 L at STP. What is the mass of the sample?

A) 2 g

B) 4 g

C) 6 g

D) 8 g

Answer: D
Diff: 2 *Page Ref: Sec. 13.7–13.9*

34) A 25-L container holds hydrogen gas at a gauge pressure of 0.25 atm and a temperature of 0°C. What mass of hydrogen is in this container?

A) 1.4 g

B) 2.8 g

C) 4.2 g

D) 5.6 g

Answer: B
Diff: 2 *Page Ref: Sec. 13.7–13.9*

35) A 100-cm^3 container has 4 g of ideal gas in it at 250 kPa. If the volume is changed to 50 cm^3 and the temperature remains constant, what is its new density?

A) 400 kg/m^3

B) 250 kg/m^3

C) 80 kg/m^3

D) 50 kg/m^3

Answer: C
Diff: 2 *Page Ref: Sec. 13.7–13.9*

36) An ideal gas occupies 600 cm^3 at 20°C. At what temperature will it occupy 1200 cm^3 if the pressure remains constant?

A) 10°C

B) 40°C

C) 100°C

D) 313°C

Answer: D
Diff: 1 *Page Ref: Sec. 13.7–13.9*

37) A constant pressure gas thermometer is initially at 28°C. If the volume of gas increases by 10%, what is the final Celsius temperature?

A) 31°C

B) 43°C

C) 58°C

D) 64°C

Answer: C
Diff: 2 *Page Ref: Sec. 13.7–13.9*

38) An ideal gas occupies 4.0 L at 20°C. What volume will it occupy at 40°C if the pressure remains constant?

A) 43 cm^3

B) 4.3 L

C) 8.0 L

D) 2.0 L

Answer: B
Diff: 1 *Page Ref: Sec. 13.7–13.9*

39) A balloon has a volume of 1.0 m^3. As it rises in the Earth's atmosphere, its volume expands. What will be its new volume if its original temperature and pressure are 20°C and 1.0 atm, and its final temperature and pressure are -40°C and 0.10 atm?

A) 2.0 m^3

B) 4.0 m^3

C) 6.0 m^3

D) 8.0 m^3

Answer: D
Diff: 2 *Page Ref: Sec. 13.7–13.9*

40) A given sample of carbon dioxide (CO_2) contains 3.01×10^{23} molecules at STP. What volume does this sample occupy?

A) 11.2 L

B) 22.4 L

C) 44.8 L

D) 32.7 L

Answer: A
Diff: 2 Page Ref: Sec. 13.7–13.9

41) 500 cm^3 of ideal gas at 40°C and 200 kPa (absolute) is compressed to 250 cm^3 and cooled to 20° C. What is the final absolute pressure?

A) 748 kPa

B) 374 kPa

C) 200 kPa

D) 100 kPa

Answer: B
Diff: 2 Page Ref: Sec. 13.7–13.9

42) 1500 cm^3 of ideal gas at STP is cooled to -20°C and put into a 1000 cm^3 container. What is the final gauge pressure?

A) 11 kPa

B) 40 kPa

C) 113 kPa

D) 141 kPa

Answer: B
Diff: 2 Page Ref: Sec. 13.7–13.9

43) An ideal gas has a density of 1.75 kg/m^3 at a gauge pressure of 160 kPa. What must be the gauge pressure if a density of 1.0 kg/m^3 is desired at the same temperature?

A) 356 kPa

B) 280 kPa

C) 91 kPa

D) 48 kPa

Answer: D
Diff: 2 Page Ref: Sec. 13.7–13.9

44) An ideal gas has a volume of 0.20 m^3, a temperature of 30°C, and a pressure of 1.0 atm. It is heated to 60°C and compressed to a volume of 0.15 m^3. What is the new pressure?

A) 1.0 atm

B) 1.2 atm

C) 1.5 atm

D) 2.7 atm

Answer: C
Diff: 2 *Page Ref: Sec. 13.7–13.9*

45) A mixture of gases contains 15 g of H_2, 14 g of N_2, and 44 g of CO_2. The mixture is in a 40 L sealed container which is at 20°C. What is the pressure in the container?

A) $3.3 \times 10^5\ N/m^2$

B) $4.4 \times 10^5\ N/m^2$

C) $5.5 \times 10^5\ N/m^2$

D) $6.6 \times 10^5\ N/m^2$

Answer: C
Diff: 2 *Page Ref: Sec. 13.7–13.9*

46) What is the average separation between air molecules at STP?

A) 3.34×10^{-7} cm

B) 4.33×10^{-7} cm

C) 5.32×10^{-7} cm

D) 5.23×10^{-7} cm

Answer: A
Diff: 3 *Page Ref: Sec. 13.7–13.9*

47) At what temperature is the average kinetic energy of an atom in helium gas equal to 6.21×10^{-21} J?

A) 200 K

B) 250 K

C) 300 K

D) 350 K

Answer: C
Diff: 1 *Page Ref: Sec. 13.10*

48) At what temperature would the rms speed of H_2 molecules equal 11,200 m/s (the Earth's escape speed)?

A) 10^2 K

B) 10^4 K

C) 10^6 K

D) 10^8 K

Answer: B

Diff: 2 *Page Ref: Sec. 13.10*

49) A cylinder contains 16 g of helium gas at STP. How much energy is needed to raise the temperature of this gas to 20°C?

A) 789 J

B) 798 J

C) 879 J

D) 998 J

Answer: D

Diff: 2 *Page Ref: Sec. 13.10*

50) If the temperature of a gas is increased from 20°C to 40°C, by what factor does the speed of the molecules increase?

A) 3%

B) 30%

C) 70%

D) 100%

Answer: A

Diff: 2 *Page Ref: Sec. 13.10*

51) A molecule has a speed of 500 m/s at 20°C. What is its speed at 80°C?

A) 500 m/s

B) 550 m/s

C) 1000 m/s

D) 2000 m/s

Answer: B

Diff: 2 *Page Ref: Sec. 13.10*

52) The molecular mass of oxygen molecules is 32, and the molecular mass of nitrogen molecules is 28. If these two gases at the same temperature, the ratio of nitrogen's rms speed to that of oxygen is ________.

A) $(8)^{1/2}:(7)^{1/2}$

B) 8:7

C) $(7)^{1/2}:(8)^{1/2}$

D) 7:8

Answer: A
Diff: 2 *Page Ref: Sec. 13.10*

53) The molecular mass of nitrogen is 14 times greater than that of hydrogen. If the molecules in these two gases have the same rms speed, the ratio of hydrogen's absolute temperature to that of nitrogen is ________.

A) $(14)^{1/2}:1$

B) $1:(14)^{1/2}$

C) 1:14

D) 14:1

Answer: C
Diff: 2 *Page Ref: Sec. 13.10*

Chapter 14 Heat

Conceptual Questions

1) Which of the following is the smallest unit of heat energy?

A) Calorie

B) Kilocalorie

C) Btu

D) Joule

Answer: D
Diff: 1 *Page Ref: Sec. 14.1*

2) The amount of heat necessary to raise the temperature of 1 gram of water by 1°C is referred to as the

A) calorie.

B) kilocalorie.

C) British thermal unit.

D) joule.

Answer: A
Diff: 1 *Page Ref: Sec. 14.1*

3) The measure of the average kinetic energy of individual molecules is referred to as

A) internal energy.

B) thermal energy.

C) temperature.

D) heat.

Answer: C
Diff: 1 *Page Ref: Sec. 14.2*

4) A cup of water is scooped up from a swimming pool of water. Compare the temperature T and the internal energy U of the water, in both the cup and the swimming pool.

A) T_{Pool} is greater than T_{Cup}, and the U is the same.

B) T_{Pool} is less than T_{Cup}, and the U is the same.

C) T_{Pool} is equal to T_{Cup}, and U_{Pool} is greater than U_{Cup}.

D) T_{Pool} is equal to T_{Cup}, and U_{Pool} is less than U_{Cup}.

Answer: C
Diff: 1 *Page Ref: Sec. 14.2*

5) The internal energy of an ideal gas depends on

A) its volume.

B) its pressure.

C) its temperature.

D) all of the above

Answer: C
Diff: 1 *Page Ref: Sec. 14.2*

6) An ideal gas at STP is first compressed until its volume is half the initial volume, and then it is allowed to expand until its pressure is half the initial pressure. All of this is done while holding the temperature constant. If the initial internal energy of the gas is U, the final internal energy of the gas will be

A) U.

B) U/3.

C) U/2.

D) 2U.

Answer: A
Diff: 2 *Page Ref: Sec. 14.2*

7) An ideal gas with internal energy U at 200°C is heated to 400°C. Its internal energy then will be

A) still U.

B) 2 U.

C) 1.4 U.

D) 1.2 U.

Answer: C
Diff: 2 *Page Ref: Sec. 14.2*

8) The reason ocean temperatures do not vary drastically is that

A) water has a relatively high rate of heat conduction.

B) water is a good radiator.

C) water has a relatively high specific heat.

D) water is a poor heat conductor.

Answer: C
Diff: 2 *Page Ref: Sec. 14.3*

9) It is a well-known fact that water has a higher specific heat capacity than iron. Now, consider equal masses of water and iron that are initially in thermal equilibrium. The same amount of heat, 30 calories, is added to each. Which statement is true?

A) They remain in thermal equilibrium.

B) They are no longer in thermal equilibrium; the iron is warmer.

C) They are no longer in thermal equilibrium; the water is warmer.

D) It is impossible to say without knowing the exact mass involved and the exact specific heat capacities.

Answer: B
Diff: 2 *Page Ref: Sec. 14.3*

10) A thermally isolated system is made up of a hot piece of aluminum and a cold piece of copper; the aluminum and the copper are in thermal contact. The specific heat capacity of aluminum is more than double that of copper. Which object experiences the greater magnitude gain or loss of heat during the time the system takes to reach thermal equilibrium?

A) the aluminum

B) the copper

C) Neither; both experience the same size gain or loss of heat.

D) It is impossible to tell without knowing the masses.

Answer: C
Diff: 2 *Page Ref: Sec. 14.4*

11) Phase changes occur

A) as the temperature decreases.

B) as the temperature increases.

C) as the temperature remains the same.

D) all of the above

Answer: C
Diff: 1 *Page Ref: Sec. 14.5*

12) The heat required to change a substance from the solid to the liquid state is referred to as the

A) heat of fusion.

B) heat of vaporization.

C) heat of melting.

D) heat of freezing.

Answer: A
Diff: 1 *Page Ref: Sec. 14.5*

13) The heat required to change a substance from the liquid to the vapor state is referred to as the

A) heat of fusion.

B) heat of vaporization.

C) heat of evaporation.

D) heat of condensation.

Answer: B
Diff: 1 *Page Ref: Sec. 14.5*

14) If heat is added to a pure substance at a steady rate,

A) its temperature will begin to rise.

B) it will eventually melt.

C) it will eventually boil.

D) More than one of the above is true.

E) None of the above is true.

Answer: D
Diff: 1 *Page Ref: Sec. 14.5*

15) When a solid melts

A) the temperature of the substance increases.

B) the temperature of the substance decreases.

C) heat energy leaves the substance.

D) heat energy enters the substance.

Answer: D
Diff: 1 *Page Ref: Sec. 14.5*

16) When a liquid freezes

A) the temperature of the substance increases.

B) the temperature of the substance decreases.

C) heat energy leaves the substance.

D) heat energy enters the substance.

Answer: C
Diff: 1 *Page Ref: Sec. 14.5*

17) When a liquid evaporates

A) the temperature of the substance increases.

B) the temperature of the substance decreases.

C) heat energy leaves the substance.

D) heat energy enters the substance.

Answer: D
Diff: 1 *Page Ref: Sec. 14.5*

18) When a vapor condenses

A) the temperature of the substance increases.

B) the temperature of the substance decreases.

C) heat energy leaves the substance.

D) heat energy enters the substance.

Answer: C
Diff: 1 *Page Ref: Sec. 14.5*

19) In a cloud formation, water vapor condenses into water droplets which get bigger and bigger until it rains. This will cause the temperature of the air in the clouds to

A) increase.

B) decrease.

C) stay constant.

D) freeze.

Answer: A
Diff: 2 *Page Ref: Sec. 14.5*

20) Turning up the flame under a pan of boiling water causes

A) the water to boil away faster.

B) the temperature of the boiling water to increase.

C) both the water to boil away faster and the temperature of the boiling water to increase.

D) none of the above

Answer: A
Diff: 1 *Page Ref: Sec. 14.5*

21) Equal masses of water at 20°C and 80°C are mixed. What is the final temperature of the mixture?

A) 40°C

B) 50°C

C) 60°C

D) 70°C

Answer: B
Diff: 2 *Page Ref: Sec. 14.5*

22) A chunk of ice (T = -20°C) is added to a thermally insulated container of cold water (T = 0°C). What happens in the container?

A) The ice melts until thermal equilibrium is established.

B) The water cools down until thermal equilibrium is established.

C) Some of the water freezes and the chunk of ice gets larger.

D) none of the above

Answer: C
Diff: 2 *Page Ref: Sec. 14.5*

23) The process whereby heat flows by means of molecular collisions is referred to as

A) conduction.

B) convection.

C) radiation.

D) inversion.

Answer: A

Diff: 1 *Page Ref: Sec. 14.6–14.8*

24) By what primary heat transfer mechanism does one end of an iron bar become hot when the other end is placed in a flame?

A) natural convection

B) conduction

C) radiation

D) forced convection

Answer: B

Diff: 1 *Page Ref: Sec. 14.6–14.8*

25) On a cold day, a piece of metal feels much colder to the touch than a piece of wood. This is due to the difference in which one of the following physical property?

A) density

B) specific heat

C) latent heat

D) thermal conductivity

Answer: D

Diff: 1 *Page Ref: Sec. 14.6–14.8*

26) If you double the thickness of a wall built from a homogeneous material, the rate of heat loss for a given temperature difference across the thickness will

A) become one-half its original value.

B) also double.

C) become one-fourth its original value.

D) none of the above

Answer: A

Diff: 1 *Page Ref: Sec. 14.6–14.8*

27) A layer of insulating material with thermal conductivity K is placed on a layer of another material of thermal conductivity 2K. The layers have equal thickness. What is the effective thermal conductivity of the composite sheet?

A) 3K

B) 1.5K

C) K/3

D) 2K/3

Answer: D
Diff: 3 *Page Ref: Sec. 14.6–14.8*

28) The process whereby heat flows by the mass movement of molecules from one place to another is referred to as

A) conduction.

B) convection.

C) radiation.

D) inversion.

Answer: B
Diff: 2 *Page Ref: Sec. 14.6–14.8*

29) By what primary heat transfer mechanism is a pot of water heated on a stove?

A) convection

B) conduction

C) radiation

D) all of the above in combination

Answer: A
Diff: 3 *Page Ref: Sec. 14.6–14.8*

30) Convection can occur

A) only in solids.

B) only in liquids.

C) only in gases.

D) only in liquids and gases.

E) in solids, liquids, and gases.

Answer: D
Diff: 1 *Page Ref: Sec. 14.6–14.8*

31) Which of the following best explains why sweating is important to humans in maintaining suitable body temperature?

A) Moisture on the skin increases thermal conductivity, thereby allowing heat to flow out of the body more effectively.

B) Evaporation of moisture from the skin extracts heat from the body.

C) The high specific heat of water on the skin absorbs heat from the body.

D) Functioning of the sweat glands absorbs energy that otherwise would go into heating the body.

E) None of the above explains the principle on which sweating depends.

Answer: B
Diff: 1 *Page Ref: Sec. 14.6–14.8*

32) A spaceship is drifting in an environment where the acceleration of gravity is essentially zero. As the air on one side of the cabin is heated by an electric heater, what is true about the convection currents caused by this heating?

A) The hot air around the heater rises and the cooler air moves in to take its place.

B) The hot air around the heater drops and the cooler air moves in to take its place.

C) The convection currents move about the cabin in a random fashion.

D) There are no convection currents.

Answer: C
Diff: 2 *Page Ref: Sec. 14.6–14.8*

33) Consider two neighboring rectangular houses built from the same materials. One of the houses has twice the length, width, and height of the other. Under identical climatic conditions, what would be true about the rate that heat would have to be supplied to maintain the same inside temperature on a cold day? Compared to the small house, the larger house would need heat supplied at

A) twice the rate.

B) 4 times the rate.

C) 8 times the rate.

D) 16 times the rate.

Answer: B
Diff: 2 *Page Ref: Sec. 14.6–14.8*

34) If the absolute temperature of a radiator is doubled, by what factor does the radiating power change?

A) 2

B) 4

C) 8

D) 16

Answer: D
Diff: 2 *Page Ref: Sec. 14.6–14.8*

35) The process whereby heat flows in the absence of any medium is referred to as

A) conduction.

B) convection.

C) radiation.

D) inversion.

Answer: C
Diff: 2 *Page Ref: Sec. 14.6–14.8*

36) By what primary heat transfer mechanism does the Sun warm the Earth?

A) convection

B) conduction

C) radiation

D) all of the above in combination

Answer: C
Diff: 1 *Page Ref: Sec. 14.6–14.8*

Quantitative Problems

1) 1700 J of work is equivalent to how much heat?

A) 7,116,000 cal

B) 7.116 kcal

C) 406 cal

D) 406 kcal

Answer: C
Diff: 1 *Page Ref: Sec. 14.1*

2) 16.5 kcal of heat is equivalent to how much work?

A) 3.94 J

B) 3940 J

C) 69.1 J

D) 69100 J

Answer: D
Diff: 1 *Page Ref: Sec. 14.1*

3) Gasoline yields 4.8×10^7 joules per kg when burned. The density of gasoline is approximately the same as that of water, and 1 gal = 3.8 L. How much energy does your car use on a trip of 100 mi if you get 25 mi per gallon?

A) 3.7×10^8 J

B) 4.6×10^8 J

C) 6.2×10^8 J

D) 7.3×10^8 J

Answer: D
Diff: 2 *Page Ref: Sec. 14.1*

4) How much heat is needed to raise the temperature of 100 g of lead (c = 0.11 kcal/kg• C°) by 15 C°?

A) 16.5 cal

B) 165 cal

C) 1500 cal

D) 15 kcal

Answer: B
Diff: 1 *Page Ref: Sec. 14.3–14.4*

5) If 40 kcal of heat is added to 2.0 kg of water, what is the resulting temperature change?

A) 80C°

B) 40C°

C) 20C°

D) 0.05C°

Answer: C
Diff: 1 *Page Ref: Sec 14.3–14.4*

6) A 4.0-kg aluminum block is originally at 10°C. If 160 kJ of heat is added to the block, what is its final temperature?

A) 24°C

B) 34°C

C) 44°C

D) 54°C

Answer: D
Diff: 1 *Page Ref: Sec. 14.3–14.4*

7) 150 kcal of heat raises the temperature of 2.0 kg of material by 400 F°. What is the material's specific heat capacity?

A) 1.35 kcal/kg•°C

B) 0.75 kcal/kg•°C

C) 0.34 kcal/kg•°C

D) 0.19 kcal/kg•°C

Answer: C
Diff: 2 *Page Ref: Sec. 14.3–14.4*

8) A person tries to heat up her bath water by adding 5.0 L of water at 80°C to 60 L of water at 30° C. What is the final temperature of the water?

A) 34°C

B) 36°C

C) 38°C

D) 40°C

Answer: A
Diff: 2 *Page Ref: Sec. 14.3–14.4*

9) A machine part consists of 0.10 kg of iron and 0.16 kg of copper. How much heat is added to the gear if the temperature increases by 35 C°?

A) 9.1×10^2 J

B) 3.8×10^3 J

C) 4.0×10^3 J

D) 4.4×10^3 J

Answer: B
Diff: 2 *Page Ref: Sec. 14.3–14.4*

10) 50 g of lead (c = 0.11 kcal/kg•°C) at 100°C is put into 75 g of water at 0°C. What is the final temperature of the mixture?

A) 2°C

B) 6.8°C

C) 25°C

D) 50°C

Answer: B
Diff: 2 *Page Ref: Sec. 14.3–14.4*

11) A 0.600-kg piece of metal is heated to 100°C and placed in an aluminum can of mass 0.200-kg which contains 0.500 kg of water initially at 17.3°C. The final equilibrium temperature of the mixture is 20.2°C, what is the specific heat of the metal?

A) 140 J/kg•C°

B) 270 J/kg•C°

C) 450 J/kg•C°

D) 900 J/kg•C°

Answer: A
Diff: 2 *Page Ref: Sec. 14.3-14.4*

12) A 0.10-kg piece of copper, initially at 95°C, is dropped into 0.20 kg of water contained in a 0.28-kg aluminum can; the water and aluminum are initially at 15°C. What is the final temperature of the system?

A) 19.2°C

B) 18.3°C

C) 17.8°C

D) 23.7°C

Answer: C
Diff: 2 *Page Ref: Sec. 14.3-14.4*

13) If 50 g of material at 100°C is mixed with 100 g of water at 0°C, the final temperature is 40°C. What is the specific heat of the material?

A) 0.33 kcal/kg•°C

B) 0.75 kcal/kg•°C

C) 1.33 kcal/kg•°C

D) 7.5 kcal/kg•°C

Answer: C
Diff: 2 *Page Ref: Sec. 14.3-14.4*

14) Two equal mass objects make up a system that is thermally isolated from its surroundings. One object has an initial temperature of 100°C and the other has an initial temperature of 0°C. What is the equilibrium temperature of the system, assuming that no phase changes take place for either object? (The hot object has a specific heat capacity that is three times that of the cold object.)

A) 25°C

B) 50°C

C) 75°C

D) 67°C

Answer: C
Diff: 2 *Page Ref: Sec. 14.3-14.4*

15) On his honeymoon, James Joule attempted to explore the relationships between various forms of energy by measuring the rise of temperature of water which had fallen down a waterfall on Mount Blanc. What maximum temperature rise would one expect for a waterfall with a vertical drop of 20 m?

A) 0.047 C°

B) 0.053 C°

C) 0.064 C°

D) 0.071 C°

Answer: A
Diff: 2 *Page Ref: Sec. 14.3–14.4*

16) The water flowing over Niagara Falls drops a distance of 50 m. Assuming that all the gravitational energy is converted to thermal energy, by what temperature does the water rise?

A) 0.10 C°

B) 0.12 C°

C) 0.37 C°

D) 0.42 C°

Answer: B
Diff: 2 *Page Ref: Sec. 14.3–14.4*

17) A 200–L electric water heater uses 2 kW. Assuming no heat loss, how long would it take to heat water in this tank from 23°C to 75°C?

A) 5 hours

B) 6 hours

C) 7 hours

D) 8 hours

Answer: B
Diff: 2 *Page Ref: Sec. 14.3–14.4*

18) A 5000–W heater is used to heat water. How long will it take to heat 20 kg of water from 20°C to 100°C?

A) 2 minutes

B) 12 minutes

C) 22 minutes

D) 32 minutes

Answer: C
Diff: 2 *Page Ref: Sec. 14.3–14.4*

19) An aluminum kettle (mass 1000 g, c = 0.22 kcal/kg °C) holds 400 g of pure water at 20°C. The kettle is placed on a 1000 W electric burner and heated to boiling. Assume that all the heat from the burner heats the kettle and its contents, and that a negligible amount of water evaporates before boiling begins. Calculate the amount of time required to bring the water to boil.

A) 3.5 min

B) 4.0 min

C) 7.3 min

D) 8.1 min

Answer: A
Diff: 3 *Page Ref: Sec. 14.3–14.4*

20) In grinding a steel knife blade (specific heat = 0.11 cal/g-°C), the metal can get as hot as 400°C. If the blade has a mass of 80 g, what is the minimum amount of water needed at 20°C if the water is not to rise above the boiling point when the hot blade is quenched in it?

A) 22 g

B) 33 g

C) 44 g

D) 55 g

Answer: B
Diff: 3 *Page Ref: Sec. 14.3–14.4*

21) How much heat must be removed from steam to change it to liquid?

A) 540 cal/g

B) 600 cal/g

C) 1 kcal/g

D) 1.8 kcal/g

Answer: A
Diff: 1 *Page Ref: Sec. 14.5*

22) Ice has a latent heat of fusion of 80 kcal/kg. How much heat is required to melt 200 g of ice?

A) 400 J

B) 160 J

C) 67 kJ

D) 16 kJ

Answer: C
Diff: 2 *Page Ref: Sec. 14.5*

23) How much heat energy is needed to change 10 kg of ice at -20°C to water at 50°C?

A) 4.2×10^5 J

B) 3.3×10^6 J

C) 4.2×10^6 J

D) 5.8×10^6 J

Answer: D
Diff: 2 *Page Ref: Sec. 14.5*

24) How much heat needs to be removed from 100 g of 85°C water to make -5°C ice?

A) 255 cal

B) 8.5 kcal

C) 16.5 kcal

D) 16.8 kcal

Answer: D
Diff: 2 *Page Ref: Sec. 14.5*

25) The heat of fusion of ice is 80 kcal/kg. When 50 g of ice at 0°C is added to 50 g of water at 25° C, what is the final temperature?

A) 0°C

B) 12.5°C

C) 17.5°C

D) 20°C

Answer: A
Diff: 2 *Page Ref: Sec. 14.5*

26) Eight grams of water initially at 100°C are poured into a cavity in a very large block of ice initially at 0°C. How many g of ice melt before thermal equilibrium is attained?

A) 100 g

B) 10 g

C) 1 g

D) An unknown amount; it cannot be calculated without first knowing the mass of the block of ice.

Answer: B
Diff: 2 *Page Ref: Sec. 14.5*

27) A block of ice at 0°C is added to a 150-g aluminum calorimeter cup that holds 200 g of water at 10°C. If all but 2.00 g of ice melt, what was the original mass of the block of ice?

A) 31.1 g

B) 38.8 g

C) 42.0 g

D) 47.6 g

Answer: A
Diff: 3 *Page Ref: Sec. 14.5*

28) If 2.0 kg of water at 0°C is to be vaporized, how much heat must be added?

A) 1080 cal

B) 1080 kcal

C) 1280 cal

D) 1280 kcal

Answer: D
Diff: 2 *Page Ref: Sec. 14.5*

29) How much heat energy is needed to change 10 kg of water at 50°C to steam at 120°C?

A) 4.2×10^5 J

B) 2.3×10^7 J

C) 4.2×10^6 J

D) 2.5×10^7 J

Answer: D
Diff: 2 *Page Ref: Sec. 14.5*

30) How much heat is required to change one gram of 0°C ice to 120°C steam?

A) 48.7 cal

B) 120 cal

C) 730 cal

D) 1505 cal

Answer: C
Diff: 2 *Page Ref: Sec. 14.5*

31) How much heat is required to change 100 g of -10°C ice to 150°C steam?

A) 74.9 kcal

B) 54 kcal

C) 749 cal

D) 594 cal

Answer: A
Diff: 3 *Page Ref: Sec. 14.5*

32) A person makes ice tea by adding ice to 1.8 kg of hot tea, initially at 80°C. How many kilograms of ice, initially at 0°C, are required to bring the mixture to 10°C?

A) 1.0 kg

B) 1.2 kg

C) 1.4 kg

D) 1.7 kg

Answer: C
Diff: 2 *Page Ref: Sec. 14.5*

33) The heat of fusion of lead is 5.9 kcal/kg, and the heat of vaporization is 207 kcal/kg, and its melting point is 328°C. How much heat is required to melt 50 g of lead initially at 23°C? (The specific heat of lead is 0.031 kcal/kg-°C.)

A) 678 cal

B) 687 cal

C) 768 cal

D) 876 cal

Answer: C
Diff: 3 *Page Ref: Sec. 14.5*

34) The thermal conductivity of concrete is 0.8 W/m-°C and the thermal conductivity of wood is 0.1 W/m-°C. How thick would a solid concrete wall have to be in order to have the same rate of flow through it as an 8-cm thick wall made of solid wood? (Assume both walls have the same surface area.)

A) 53 cm

B) 64 cm

C) 71 cm

D) 85 cm

Answer: B
Diff: 1 *Page Ref: Sec. 14.6-14.8*

35) The thermal conductivity of aluminum is twice that of brass. Two rods (one aluminum and the other brass) are joined together end to end in excellent thermal contact. The rods are of equal lengths and radii. The free end of the brass rod is maintained at 0°C and the aluminum's free end is heated to 200°C. If no heat escapes from the sides of the rods, what is the temperature at the interface between the two metals?

A) 76°C

B) 133°C

C) 148°C

D) 155°C

Answer: B
Diff: 2 *Page Ref: Sec. 14.6-14.8*

36) A window glass 0.50–cm thick has dimensions of 3.0 m by 1.5 m. If the outside temperature is −10°C and the inside temperature 20°C, what is the rate of heat conduction through the window?

A) 13 kW

B) 20 kW

C) 23 kW

D) 30 kW

Answer: C
Diff: 2 *Page Ref: Sec. 14.6–14.8*

37) A window glass 0.50–cm thick has dimensions of 3.0 m by 1.5 m. If the outside temperature is −10°C and the inside temperature is 20°C, how much heat flows through the window in one hour by conduction only?

A) 50 MJ

B) 60 MJ

C) 70 MJ

D) 80 MJ

Answer: D
Diff: 2 *Page Ref: Sec. 14.6–14.8*

38) How much heat will flow in 1.0 hour through a 2.0 m × 2.0 m section of concrete ($k = 2.0 \times 10^{-4}$ kcal/s•m•°C) 10 cm thick if the inside temperature is 21°C and the outside temperature is 4°C?

A) 0.136 cal

B) 136 cal

C) 490 cal

D) 490 kcal

Answer: D
Diff: 2 *Page Ref: Sec. 14.6–14.8*

39) How long will it take to transfer 1,000,000 cal of heat through a 2.0 m^2 pane of 0.30 cm thick glass ($k = 2.0 \times 10^{-4}$ kcal/s•m•°C) if the temperature differential is 10°C?

A) 208 hr

B) 20.8 hr

C) 12.5 min

D) 75 s

Answer: C
Diff: 2 *Page Ref: Sec. 14.6–14.8*

40) What is the outside temperature if 4000 kcal of heat is lost through a 4.0 m^2 pane of 0.30 cm thick glass (k = 2.0×10^{-4} kcal/s•m•°C) in one hour from a house kept at 20°C?

A) 0°C

B) 4°C

C) 16°C

D) 24°C

Answer: C

Diff: 3 *Page Ref: Sec. 14.6–14.8*

41) In an electric furnace used for refining steel, the temperature is monitored by measuring the radiant power emitted through a small hole of area 0.5 cm^2. The furnace acts like a blackbody radiator. If it is to be maintained at a temperature of 1650°C, at what level should the power radiated through the hole be maintained?

A) 20 W

B) 30 W

C) 40 W

D) 50 W

Answer: C

Diff: 1 *Page Ref: Sec. 14.6–14.8*

42) At what rate is the human body radiating energy when it is at 33°C? Take the body surface area to be 1.4 m^2, and approximate the body as a blackbody.

A) 600 W

B) 700 W

C) 800 W

D) 900 W

Answer: B

Diff: 1 *Page Ref: Sec. 14.6–14.8*

43) What temperature exists inside a solar collector (effective collection area of 15 m^2) on a bright sunny day when the outside temperature is +20°C? Assume that the collector is thermally insulated, that the Sun radiates the collector with a power per unit area of 600 W/m^2, and that the collector acts as a perfect blackbody.

A) 73°C

B) 93°C

C) 107°C

D) 154°C

Answer: B

Diff: 3 *Page Ref: Sec. 14.6–14.8*

Chapter 15 The Laws of Thermodynamics

Conceptual Questions

1) The process shown on the T–V graph is an

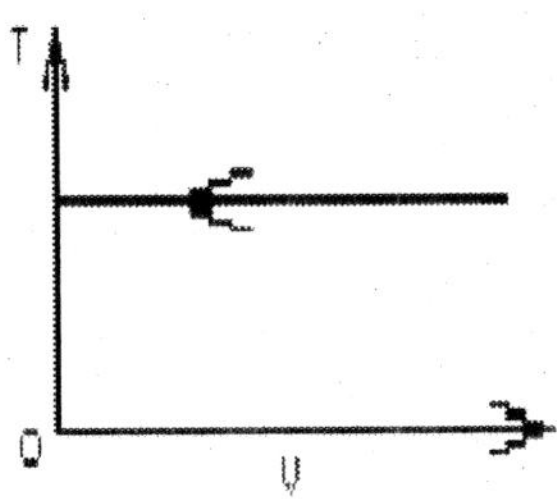

A) adiabatic compression.

B) isothermal compression.

C) isochoric compression.

D) isobaric compression.

Answer: B
Diff: 1 *Page Ref: Sec. 15.1–15.2*

2) In an isothermal process, there is no change in

A) pressure.

B) temperature.

C) volume.

D) heat.

Answer: B
Diff: 1 *Page Ref: Sec. 15.1–15.2*

3) When the first law of thermodynamics, $Q = \Delta U + W$, is applied to an ideal gas that is taken through an isothermal process,

A) $\Delta U = 0$

B) $W = 0$

C) $Q = 0$

D) none of the above

Answer: A
Diff: 2 *Page Ref: Sec. 15.1–15.2*

4) A gas is expanded to twice its original volume with no change in its temperature. This process is

A) isothermal.

B) isochoric.

C) isobaric.

D) adiabatic.

Answer: A
Diff: 1 *Page Ref: Sec. 15.1–15.2*

5) An ideal gas is compressed isothermally from 30 L to 20 L. During this process, 6.0 J of energy is expended by the external mechanism that compressed the gas. What is the change of internal energy for this gas?

A) 6.0 J

B) zero

C) -6.0 J

D) none of the above

Answer: B
Diff: 2 *Page Ref: Sec. 15.1–15.2*

6) An ideal gas is compressed to one-half its original volume during an isothermal process. The final pressure of the gas

A) increases to twice its original value.

B) increases to less than twice its original value.

C) increases to more than twice its original value.

D) does not change.

Answer: A
Diff: 1 *Page Ref: Sec. 15.1–15.2*

7) An ideal gas is expanded isothermally from 20 L to 30 L. During this process, 6 J of energy is expended by the external mechanism that expanded the gas. Which of the following statements is correct?

A) 6 J of energy flow from surroundings into the gas.

B) 6 J of energy flow from the gas into the surroundings.

C) No energy flows into or from the gas since this process is isothermal.

D) None of the above statements is correct.

Answer: A
Diff: 2 *Page Ref: Sec. 15.1–15.2*

8) A gas is quickly compressed in an isolated environment. During the event, the gas exchanged no heat with its surroundings. This process is

A) isothermal.

B) isochoric.

C) isobaric.

D) adiabatic.

Answer: D
Diff: 1 *Page Ref: Sec. 15.1-15.2*

9) When the first law of thermodynamics, $Q = \Delta U + W$, is applied to an ideal gas that is taken through an adiabatic process,

A) $\Delta U = 0$.

B) $W = 0$.

C) $Q = 0$.

D) none of the above

Answer: C
Diff: 1 *Page Ref: Sec. 15.1-15.2*

10) A monatomic ideal gas is compressed to one-half its original volume during an adiabatic process. The final pressure of the gas

A) increases to twice its original value.

B) increases to less than twice its original value.

C) increases to more than twice its original value.

D) does not change.

Answer: C
Diff: 2 *Page Ref: Sec. 15.1-15.2*

11) Consider two cylinders of gas identical in all respects except that one contains O_2 and the other He. Both hold the same volume of gas at STP and are closed by a movable piston at one end. Both gases are now compressed adiabatically to one-third their original volume. Which gas will show the greater temperature increase?

A) the O_2

B) the He

C) Neither; both will show the same increase.

D) It's impossible to tell from the information given.

Answer: B
Diff: 3 *Page Ref: Sec. 15.1-15.2*

12) Consider two cylinders of gas identical in all respects except that one contains O_2 and the other He. Both hold the same volume of gas at STP and are closed by a movable piston at one end. Both gases are now compressed adiabatically to one-third their original volume. Which gas will show the greater pressure increase?

A) the O_2

B) the He

C) Neither; both will show the same increase.

D) It's impossible to tell from the information given.

Answer: B
Diff: 3 *Page Ref: Sec. 15.1-15.2*

13) The process shown on the PV diagram is an

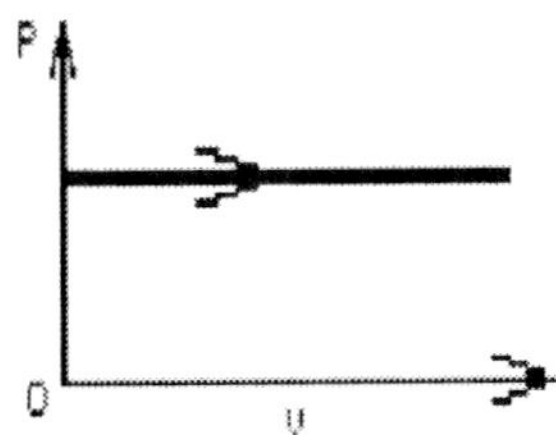

A) adiabatic expansion.

B) isothermal expansion.

C) isometric expansion.

D) isobaric expansion.

Answer: D
Diff: 1 *Page Ref: Sec. 15.1-15.2*

14) In an isobaric process, there is no change in

A) pressure.

B) temperature.

C) volume.

D) internal energy.

Answer: A
Diff: 1 *Page Ref: Sec. 15.1-15.2*

15) When the first law of thermodynamics, $Q = \Delta U + W$, is applied to an ideal gas that is taken through an isobaric process,

A) $\Delta U = 0$.

B) $W = 0$.

C) $Q = 0$.

D) none of the above

Answer: D
Diff: 2 *Page Ref: Sec. 15.1–15.2*

16) A gas is allowed to expand at constant pressure as heat is added to it. This process is

A) isothermal.

B) isochoric.

C) isobaric.

D) adiabatic.

Answer: C
Diff: 1 *Page Ref: Sec. 15.1–15.2*

17) Ten joules of heat energy are transferred to a sample of ideal gas at constant pressure. As a result, the internal energy of the gas

A) increases by 10 J.

B) increases by less than 10 J.

C) increases by more than 10 J.

D) remains unchanged.

Answer: B
Diff: 2 *Page Ref: Sec. 15.1–15.2*

18) The process shown on the PV diagram is

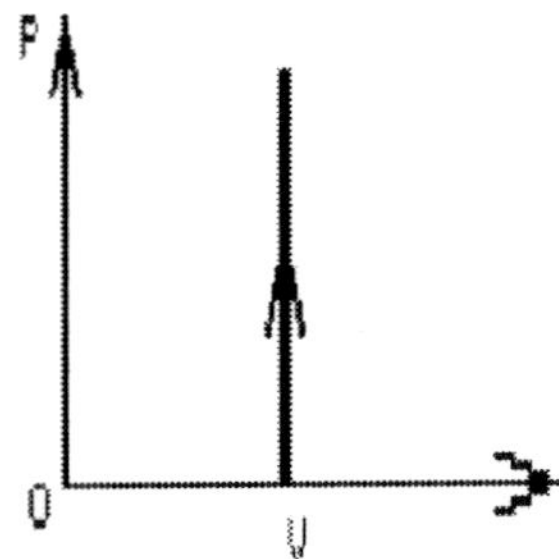

A) adiabatic.

B) isothermal.

C) isochoric.

D) isobaric.

Answer: C
Diff: 1 *Page Ref: Sec. 15.1–15.2*

19) In an isochoric process, there is no change in

A) pressure.

B) temperature.

C) volume.

D) internal energy.

Answer: C
Diff: 1 *Page Ref: Sec. 15.1–15.2*

20) When the first law of thermodynamics, $Q = \Delta U + W$, is applied to an ideal gas that is taken through an isochoric process,

A) $\Delta U = 0$.

B) $W = 0$.

C) $Q = 0$.

D) none of the above

Answer: B
Diff: 2 *Page Ref: Sec. 15.1–15.2*

21) A gas is confined to a rigid container that cannot expand as heat energy is added to it. This process is

A) isothermal.

B) isochoric.

C) isobaric.

D) adiabatic.

Answer: B
Diff: 1 *Page Ref: Sec. 15.1–15.2*

22) Ten joules of heat energy are transferred to a sample of ideal gas at constant volume. As a result, the internal energy of the gas

A) increases by 10 J.

B) increases by less than 10 J.

C) increases by more than 10 J.

D) remains unchanged.

Answer: A
Diff: 2 *Page Ref: Sec. 15.1–15.2*

23) State the first law of thermodynamics.

Answer: The change in internal energy of a closed system will be equal to the energy added to the system by heating minus the work done by the system on the surroundings.
Diff: 1 *Page Ref: Sec. 15.1–15.2*

24) Is it possible to transfer heat from a hot reservoir to a cold reservoir?

A) No.

B) Yes; this will happen naturally.

C) Yes, but work will have to be done.

D) Theoretically yes, but it hasn't been accomplished yet.

Answer: B
Diff: 1 *Page Ref: Sec. 15.4*

25) Is it possible to transfer heat from a cold reservoir to a hot reservoir?

A) No.

B) Yes; this will happen naturally.

C) Yes, but work will have to be done.

D) Theoretically yes, but it hasn't been accomplished yet.

Answer: C
Diff: 1 *Page Ref: Sec. 15.4*

26) State the second law of thermodynamics according to Clausius.

Answer: Heat can flow spontaneously from a hot object to a cold object; heat will not flow spontaneously from a cold object to a hot object.
or
No device is possible whose sole effect is to transfer heat from one system at a temperature T_L into a second system at a higher temperature T_H.

Diff: 1 *Page Ref: Sec. !5.4*

27) A gas is taken through the cycle illustrated here. During one cycle, how much work is done by an engine operating on this cycle?

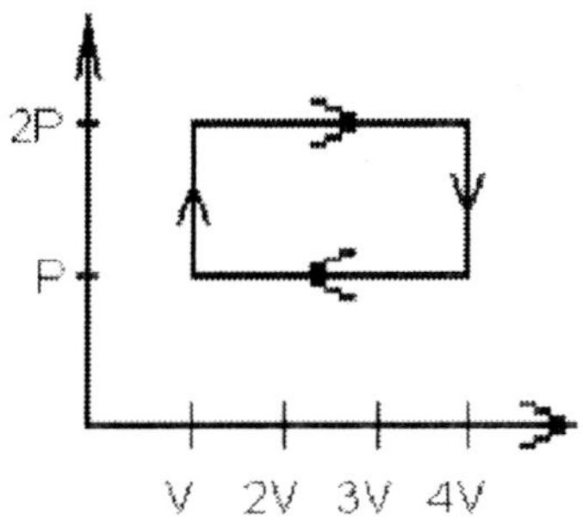

A) PV
B) 2PV
C) 3PV
D) 4PV

Answer: C
Diff: 1 *Page Ref: Sec. 15.5*

28) The efficiency of a heat engine is defined as the ratio of
A) the heat input at the high temperature to the heat output at the low temperature.
B) the heat output at the low temperature to the heat input at the high temperature.
C) the work it does to the heat input at the high temperature.
D) the work it does to the heat output at the low temperature.

Answer: C
Diff: 1 *Page Ref: Sec. 15.5*

29) If the theoretical efficiency of a Carnot engine is to be 100%, the heat sink must be
A) at absolute zero.
B) at 0°C.
C) at 100°C.
D) infinitely hot.

Answer: A
Diff: 2 *Page Ref: Sec. 15.5*

30) A Carnot cycle consists of

A) two adiabats and two isobars.

B) two isobars and two isotherms.

C) two isotherms and two isomets.

D) two adiabats and two isotherms.

Answer: D
Diff: 2 *Page Ref: Sec. 15.5*

31) Give the Kelvin–Planck statement of the second law of thermodynamics.

Answer: No device is possible whose sole effect is to transform a given amount of heat completely into work.
Diff: 1 *Page Ref: Sec. 15.5*

32) The coefficient of performance (COP) of a refrigerator is defined as the ratio of

A) the heat removed from the inside to the heat expelled to the outside.

B) the heat expelled to the outside to the heat removed from the inside.

C) the heat removed from the inside to the work done to remove the heat.

D) the heat expelled to the outside to the work done to remove the heat.

Answer: C
Diff: 1 *Page Ref: Sec. 15.6*

33) The coefficient of performance (COP) of a heat pump is defined as the ratio of

A) the heat delivered to the inside to the heat taken from the outside.

B) the heat taken from the outside to the heat delivered to the inside.

C) the heat delivered to the inside to the work done to move the heat.

D) the heat taken from the outside to the work done to move the heat.

Answer: C
Diff: 1 *Page Ref: Sec. 15.6*

34) When water freezes, the entropy of the water

A) increases.

B) decreases.

C) does not change.

D) could either increase or decrease; it depends on other factors.

Answer: B
Diff: 1 *Page Ref: Sec. 15.7*

35) According to the second law of thermodynamics, for any process that may occur within an isolated system, which one of the choices applies?

A) Entropy remains constant.

B) Entropy increases.

C) Entropy decreases.

D) Both A and B are possible.

E) Both A and C are possible.

Answer: D
Diff: 2 *Page Ref: Sec. 15.7*

36) Give a general statement of the second law of thermodynamics.

Answer: The total entropy of any system plus that of its environment increases as a result of any natural process.
or
Natural processes tend to move toward a state of greater disorder.
Diff: 1 *Page Ref: Sec. 15.7–15.8*

37) The second law of thermodynamics leads us to conclude that

A) the total energy of the universe is constant.

B) disorder in the universe is increasing with the passage of time.

C) it is theoretically possible to convert heat into work with 100% efficiency.

D) the average temperature of the universe is increasing with the passage of time.

Answer: B
Diff: 1 *Page Ref: Sec. 15.8*

Quantitative Problems

1) During an isothermal process, 5.0 J of heat is removed from an ideal gas. What is the change in internal energy?

A) zero

B) 2.5 J

C) 5.0 J

D) 10 J

Answer: A
Diff: 1 *Page Ref: Sec. 15.1–15.2*

2) During an isothermal process, 5.0 J of heat is removed from an ideal gas. What is the work done in the process?

A) zero

B) 5.0 J

C) -5.0 J

D) none of the above

Answer: C
Diff: 1 *Page Ref: Sec. 15.1-15.2*

3) The work done on an ideal gas system in an isothermal process is -400 J. What is the change in internal energy?

A) zero

B) -400 J

C) 400 J

D) none of the above

Answer: A
Diff: 1 *Page Ref: Sec. 15.1-15.2*

4) 200 J of work is done in compressing a gas adiabatically. What is the change in internal energy of the gas?

A) zero

B) 100 J

C) 200 J

D) There is not enough information to determine.

Answer: C
Diff: 1 *Page Ref: Sec. 15.1-15.2*

5) An ideal gas undergoes an adiabatic process while doing 25 J of work. What is the change in internal energy?

A) zero

B) 25 J

C) -25 J

D) none of the above

Answer: C
Diff: 1 *Page Ref: Sec. 15.1-15.2*

6) In an isochoric process, the internal energy of a system decreases by 50 J. What is the work done?

A) zero

B) 50 J

C) -50 J

D) none of the above

Answer: A

Diff: 1 *Page Ref: Sec. 15.1-15.2*

7) In an isochoric process, the internal energy of a system decreases by 50 J. What is the heat exchange?

A) zero

B) 50 J

C) -50 J

D) none of the above

Answer: C

Diff: 1 *Page Ref: Sec. 15.1-15.2*

8) A certain amount of a monatomic gas is maintained at constant volume as it is cooled by 50 K. This feat is accomplished by removing 400 J of energy from the gas. How much work is done by the gas?

A) zero

B) 400 J

C) -400 J

D) none of the above

Answer: A

Diff: 1 *Page Ref: Sec. 15.1-15.2*

9) A monatomic gas is cooled by 50 K at constant volume when 831 J of energy is removed from it. How many moles of gas are in the sample?

A) 2.50 mol

B) 1.50 mol

C) 1.33 mol

D) none of the above

Answer: C

Diff: 2 *Page Ref: Sec. 15.1-15.2*

10) A system consists of 3.0 kg of water at 80°C. 30 J of work is done on the system by stirring with a paddle wheel, while 66 J of heat is removed. What is the change in internal energy of the system?

A) 36 J

B) -36 J

C) 96 J

D) -96 J

Answer: B
Diff: 2 *Page Ref: Sec. 15.1-15.2*

11) A heat engine receives 7000 J of heat and loses 3000 J in each cycle. What is the efficiency?

A) 57%

B) 30%

C) 70%

D) 43%

Answer: A
Diff: 1 *Page Ref: Sec. 15.5*

12) A heat engine has an efficiency of 35.0% and receives 150 J of heat per cycle. How much work does it perform in each cycle?

A) zero

B) 52.5 J

C) 97.5 J

D) 150 J

Answer: B
Diff: 1 *Page Ref: Sec. 15.5*

13) A heat engine has an efficiency of 35.0% and receives 150 J of heat per cycle. How much heat does it exhaust in each cycle?

A) zero

B) 52.5 J

C) 97.5 J

D) 150 J

Answer: C
Diff: 2 *Page Ref: Sec. 15.5*

14) A heat engine absorbs 64 kcal of heat each cycle and exhausts 42 kcal. Calculate the efficiency of each cycle.

A) 34%

B) 66%

C) 50%

D) 150%

Answer: A
Diff: 2 Page Ref: Sec. 15.5

15) A heat engine absorbs 64 kcal of heat each cycle and exhausts 42 kcal. Calculate the work done each cycle.

A) 22 kcal

B) 42 kcal

C) 64 kcal

D) 106 kcal

Answer: A
Diff: 2 Page Ref: Sec. 15.5

16) One of the most efficient engines built so far has the following characteristics: combustion chamber temperature = 1900°C, exhaust temperature = 430°C, 7.0×10^9 cal of fuel produces 1.4×10^{10} J of work in one hour. What is the actual efficiency of this engine?

A) 32%

B) 48%

C) 52%

D) 68%

Answer: B
Diff: 1 Page Ref: Sec. 15.5

17) One of the most efficient engines built so far has the following characteristics: combustion chamber temperature = 1900°C, exhaust temperature = 430°C, 7.0×10^9 cal of fuel produces 1.4×10^{10} J of work in one hour. What is the Carnot efficiency of this engine?

A) 32%

B) 48%

C) 52%

D) 68%

Answer: D
Diff: 1 Page Ref: Sec. 15.5

18) One of the most efficient engines built so far has the following characteristics: combustion chamber temperature = 1900°C, exhaust temperature = 430°C, 7.0×10^9 cal of fuel produces 1.4×10^{10} J of work in one hour. What is the power output, in hp, of this engine?

A) 5.2 kW

B) 6.1 kW

C) 7.4 kW

D) 8.3 kW

Answer: A
Diff: 2 *Page Ref: Sec. 15.5*

19) A coal-fired plant generates 600 MW of electric power. The plant uses 4.8×10^6 kg of coal each day. The heat of combustion of coal is 3.3×10^7 J/kg. The steam that drives the turbines is at a temperature of 300°C, and the exhaust water is at 37°C. What is the overall efficiency of the plant for generating electric power?

A) 33%

B) 37%

C) 46%

D) 54%

Answer: A
Diff: 1 *Page Ref: Sec. 15.5*

20) A coal-fired plant generates 600 MW of electric power. The plant uses 4.8×10^6 kg of coal each day. The heat of combustion of coal is 3.3×10^7 J/kg. The steam that drives the turbines is at a temperature of 300°C, and the exhaust water is at 37°C. What is the Carnot efficiency?

A) 33%

B) 37%

C) 46%

D) 54%

Answer: C
Diff: 1 *Page Ref: Sec. 15.5*

21) A coal-fired plant generates 600 MW of electric power. The plant uses 4.8×10^6 kg of coal each day. The heat of combustion of coal is 3.3×10^7 J/kg. The steam that drives the turbines is at a temperature of 300°C, and the exhaust water is at 37°C. How much thermal energy is exhausted each day?

A) 1.1×10^{14} J

B) 2.2×10^{14} J

C) 3.3×10^{14} J

D) 600 MJ

Answer: A
Diff: 2 *Page Ref: Sec. 15.5*

22) What is the Carnot efficiency of an engine which operates between 450 K and 310 K?

A) 31%

B) 41%

C) 59%

D) 69%

Answer: A
Diff: 1 *Page Ref: Sec. 15.5*

23) What is the maximum theoretical efficiency possible for an engine operating between 100°C and 400°C?

A) 25%

B) 45%

C) 55%

D) 75%

Answer: B
Diff: 2 *Page Ref: Sec. 15.5*

24) The efficiency of a Carnot engine is 35.0%. What is the temperature of the cold reservoir if the temperature of the hot reservoir is 500 K?

A) 175 K

B) 325 K

C) 269 K

D) 231 K

Answer: B
Diff: 1 *Page Ref: Sec. 15.5*

25) A heat engine operating between 40°C and 380°C has an efficiency 60% of that of a Carnot engine operating between the same temperatures. If the engine absorbs heat at a rate of 60 kW, at what rate does it exhaust heat?

A) 36 kW

B) 41 kW

C) 57 kW

D) 60 kW

Answer: B
Diff: 3 *Page Ref: Sec. 15.5*

26) A refrigerator removes heat from the freezing compartment at the rate of 20 kJ and ejects 24 kJ into a room per cycle. How much work is required in each cycle?

A) 4 kJ

B) 20 kJ

C) 24 kJ

D) 44 kJ

Answer: A
Diff: 2 *Page Ref: Sec. 15.6*

27) A refrigerator removes heat from the freezing compartment at the rate of 20 kJ and ejects 24 kJ into a room per cycle. What is the coefficient of performance?

A) 0.20

B) 0.50

C) 2.0

D) 5.0

Answer: D
Diff: 2 *Page Ref: Sec. 15.6*

28) During each cycle of operation, a refrigerator absorbs 230 J of heat from the freezer and expels 356 J of heat to the room. How much work input is required in each cycle?

A) 712 J

B) 586 J

C) 460 J

D) 126 J

Answer: D
Diff: 2 *Page Ref: Sec. 15.6*

29) What is the change in entropy when 50 g of ice melt at 0°C?

A) 14.7 cal/K

B) 4.0 kcal/K

C) -4.0 kcal/K

D) -14.7 cal/K

Answer: A
Diff: 1 *Page Ref: Sec. 15.7*

30) When 0.50 kg of ice freezes, the change in entropy is

A) zero.

B) 610 J/K.

C) -610 J/K.

D) none of the above

Answer: C
Diff: 1 *Page Ref: Sec. 15.7*

31) 1.0 kg of steam at 100°C condenses to water at 100°C. What is the change in entropy in the process?

A) zero

B) 6.1×10^3 J/K

C) -6.1×10^3 J/K

D) none of the above

Answer: C
Diff: 1 *Page Ref: Sec. 15.7*

32) A container of ideal gas at STP undergoes an isothermal expansion and its entropy changes by 3.7 J/° K. How much work does it do?

A) zero

B) 1.0×10^3 J/K

C) -1.0×10^3 J/K

D) none of the above

Answer: B
Diff: 2 *Page Ref: Sec. 15.7*

33) A piece of metal at 80°C is placed in 1.2 L of water at 72°C. The system is thermally isolated and reaches a final temperature of 75°C. Estimate the approximate change in entropy for this process.

A) 0.118 cal/K

B) 2.5 cal/K

C) 3.5 cal/K

D) 4.5 cal/K

Answer: A
Diff: 3 *Page Ref: Sec. 15.7*

Chapter 16 Electric Charge and Electric Field

Conceptual Questions

1) State the law of conservation of electric charge.

Answer: The net amount of electric charge produced in any process is zero.
or
No net electric charge can be created or destroyed.
Diff: 1 *Page Ref: Sec. 16.1–16.4*

2) Is it possible for two negative charges to attract each other?

A) Yes, they always attract.

B) Yes, they will attract if they are close enough.

C) Yes, they will attract if one carries a larger charge than the other.

D) No, they will never attract.

Answer: D
Diff: 1 *Page Ref: Sec. 16.1–16.4*

3) Is it possible for a positive and a negative charge to attract each other?

A) Yes, they always attract.

B) Yes, they will attract if they are close enough.

C) Yes, they will attract if one carries a larger charge than the other.

D) No, they will never attract.

Answer: A
Diff: 1 *Page Ref: Sec. 16.1–16.4*

4) A glass rod is rubbed with a piece of silk. During the process the glass rod acquires a positive charge and the silk

A) acquires a positive charge also.

B) acquires a negative charge.

C) remains neutral.

D) could either be positively charged or negatively charged. It depends on how hard the rod was rubbed.

Answer: B
Diff: 1 *Page Ref: Sec. 16.1–16.4*

5) A proton carries a

A) positive charge.

B) neutral charge.

C) negative charge.

D) variable charge.

Answer: A

Diff: 1 *Page Ref: Sec. 16.1–16.4*

6) The model of the atom shows a

A) neutrally charged nucleus surrounded by both protons and electrons.

B) nucleus consisting of both protons and neutrons, surrounded by a cloud of electrons.

C) nucleus consisting of both electrons and neutrons, surrounded by a cloud of protons.

D) nucleus consisting of both protons and electrons, surrounded by a cloud of neutrons

Answer: B

Diff: 1 *Page Ref: Sec. 16.1–16.4*

7) A neutral atom always has

A) more neutrons than protons.

B) more protons than electrons.

C) the same number of neutrons as protons.

D) the same number of protons as electrons.

Answer: D

Diff: 1 *Page Ref: Sec. 16.1–16.4*

8) An atom has more electrons than protons. The atom is

A) a positive ion.

B) a negative ion.

C) a superconductor.

D) impossible.

Answer: B

Diff: 1 *Page Ref: Sec. 16.1–16.4*

9) Materials in which the electrons are bound very tightly to the nuclei are referred to as

A) insulators.

B) conductors.

C) semiconductors.

D) superconductors.

Answer: A

Diff: 1 *Page Ref: Sec. 16.1–16.4*

10) Materials in which the electrons are bound very loosely to the nuclei and can move about freely within the material are referred to as

   A) insulators.

   B) conductors.

   C) semiconductors.

   D) superconductors.

   Answer: B
   Diff: 1 *Page Ref: Sec. 16.1–16.4*

11) A negatively charged rod is brought near one end of an uncharged metal bar. The end of the metal bar farthest from the charged rod will be charged

   A) positive.

   B) negative.

   C) neutral.

   D) none of the given answers

   Answer: B
   Diff: 2 *Page Ref: Sec. 16.1–16.4*

12) Sphere A carries a net positive charge, and sphere B is neutral. They are placed near each other on an insulated table. Sphere B is briefly touched with a wire that is grounded. Which statement is correct?

   A) Sphere B remains neutral.

   B) Sphere B is now positively charged.

   C) Sphere B is now negatively charged,

   D) The charge on sphere B cannot be determined without additional information.

   Answer: C
   Diff: 2 *Page Ref: Sec. 16.1–16.4*

13) How can a negatively charged rod charge an electroscope positively?

   A) by conduction

   B) by induction

   C) by deduction

   D) It cannot.

   Answer: B
   Diff: 1 *Page Ref: Sec. 16.1–16.4*

14) An originally neutral electroscope is briefly touched with a positively charged glass rod. The electroscope

A) remains neutral.

B) becomes negatively charged.

C) becomes positively charged.

D) could become either positively or negatively charged, depending on the time of contact.

Answer: C
Diff: 1 Page Ref: Sec. 16.1–16.4

15) An originally neutral electroscope is grounded briefly while a positively charged glass rod is held near it. After the glass rod is removed, the electroscope

A) remains neutral.

B) is negatively charged.

C) is positively charged.

D) could be either positively or negatively charged, depending on how long the contact with ground lasted.

Answer: B
Diff: 2 Page Ref: Sec. 16.1–16.4

16) A positive object touches a neutral electroscope, and the leaves separate. Then a negative object is brought near the electroscope, but does not touch it. What happens to the leaves?

A) They separate further.

B) They move closer together.

C) They are unaffected.

D) cannot be determined without further information

Answer: B
Diff: 2 Page Ref: Sec. 16.1–16.4

17) A large negatively charged object is placed on an insulated table. A neutral metallic ball rolls straight toward the object, but stops before it touches it. A second neutral metallic ball rolls along the path followed by the first ball, strikes the first ball, and stops. The first ball rolls forward, but does not touch the negative object. At no time does either ball touch the negative object. What is the final charge on each ball?

A) The first ball is positive, and the second ball is negative.

B) The first ball is negative, and the second ball is positive.

C) Both balls remain neutral.

D) Both balls are positive.

Answer: A
Diff: 3 Page Ref: Sec. 16.1–16.4

18) Charge is

A) quantized.

B) conserved.

C) invariant.

D) all of the given answers

Answer: D
Diff: 1 *Page Ref: Sec. 16.1–16.5*

19) What are the units of the Coulomb constant k, which appears in Coulomb's law?

A) N•m/C

B) N/C

C) N^2•m/C^2

D) N•m^2/C^2

Answer: D
Diff: 1 *Page Ref: Sec. 16.5–16.6*

20) Two charged objects are separated by a distance d. The first charge is larger in magnitude than the second charge.

A) The first charge exerts a larger force on the second charge.

B) The second charge exerts a larger force on the first charge.

C) The charges exert forces on each other equal in magnitude and opposite in direction.

D) The charges exert forces on each other equal in magnitude and pointing in the same direction.

Answer: C
Diff: 1 *Page Ref: Sec. 16.5–16.6*

21) Sphere A carries a net charge and sphere B is neutral. They are placed near each other on an insulated table. Which statement best describes the electrostatic force between them?

A) There is no force between them since one is neutral.

B) There is a force of repulsion between them.

C) There is a force of attraction between them.

D) The force is attractive if A is charged positively and repulsive if A is charged negatively.

Answer: C
Diff: 2 *Page Ref: Sec. 16.5–16.6*

22) Two charged objects attract each other with a certain force. If the charges on both objects are doubled with no change in separation, the force between them

A) quadruples.

B) doubles.

C) halves.

D) increases, but we can't say how much without knowing the distance between them.

Answer: A
Diff: 2 *Page Ref: Sec. 16.5-16.6*

23) Two charges are separated by a distance d and exert mutual attractive forces of F on each other. If the charges are separated by a distance of d/3, what are the new mutual forces?

A) F/9

B) F/3

C) 3F

D) 9F

Answer: D
Diff: 2 *Page Ref: Sec. 16.5-16.6*

24) Two charged objects attract each other with a force F. What happens to the force between them if one charge is doubled, the other charge is tripled, and the separation distance between their centers is reduced to one-fourth its original value? The force is now equal to

A) 16F.

B) 24F.

C) (3/8)F.

D) 96F.

Answer: D
Diff: 2 *Page Ref: Sec. 16.5-16.6*

25) An electron and a proton are separated by a distance of 1.0 m. What happens to the magnitude of the force on the proton if a second electron is placed next to the first electron?

A) It quadruples.

B) It doubles.

C) It will not change.

D) It goes to zero.

Answer: B
Diff: 1 *Page Ref: Sec. 16.5-16.6*

26) An electron and a proton are separated by a distance of 1.0 m. What happens to the magnitude of the force on the first electron if a second electron is placed next to the proton?

A) It doubles.

B) It does not change.

C) It is reduced to half.

D) It becomes zero.

Answer: D
Diff: 1 *Page Ref: Sec. 16.5–16.6*

27) An electron and a proton are separated by a distance of 1.0 m. What happens to the size of the force on the proton if the electron is moved 0.50 m closer to the proton?

A) It increases to 4 times its original value.

B) It increases to 2 times its original value.

C) It decreases to one-half its original value.

D) It decreases to one-fourth its original value.

Answer: A
Diff: 1 *Page Ref: Sec. 16.5–16.5*

28) A point charge of +Q is placed at the center of a square. When a second point charge of -Q is placed at one of the square's corners, it is observed that an electrostatic force of 2.0 N acts on the positive charge at the square's center. Now, identical charges of -Q are placed at the other three corners of the square. What is the magnitude of the net electrostatic force acting on the positive charge at the center of the square?

A) zero

B) 2.8 N

C) 4.0 N

D) 8.0 N

Answer: A
Diff: 2 *Page Ref: Sec. 16.5–16.6*

29) A point charge of +Q is placed at the centroid of an equilateral triangle. When a second charge of +Q is placed at one of the triangle's vertices, an electrostatic force of 4.0 N acts on it. What is the magnitude of the force that acts on the center charge due to a third charge of +Q placed at one of the other vertices?

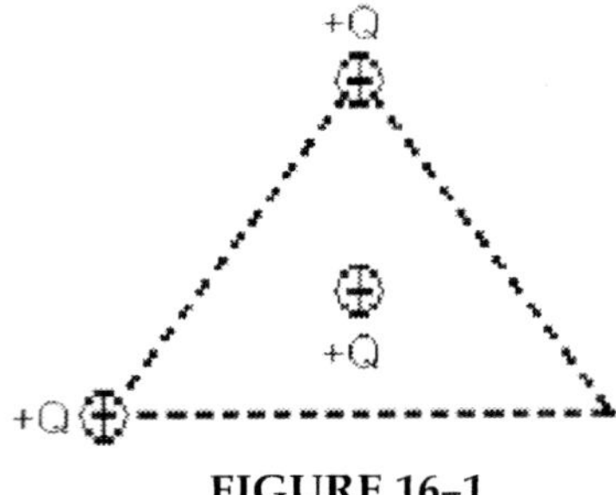

FIGURE 16–1

A) zero
B) 4.0 N
C) 8.0 N
D) 16 N

Answer: B
Diff: 3 *Page Ref: Sec. 16.5–16.6*

30) Which of the following is not a vector?
A) electric force
B) electric field
C) electric charge
D) electric line of force

Answer: C
Diff: 1 *Page Ref: Sec. 16.1–16.8*

31) At twice the distance from a point charge, the strength of the electric field
A) is four times its original value.
B) is twice its original value.
C) is one-half its original value.
D) is one-fourth its original value.

Answer: D
Diff: 1 *Page Ref: Sec. 16.7–16.8*

32) Is it possible to have a zero electric field value between a negative and positive charge along the line joining the two charges?

A) Yes, if the two charges are equal in magnitude.

B) Yes, regardless of the magnitude of the two charges.

C) No, a zero electric field cannot exist between the two charges.

D) cannot be determined without knowing the separation between the two charges

Answer: C
Diff: 1 *Page Ref: Sec. 16.7–16.8*

33) Is it possible to have a zero electric field value between two positive charges along the line joining the two charges?

A) Yes, if the two charges are equal in magnitude.

B) Yes, regardless of the magnitude of the two charges.

C) No, a zero electric field cannot exist between the two charges.

D) cannot be determined without knowing the separation between the two charges

Answer: B
Diff: 1 *Page Ref: Sec. 16.7–16.8*

34) Electric field lines near psitive point charges

A) circle clockwise.

B) circle counter-clockwise.

C) radiate inward.

D) radiate outward.

Answer: D
Diff: 1 *Page Ref: Sec. 16.7–16.8*

35) The electric field shown

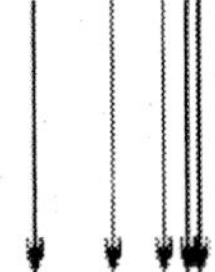

FIGURE 16–2

A) increases to the right.

B) increases down.

C) decreases to the right.

D) decreases down.

E) is uniform.

Answer: A
Diff: 2 *Page Ref: Sec. 16.7–16.8*

36) Can electric field lines intersect in free space?

A) Yes, but only at the midpoint between two equal like charges.

B) Yes, but only at the midpoint between a positive and a negative charge.

C) Yes, but only at the centroid of an equilateral triangle with like charges at each corner.

D) No.

Answer: D
Diff: 2 *Page Ref: Sec. 16.7–16.8*

37) A solid block of metal in electrostatic equilibrium is placed in a uniform electric field. Give a statement concerning the electric field in the block's interior.

A) The interior field points in a direction opposite to the exterior field.

B) The interior field points in a direction that is at right angles to the exterior field.

C) The interior points in a direction that is parallel to the exterior field.

D) There is no electric field in the block's interior.

Answer: D
Diff: 2 *Page Ref: Sec. 16.9*

38) If a solid metal sphere and a hollow metal sphere of equal diameters are each given the same charge, the electric field (E) midway between the center and the surface is

A) greater for the solid sphere than for the hollow sphere.

B) greater for the hollow sphere than for the solid sphere.

C) zero for both.

D) equal in magnitude for both, but one is opposite in direction from the other.

Answer: C
Diff: 2 *Page Ref: Sec. 16.9*

39) A cubic block of aluminum rests on a wooden table in a region where a uniform electric field is directed straight upward. What can be said concerning the charge on the block's top surface?

A) The top surface is charged positively.

B) The top surface is charged negatively.

C) The top surface is neutral.

D) The top surface's charge cannot be determined without further information.

Answer: A
Diff: 2 *Page Ref: Sec. 16.9*

40) If a conductor is in electrostatic equilibrium near an electric charge

A) the total charge on the conductor must be zero.

B) the force between the conductor and the charge must be zero.

C) the total electric field of the conductor must be zero.

D) the electric field on the surface of the conductor is perpendicular to the surface.

Answer: D
Diff: 2 *Page Ref: Sec. 16.9*

41) A positive point charge is enclosed in a hollow metallic sphere that is grounded. As compared to the case without the hollow sphere, the electric field at a point directly above the hollow sphere has

A) diminished to zero.

B) diminished somewhat.

C) increased somewhat.

D) not changed.

Answer: A
Diff: 3 *Page Ref: Sec. 16.9*

42) State three properties of conductors in static equilibrium.

Answer: (1) The electric field inside a conductor is zero in the static situation.
(2) Any net charge on a conductor distributes itself on the surface.
(3) The electric field is always perpendicular to the surface outside of a conductor.
Diff: 1 *Page Ref: Sec. 16.9*

43) State Gauss's law.

Answer: The total flux summed over any closed surface is equal to the net charge enclosed by the surface divided by ε_0.
Diff: 1 *Page Ref: Sec. 16–10*

Quantitative Problems

1) The charge carried by one electron is e = -1.6×10^{-19} C. The number of electrons necessary to produce a charge of -1.0 C is

A) 6.25×10^{18}.

B) 6.25×10^{9}.

C) 1.6×10^{19}.

D) none of the given answers

Answer: A
Diff: 1 *Page Ref: Sec. 16.5–16.6*

2) A piece of plastic has a net charge of +2.00 μC. How many more protons than electrons does this piece of plastic have?

A) 1.25×10^{13}

B) 1.25×10^{19}

C) 2.50×10^{13}

D) 2.50×10^{19}

Answer: A
Diff: 1 *Page Ref: Sec. 16.5–16.6*

3) What is the charge on 1 kg of protons?

A) 1.0 C

B) 1000 C

C) 9.6×10^7 C

D) 6.0×10^{26} C

Answer: C
Diff: 2 *Page Ref: Sec. 16.5–16.6*

4) An atomic nucleus has a charge of +40e. An electron is 10^{-9} m from the nucleus. What is the force on the electron?

A) 2.9 nN

B) 1000 C

C) 3.7 nN

D) 6.8 nN

E) 9.2 nN

Answer: E
Diff: 1 *Page Ref: Sec. 16.5–16.6*

5) Two point charges, separated by 1.5 cm, have charge values of 2.0 and -4.0 μC, respectively. What is the magnitude of the electric force between them?

A) 400 N

B) 360 N

C) 320 N

D) 160 N

Answer: C
Diff: 1 *Page Ref: Sec. 16.5–16.6*

6) A 1.0-C charge is 15 m from a second charge, and the force between them is 1.0 N. What is the magnitude of the second charge?

A) 25 C

B) 1.0 C

C) 0.025 C

D) 25 nC

Answer: D
Diff: 1 *Page Ref: Sec. 16.5–16.5*

7) Two 1.0-C charges have a force between them of 1.0 N. How far apart are they?

A) 95 km

B) 9.5 m

C) 4.0 m

D) 4.0 mm

Answer: A
Diff: 1 *Page Ref: Sec. 16.5–16.5*

8) The force between a 30-μC charge and a -90-μC charge is 1.8 N. How far apart are they?

A) 1.9 m

B) 2.3 m

C) 3.7 m

D) 4.2 m

Answer: C
Diff: 1 *Page Ref: Sec. 16.5–16.5*

9) Two point charges, initially 2.0 cm apart, experience a 1.0-N force. If they are moved to a new separation of 8.0 cm, what is the electric force between them?

A) 4.0 N

B) 16 N

C) 1/4 N

D) 1/16 N

Answer: D
Diff: 2 *Page Ref: Sec. 16.5–16.6*

10) Three identical point charges of 2.0 μC are placed on the x-axis. The first charge is at the origin, the second to the right at $x = 50$ cm, and the third is at the 100 cm mark. What are the magnitude and direction of the electrostatic force which acts on the charge at the origin?

A) 0.18 N left

B) 0.18 N right

C) 0.36 N left

D) 0.36 N right

Answer: A
Diff: 2 *Page Ref: Sec. 16.5–16.5*

11) Three point charges are placed on the x-axis. A charge of +2.0 μC is placed at the origin, -2.0 μC to the right at x = 50 cm, and +4.0 μC at the 100 cm mark. What are the magnitude and direction of the electrostatic force which acts on the charge at the origin?

A) 0.072 N right

B) 0.072 N left

C) 0.14 N right

D) 0.14 N left

Answer: A
Diff: 2 *Page Ref: Sec. 16.5–16.6*

12) Three point charges are located at the following positions: Q_1 = 2.00 μC at x = 1.00 m; Q_2 = 3.00 μC at x = 0; Q_3 = -5.00 μC at x = -1.00 m. What is the magnitude of the force on the 3.00-μC charge?

A) 5.40×10^{-2} N

B) 0.135 N

C) 8.10×10^{-2} N

D) 0.189 N

Answer: D
Diff: 2 *Page Ref: Sec. 16.5–16.6*

13) A point charge of +Q is placed at the center of a square, and a second point charge of -Q is placed at the upper-left corner. It is observed that an electrostatic force of 2.0 N acts on the positive charge at the center. What is the magnitude of the force that acts on the center charge if a third charge of -Q is placed at the lower-left corner?

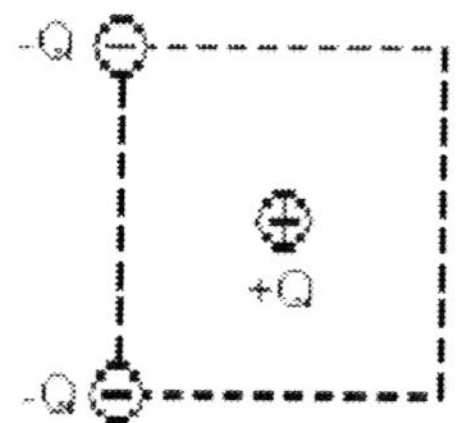

FIGURE 16-3

A) zero

B) 2.8 N

C) 4.0 N

D) 5.3 N

Answer: B
Diff: 2 *Page Ref: Sec. 16.5–16.6*

14) A point charge of +Q is placed at the centroid of an equilateral triangle. When a second charge of +Q is placed at one of the triangle's vertices, an electrostatic force of 4.0 N acts on it. What is the magnitude of the force that acts on the center charge due to a third charge of +Q placed at one of the other vertices?

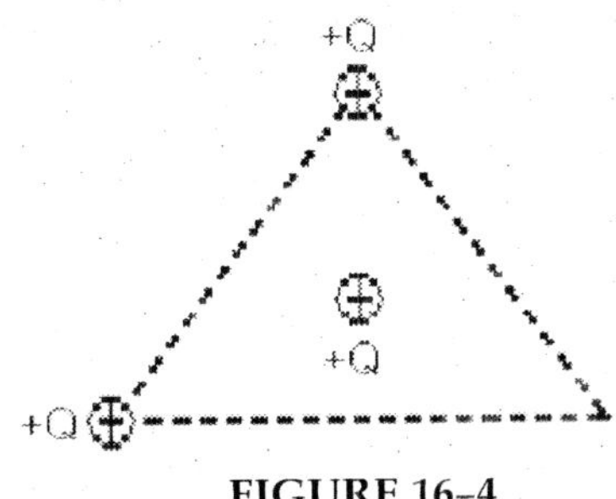

FIGURE 16-4

A) zero

B) 4.0 N

C) 8.0 N

D) 16 N

Answer: B
Diff: 2 *Page Ref: Sec. 16.5-16.6*

15) Q1 = 6.0 nC is at (0.30 m, 0); Q2 = -1.0 nC is at (0, 0.10 m); Q3 = 5.0 nC is at (0, 0). What is the magnitude of the net force on the 5.0 nC charge?

A) 3.0×10^{-6} N

B) 4.5×10^{-6} N

C) 5.4×10^{-6} N

D) 7.2×10^{-6} N

Answer: C
Diff: 2 *Page Ref: Sec. 16.5-16.6*

16) Q1 = 6.0 nC is at (0.30 m, 0); Q2 = -1.0 nC is at (0, 0.10 m); Q3 = 5.0 nC is at (0, 0). What is the direction of the net force on the 5.0 nC charge?

A) 34° above +x axis

B) 34° above -x axis

C) 56° above +x axis

D) 56° above -x axis

Answer: D
Diff: 2 *Page Ref: Sec. 16.5-16.6*

17) Three identical charges of 3.0 μC are placed at the vertices of an equilateral triangle which measures 30 cm on a side. What is the magnitude of the electrostatic force which acts on any one of the charges?

A) 1.6 N

B) 1.8 N

C) 2.0 N

D) 2.2 N

Answer: A
Diff: 2 *Page Ref: Sec. 16.5–16.6*

18) Consider point charges of +Q and +4Q, which are separated by 3.0 m. At what point, on a line between the two charges, would it be possible to place a charge of -Q such that the electrostatic force acting on it would be zero?

A) There is no such point possible.

B) 1.0 m from the +Q charge

C) 1.0 m from the +4Q charge

D) 0.60 m from the +Q charge

Answer: B
Diff: 2 *Page Ref: Sec. 16.5–16.6*

19) A +3.0-C charge is at the origin and a +9.0-C charge is at x = 4.0 m. Where on the x-axis can a third charge be placed so the net force on it is zero?

A) x = 0.50 m

B) x = 0.60 m

C) x = 1.5 m

D) x = 2.4 m

Answer: C
Diff: 2 *Page Ref: Sec. 16.5–16.6*

20) Charge +2q is placed at the origin and charge -q is placed at x = 2a. Where can a third positive charge +q be placed so that the force on it is zero?

A) 3.4a

B) 6.8a

C) 8.6a

D) 9.3a

Answer: B
Diff: 3 *Page Ref: Sec. 16.5–16.6*

21) A copper penny has a mass of 3.0 g. A total of 4.0×10^{12} electrons are transferred from one neutral penny to another. If the electrostatic force of attraction between the pennies is equal to the weight of a penny, what is the separation between them?

A) 31 cm

B) 33 cm

C) 35 cm

D) 37 cm

Answer: C
Diff: 2 *Page Ref: Sec. 16.5–16.6*

22) An electron is held up against the force of gravity by the attraction of a fixed proton some distance above it. How far above the electron is the proton?

A) 1.5 m

B) 2.3 m

C) 3.7 m

D) 5.1 m

Answer: D
Diff: 2 *Page Ref: Sec. 16.5–16.6*

23) Two 0.20-g metal spheres are hung from a common point by nonconducting threads which are 30 cm long. Both are given identical charges, and the electrostatic repulsion forces them apart until the angle between the threads is 20°. How much charge was placed on each sphere?

A) 10 nC

B) 15 nC

C) 20 nC

D) 25 nC

Answer: C
Diff: 3 *Page Ref: Sec. 16.5–16.6*

24) An atomic nucleus has a charge of +40e. What is the magnitude of the electric field at a distance of 1.0 m from the nucleus?

A) 5.6×10^{-8} N/C

B) 5.8×10^{-8} N/C

C) 6.0×10^{-8} N/C

D) 6.2×10^{-8} N/C

Answer: B
Diff: 1 *Page Ref: Sec. 16.7–16.8*

25) What are the magnitude and direction of the electric field at a distance of 1.50 m from a 50.0-nC charge?

A) 20 N/C away from the charge

B) 20 N/C toward the charge

C) 200 N/C away from the charge

D) 200 N/C toward the charge

Answer: C
Diff: 1 *Page Ref: Sec. 16.7-16.8*

26) A 5.0-C charge is 10 m from a small test charge. What is the magnitude of the electric field at the location of the test charge?

A) 4.5×10^6 N/C

B) 4.5×10^7 N/C

C) 4.5×10^8 N/C

D) 4.5×10^9 N/C

Answer: C
Diff: 1 *Page Ref: Sec. 16.7-16.8*

27) A 5.0-C charge is 10 m from a small test charge. What is the direction of the electric field?

A) toward the 5.0 C

B) away from the 5.0 C

C) perpendicular to a line joining the charges

D) none of the given answers

Answer: B
Diff: 2 *Page Ref: Sec. 16.7-16.8*

28) A 5.0-C charge is 10 m from a small test charge. What is the magnitude of the force experienced by a 1.0 nC charge placed at the location of the test charge?

A) 0.045 N

B) 0.45 N

C) 4.5 N

D) 45 N

Answer: B
Diff: 2 *Page Ref: Sec. 16.7-16.8*

29) Two point charges each have a value of 3.0 C and are separated by a distance of 4.0 m. What is the electric field at a point midway between the two charges?

A) zero

B) 9.0×10^7 N/C

C) 18×10^7 N/C

D) 4.5×10^7 N/C

Answer: A
Diff: 2 *Page Ref:* Sec. 16.7–16.8

30) A 5.0-μC charge is placed at the 0 cm mark of a meter stick and a -4.0 μC charge is placed at the 50 cm mark. What is the electric field at the 30 cm mark?

A) 4.0×10^5 N/C

B) 5.0×10^5 N/C

C) 9.0×10^5 N/C

D) 1.4×10^6 N/C

Answer: D
Diff: 2 *Page Ref:* Sec. 16.7–16.8

31) A 5.0-μC charge is placed at the 0 cm mark of a meter stick and a -4.0 μC charge is placed at the 50 cm mark. At what point on a line joining the two charges is the electric field zero?

A) 1.4 m from the 0 cm mark

B) 2.9 m from the 0 cm mark

C) 3.3 m from the 0 cm mark

D) 4.7 m from the 0 cm mark

Answer: D
Diff: 2 *Page Ref:* Sec. 16.7–16.8

32) Two point charges of +3.0 μC and -7.0 μC are placed at x = 0 and x = 0.20 m. What is the magnitude of the electric field at the point midway between them?

A) 1.8×10^6 N/C

B) 3.6×10^6 N/C

C) 4.5×10^6 N/C

D) 9.0×10^6 N/C

Answer: D
Diff: 2 *Page Ref:* Sec. 16.7–16.8

33) Three 3.0 μC charges are at the three corners of an square of side 0.50 m. The last corner is occupied by a -3.0 μC charge. Find the electric field at the center of the square.

A) 2.2×10^5 N/C

B) 4.3×10^5 N/C

C) 6.1×10^5 N/C

D) 9.3×10^5 N/C

Answer: B

Diff: 3 *Page Ref: Sec. 16.7-16.8*

34) Consider a square which is 1.0 m on a side. Charges are placed at the corners of the square as follows: +4.0 μC at (0, 0); +4.0 μC at (1, 1); +3.0 μC at (1, 0); -3.0 μC at (0, 1). What is the magnitude of the electric field at the square's center?

A) 1.1×10^5 N/C

B) 1.3×10^5 N/C

C) 1.5×10^5 N/C

D) 1.7×10^5 N/C

Answer: A

Diff: 3 *Page Ref: Sec. 16.7-16.8*

35) A force of 10 N acts on a charge of 5.0 μC when it is placed in a uniform electric field. What is the magnitude of this electric field?

A) 50 MN/C

B) 2.0 MN/C

C) 0.50 MN/C

D) 1000 MN/C

Answer: B

Diff: 1 *Page Ref: Sec. 16.7-16.8*

36) A particle with a charge of 4.0 μC has a mass of 5.0×10^{-3} kg. What electric field directed upward will exactly balance the weight of the particle?

A) 4.1×10^2 N/C

B) 8.2×10^2 N/C

C) 1.2×10^4 N/C

D) 5.1×10^6 N/C

Answer: C

Diff: 2 *Page Ref: Sec. 16.7-16.8*

37) A Styrofoam ball of mass 0.120 g is placed in an electric field of 6000 N/C pointing downward. What charge must be placed on the ball for it to be suspended?

A) -16.0 nC

B) -57.2 nC

C) -125 nC

D) -196 nC

Answer: D
Diff: 2 *Page Ref: Sec. 16.7-16.8*

38) A foam ball of mass 0.150 g carries a charge of -2.00 nC. The ball is placed inside a uniform electric field, and is suspended against the force of gravity. What are the magnitude and direction of the electric field?

A) 573 kN/C down

B) 573 kN/C up

C) 735 kN/C down

D) 735 kN/C up

Answer: C
Diff: 2 *Page Ref: Sec. 16.7-16.8*

39) A metal sphere of radius 10 cm carries a charge of +2.0 μC. What is the magnitude of the electric field 5.0 cm from the sphere's surface?

A) 4.0×10^5 N/C

B) 8.0×10^5 N/C

C) 4.0×10^7 N/C

D) 8.0×10^7 N/C

Answer: B
Diff: 2 *Page Ref: Sec. 16.10*

40) A metal sphere of radius 2.0 cm carries a charge of 3.0 μC. What is the electric field 6.0 cm from the center of the sphere?

A) 4.2×10^6 N/C

B) 5.7×10^6 N/C

C) 7.5×10^6 N/C

D) 9.3×10^6 N/C

Answer: C
Diff: 2 *Page Ref: Sec. 16.10*

Chapter 17 Electric Potential

Conceptual Questions

1) Which of the following is not a vector?

A) electric force

B) electric field

C) electric potentia;

D) electric line of force

Answer: C

Diff: 1 *Page Ref: Sec. 17.1-17.8*

2) One joule per coulomb is a

A) newton.

B) volt.

C) electron-volt.

D) farad.

Answer: B

Diff: 1 *Page Ref: Sec. 17.1-17.3*

3) Two identical aluminum objects are insulated from their surroundings. Object A has a net charge of excess electrons. Object B is grounded. Which object is at a higher potential?

A) A

B) B

C) Both are at the same potential.

D) cannot be determined without more information

Answer: B

Diff: 2 *Page Ref: Sec. 17.1-17.3*

4) For a proton moving in the direction of the electric field

A) its potential energy increases and its electric potential decreases.

B) its potential energy decreases and its electric potential increases.

C) its potential energy increases and its electric potential increases.

D) its potential energy decreases and its electric potential decreases.

Answer: D

Diff: 2 *Page Ref: Sec. 17.1-17.3*

5) For an electron moving in a direction opposite to the electric field

A) its potential energy increases and its electric potential decreases.

B) its potential energy decreases and its electric potential increases.

C) its potential energy increases and its electric potential increases.

D) its potential energy decreases and its electric potential decreases.

Answer: B

Diff: 2 *Page Ref: Sec. 17.1–17.3*

6) Several electrons are placed on a hollow conducting sphere. They

A) clump together on the sphere's outer surface.

B) clump together on the sphere's inner surface.

C) become uniformly distributed on the sphere's outer surface.

D) become uniformly distributed on the sphere's inner surface.

Answer: C

Diff: 2 *Page Ref: Sec. 17.1–17.3*

7) A small charged ball is accelerated from rest to a speed v by a 500 V potential difference. If the potential difference is changed to 2000 V, what will the new speed of the ball be?

A) v

B) 2v

C) 4v

D) 16v

Answer: B

Diff: 2 *Page Ref: Sec. 17.1–17.3*

8) A surface on which all points are at the same potential is referred to as

A) a constant electric force surface.

B) a constant electric field surface.

C) an equipotential surface.

D) an equivoltage surface.

Answer: C

Diff: 2 *Page Ref: Sec. 17.1–17.3*

9) A negative charge is moved from point A to point B along an equipotential surface.

A) The negative charge performs work in moving from point A to point B.

B) Work is required to move the negative charge from point A to point B.

C) Work is both required and performed in moving the negative charge from point A to point B.

D) No work is required to move the negative charge from point A to point B.

Answer: D

Diff: 1 *Page Ref: Sec. 17.1–17.3*

10) An equipotential surface must be

A) parallel to the electric field at any point.

B) perpendicular to the electric field at any point.

Answer: B
Diff: 1 Page Ref: Sec. 17.1–17.3

11) The energy acquired by a particle carrying a charge equal to that on the electron as a result of moving through a potential difference of one volt is referred to as

A) a joule.

B) an electron–volt.

C) a proton–volt.

D) a coulomb.

Answer: B
Diff: 1 Page Ref: Sec. 17.4

12) The electron–volt is a unit of

A) voltage.

B) current.

C) power.

D) energy.

Answer: D
Diff: 1 Page Ref: Sec. 17.4

13) One electron–volt corresponds to

A) 8.0×10^{-20} J.

B) 1.6×10^{-19} J.

C) 9.5×10^{-17} J.

D) 1.9×10^{-16} J.

Answer: B
Diff: 1 Page Ref: Sec. 17.4

14) The absolute potential at a distance of 2.0 m from a positive point charge is 100 V. What is the absolute potential 4.0 m away from the same point charge?

A) 25 V

B) 50 V

C) 200 V

D) 400 V

Answer: B
Diff: 2 Page Ref: Sec. 17.5

15) The absolute potential at a distance of 2.0 m from a negative point charge is −100 V. What is the absolute potential 4.0 m away from the same point charge?

A) −25 V

B) −50 V

C) −200 V

D) −400 V

Answer: B
Diff: 2 *Page Ref: Sec. 17.5*

16) The absolute potential at the exact center of a square is 3.0 V when a charge of +Q is located at one of the square's corners. What is the absolute potential at the square's center when each of the other corners is also filled with a charge of +Q?

A) zero

B) 3.0 V

C) 9.0 V

D) 12 V

Answer: D
Diff: 2 *Page Ref: Sec. 17.5*

17) The absolute potential at the center of a square is 3.0 V when a charge of +Q is located at one of the square's corners. What is the absolute potential at the square's center when a second charge of −Q is placed at one of the remaining corners?

A) zero

B) 3.0 V

C) 6.0 V

D) 9.0 V

Answer: A
Diff: 2 *Page Ref: Sec. 17.5*

18) Electric dipoles always consist of two charges that are

A) equal in magnitude; opposite in sign.

B) equal in magnitude; both are negative.

C) equal in magnitude; both are positive.

D) unequal in magnitude; opposite in sign.

Answer: A
Diff: 1 *Page Ref: Sec. 17.6*

19) One coulomb per volt is a

A) joule.

B) electron-volt.

C) farad.

D) watt.

Answer: C
Diff: 1 *Page Ref: Sec. 17.7-17.9*

20) Two parallel-plate capacitors are identical in every respect except that one has twice the plate area of the other. If the smaller capacitor has capacitance C, the larger one has capacitance

A) C/2.

B) C.

C) 2C.

D) 4C.

Answer: C
Diff: 1 *Page Ref: Sec. 17.7-17.9*

21) A parallel-plate capacitor has a capacitance of C. If the area of the plates is doubled and the distance between the plates is halved, what is the new capacitance?

A) C/4

B) C/2

C) 2C

D) 4C

Answer: D
Diff: 2 *Page Ref: Sec. 17.7-17.9*

22) A battery charges a parallel-plate capacitor fully and then is removed. The plates are immediately pulled apart. (With the battery disconnected, the amount of charge on the plates remains constant.) What happens to the potential difference between the plates as they are being separated?

A) It increases.

B) It decreases.

C) It remains constant.

D) cannot be determined from the information given

Answer: A
Diff: 2 *Page Ref: Sec. 17.7-17.9*

23) If the electric field between the plates of a given capacitor is weakened, the capacitance of that capacitor

A) increases.

B) decreases.

C) does not change.

D) cannot be determined from the information given

Answer: C
Diff: 1 *Page Ref: Sec. 17.7–17.9*

24) The plates of a parallel-plate capacitor are maintained with constant voltage by a battery as they are pulled apart. During this process, the amount of charge on the plates must

A) increase.

B) decrease.

C) remain constant.

D) either increase or decrease. There is no way to tell from the information given.

Answer: B
Diff: 2 *Page Ref: Sec. 17.7–17.9*

25) The plates of a parallel-plate capacitor are maintained with constant voltage by a battery as they are pulled apart. What happens to the strength of the electric field during this process?

A) It increases.

B) It decreases.

C) It remains constant.

D) cannot be determined from the information given

Answer: B
Diff: 2 *Page Ref: Sec. 17.7–17.9*

26) State three reasons for adding a dielectric material between the plates of a capacitor.

Answer: (1) Dielectrics do not break down (allowing electric charge to flow) as readily as air, so a higher voltage can be applied without charge passing across the gap.
(2) A dielectric allows the plates to be placed closer together without touching thus allowing an increased capacitance because the plate separation is less.
(3) If a dielectric fills the space between the two conductors, it increases the capacitance.
Diff: 1 *Page Ref: Sec. 17.7–17.9*

27) A dielectric material such as paper is placed between the plates of a capacitor. What happens to the capacitance?

A) no change

B) becomes larger

C) becomes smaller

D) becomes infinite

Answer: B
Diff: 2 *Page Ref: Sec. 17.7–17.9*

28) A dielectric material such as paper is placed between the plates of a capacitor holding a fixed charge. What happens to the electric field between the plates?

A) no change

B) becomes stronger

C) becomes weaker

D) reduces to zero

Answer: C
Diff: 2 *Page Ref: Sec. 17.7–17.9*

29) A parallel–plate capacitor is connected to a battery and becomes fully charged. The capacitor is then disconnected, and the separation between the plates is increased in such a way that no charge leaks off. The energy stored in this capacitor has

A) increased.

B) decreased.

C) not changed.

D) become zero.

Answer: A
Diff: 2 *Page Ref: Sec. 17.7–17.9*

30) Doubling the capacitance of a capacitor holding a constant charge causes the energy stored in that capacitor to

A) quadruple.

B) double.

C) decrease to one half.

D) decrease to one fourth.

Answer: D
Diff: 1 *Page Ref: Sec. 17.7–17.9*

31) Doubling the voltage across a given capacitor causes the energy stored in that capacitor to

A) quadruple.

B) double.

C) reduce to one half.

D) reduce to one fourth.

Answer: A
Diff: 1 *Page Ref: Sec. 17.7–17.9*

Quantitative Problems

1) It takes 50 J of energy to move 10 C of charge from point A to point B. What is the potential difference between points A and B?

A) 500 V

B) 50 V

C) 5.0 V

D) 0.50 V

Answer: C
Diff: 1 *Page Ref: Sec. 17.1–17.4*

2) The net work done in moving an electron from point A, where the potential is –50 V, to point B, where the potential is +50 V, is

A) $+1.6 \times 10^{-17}$ J.

B) -1.6×10^{-17} J.

C) zero.

D) none of the given answers

Answer: B
Diff: 2 *Page Ref: Sec. 17.1–17.4*

3) A proton, initially at rest, is accelerated through an electric potential difference of 500 V. What is the kinetic energy of the proton?

A) 500 J

B) 8.0×10^{-17} J

C) 1.6×10^{-19} J

D) zero

Answer: B
Diff: 1 *Page Ref: Sec. 17.1–17.4*

4) A proton, initially at rest, is accelerated through an electric potential difference of 500 V. What is the speed of the proton?

A) 2.2×10^{5} m/s

B) 3.1×10^{5} m/s

C) 9.6×10^{10} m/s

D) zero

Answer: B
Diff: 2 *Page Ref: Sec. 17.1–17.4*

5) Starting from rest, a proton falls through a potential difference of 1200 V. What speed does it acquire?

A) 1.2×10^5 m/s

B) 2.4×10^5 m/s

C) 3.6×10^5 m/s

D) 4.8×10^5 m/s

Answer: D
Diff: 2 *Page Ref: Sec. 17.1–17.4*

6) How much work does 9.0 V do in moving 8.5×10^{18} electrons?

A) 12 J

B) 7.7 J

C) 1.4 J

D) 1.1 J

Answer: A
Diff: 2 *Page Ref: Sec. 17.1–17.4*

7) A stationary electron is accelerated through a potential difference of 500 V. What is the velocity of the electron afterward?

A) 1.3×10^6 m/s

B) 2.6×10^6 m/s

C) 1.3×10^7 m/s

D) 2.6×10^7 m/s

Answer: C
Diff: 2 *Page Ref: Sec. 17.1–17.4*

8) A 4.0-g object carries a charge of 20 μC. The object is accelerated from rest through a potential difference, and afterward the ball is moving at 2.0 m/s. What is the magnitude of the potential difference?

A) 800 kV

B) 400 kV

C) 800 V

D) 400 V

Answer: D
Diff: 2 *Page Ref: Sec. 17.1–17.4*

9) A 6.0–V battery maintains the electrical potential difference between two parallel metal plates separated by 1.0 mm. What is the electric field between the plates?

A) 6.0 V/m

B) 600 V/m

C) 6000 V/m

D) zero

Answer: C
Diff: 1 *Page Ref: Sec. 17.1–17.4*

10) A uniform electric field, with a magnitude of 500 V/m, is directed parallel to the +x axis. If the potential at x = 5.0 m is 2500 V, what is the potential at x = 2.0 m?

A) 500 V

B) 1000 V

C) 2000 V

D) 4000 V

Answer: D
Diff: 2 *Page Ref: Sec. 17.1–17.4*

11) Consider a uniform electric field of 50 N/C directed toward the east. If the voltage measured relative to ground at a given point is 80 V, what is the voltage at a point 1.0 m directly west of that point?

A) 30 V

B) 50 V

C) 80 V

D) 130 V

Answer: D
Diff: 2 *Page Ref: Sec. 17.1–17.4*

12) A proton moves 0.10 m along the direction of an electric field of magnitude 3.0 V/m. What is the change in kinetic energy of the proton?

A) 4.8×10^{-20} J

B) 3.2×10^{-20} J

C) 1.6×10^{-20} J

D) 8.0×10^{-21} J

Answer: A
Diff: 2 *Page Ref: Sec. 17.1–17.4*

13) Two parallel plates, separated by 0.20 m, are connected to a 12-V battery. An electron released from rest at a location 0.10 m from the negative plate. When the electron arrives at a distance 0.050 m from the positive plate, what is the potential difference between the initial and final points?

A) 2.4 V

B) 3.0 V

C) 4.8 V

D) 6.0 V

Answer: B
Diff: 2 *Page Ref: Sec. 17.1-17.4*

14) Two parallel plates, separated by 0.20 m, are connected to a 12-V battery. An electron released from rest at a location 0.10 m from the negative plate. When the electron arrives at a distance 0.050 m from the positive plate, how much kinetic energy does the electron gain?

A) 2.4×10^{-19} J

B) 4.8×10^{-19} J

C) 7.2×10^{-19} J

D) 9.6×10^{-19} J

Answer: B
Diff: 2 *Page Ref: Sec. 17.1-17.4*

15) Two parallel plates, separated by 0.20 m, are connected to a 12-V battery. An electron released from rest at a location 0.10 m from the negative plate. When the electron arrives at a distance 0.050 m from the positive plate, what is the speed of the electron?

A) 5.0×10^{5} m/s

B) 1.0×10^{6} m/s

C) 5.0×10^{6} m/s

D) 1.0×10^{7} m/s

Answer: B
Diff: 2 *Page Ref: Sec. 17.1-17.4*

16) Consider a uniform electric field of 50 N/C directed toward the east. If the voltage measured relative to ground at a given point in the field is 80 V, what is the voltage at a point 1.0 m directly east of the point?

A) 15 V

B) 30 V

C) 90 V

D) 130 V

Answer: B
Diff: 2 *Page Ref: Sec. 17.1-17.4*

17) Consider a uniform electric field of 50 N/C directed toward the east. If the voltage measured relative to ground at a given point in the field is 80 V, what is the voltage at a point 1.0 m directly south of that point?

A) zero

B) 30 V

C) 50 V

D) 80 V

Answer: D
Diff: 2 *Page Ref: Sec. 17.1-17.4*

18) If a Cu^{2+} ion drops through a potential difference of 12 V, it will acquire a kinetic energy (in the absence of friction) of

A) 3.0 eV.

B) 6.0 eV.

C) 12 eV.

D) 24 eV.

Answer: D
Diff: 1 *Page Ref: Sec. 17.1-17.4*

19) What is the potential at a distance of 5.0×10^{-10} m from a nucleus of charge +50e?

A) 120 V

B) 140 V

C) 170 V

D) 210 V

Answer: B
Diff: 2 *Page Ref: Sec. 17.5*

20) Two 3.00-μC charges are at the ends of a meter stick. Find the electrical potential for the center of the meter stick.

A) zero

B) 2.70×10^4 V

C) 5.40×10^4 V

D) 1.08×10^5 V

Answer: D
Diff: 2 *Page Ref: Sec. 17.5*

21) A 5.0-nC charge is at (0, 0) and a -2.0-nC charge is at (3.0 m, 0). If the potential is taken to be zero at infinity, what is the electric potential at point (0, 4.0 m)?

A) 15 V

B) 3.6 V

C) 11 V

D) 7.7 V

Answer: D
Diff: 1 *Page Ref: Sec. 17.5*

22) A 5.0-nC charge is at (0, 0) and a -2.0-nC charge is at (3.0 m, 0). If the potential is taken to be zero at infinity, what is the electric potential energy of a 1.0-nC charge at point (0, 4.0 m)?

A) 1.5×10^{-8} J

B) 3.6×10^{-9} J

C) 1.1×10^{-8} J

D) 7.7×10^{-9} J

Answer: D
Diff: 2 *Page Ref: Sec. 17.5*

23) A 5.0-nC charge is at (0, 0) and a -2.0-nC charge is at (3.0 m, 0). If the potential is taken to be zero at infinity, what is the work required to bring a 1.0-nC charge from infinity to point (0, 4.0 m)?

A) 1.5×10^{-8} J

B) 3.6×10^{-9} J

C) 1.1×10^{-8} J

D) 7.7×10^{-9} J

Answer: D
Diff: 2 *Page Ref: Sec. 17.5*

24) Four charges of equal charge +q are placed at the corners of a rectangle of sides a and b. What is the potential at the center of the rectangle if q = 2.0 μC, a = 3.0 cm, and b = 4.0 cm?

A) 1.3×10^{6} V

B) 2.9×10^{6} V

C) 3.5×10^{6} V

D) 7.8×10^{6} V

Answer: B
Diff: 2 *Page Ref: Sec. 17.5*

25) A square is 1.0 m on a side. Charges of +4.0 μC are placed in two diagonally opposite corners. In the other two corners are placed charges of +3.0 μC and -3.0 μC. What is the absolute potential in the square's center?

A) 1.0×10^4 V

B) 1.0×10^5 V

C) 1.0×10^6 V

D) infinite

Answer: B
Diff: 2 *Page Ref: Sec. 17.5*

26) An alpha particle (charge +2e, mass 6.64×10^{-27}) moves head-on at a fixed gold nucleus (charge +79e). If the distance of closest approach is 2.0×10^{-10} m, what was the initial speed of the alpha particle?

A) 2.3×10^5 m/s

B) 4.6×10^5 m/s

C) 2.3×10^6 m/s

D) 4.6×10^6 m/s

Answer: A
Diff: 3 *Page Ref: Sec. 17.5*

27) How much energy is necessary to place three charges, each of 2.0 μC, at the corners of an equilateral triangle of side 2.0 cm?

A) 4.5 J

B) 5.4 J

C) 6.7 J

D) 7.6 J

Answer: B
Diff: 1 *Page Ref: Sec. 17.5*

28) What charge appears on the plates of a 2.0-μF capacitor when it is charged to 100 V?

A) 50 μC

B) 100 μC

C) 150 μC

D) 200 μC

Answer: D
Diff: 1 *Page Ref: Sec. 17.7-17.9*

29) A parallel-plate capacitor has plates of area 0.50 m^2 separated by a distance of 2.0 mm. What is this capacitor's capacitance?

A) 250 F

B) 50 F

C) 2.2×10^{-9} F

D) 4.4×10^{-10} F

Answer: C
Diff: 1 *Page Ref: Sec. 17.7-17.9*

30) A parallel-plate capacitor is filled with air, and the plates are separated by 0.050 mm. If the capacitance is 17.3 pF, what is the plate area?

A) 4.9×19^{-5} m^2

B) 9.8×10^{-5} m^2

C) 2.4×10^{-4} m^2

D) 4.8×10^{-4} m^2

Answer: B
Diff: 2 *Page Ref: Sec. 17.7-17.9*

31) A parallel-plate capacitor has plates of area 0.20 m^2 separated by a distance of 1.0 mm. What is the strength of the electric field between these plates when this capacitor is connected to a 6.0-V battery?

A) 1200 N/C

B) 3000 N/C

C) 6000 N/C

D) 1500 N/C

Answer: C
Diff: 2 *Page Ref: Sec. 17.7-17.9*

32) A parallel-plate capacitor has a plate separation of 5.0 cm. If the potential difference between the plates is 2000 V, with the top plate at the higher potential, what is the electric field between the plates?

A) 100 N/C upward

B) 100 N/C downward

C) 40000 N/C upward

D) 40000 N/C downward

Answer: D
Diff: 2 *Page Ref: Sec. 17.7-17.9*

33) A 6.0-μF air capacitor is connected across a 100-V battery. After the battery fully charges the capacitor, the capacitor is immersed in transformer oil (dielectric constant = 4.5). How much additional charge flows from the battery, which remained connected during the process?

A) 1.2 mC

B) 1.7 mC

C) 2.1 mC

D) 2.5 mC

Answer: C
Diff: 2 *Page Ref: Sec. 17.7-17.9*

34) A charge of 60 μC is placed on a 15 μF capacitor. How much energy is stored in the capacitor?

A) 120 J

B) 4.0 J

C) 240 μJ

D) 120 μJ

Answer: D
Diff: 1 *Page Ref: Sec. 17.7-17.9*

35) 20 V is placed across a 15 μF capacitor. What is the energy stored in the capacitor?

A) 150 μJ

B) 300 μJ

C) 3.0 mJ

D) 6.0 mJ

Answer: C
Diff: 1 *Page Ref: Sec. 17.7-17.9*

36) A charge of 2.00 μC flows onto the plates of a capacitor when it is connected to a 12.0-V battery. How much work was done in charging this capacitor?

A) 24.0 μJ

B) 12.0 μJ

C) 144 μJ

D) 576 J

Answer: B
Diff: 1 *Page Ref: Sec. 17.7-17.9*

37) If a 10-μF capacitor is charged so that it stores 2.0×10^{-3} J of energy, what is the voltage across it?

A) 5.0 V

B) 10 V

C) 15 V

D) 20 V

Answer: D
Diff: 2 *Page Ref: Sec. 17.7-17.9*

38) A parallel-plate capacitor consists of plates of area 1.5×10^{-4} m^2 and separated by 1.0 mm. The capacitor is connected to a 12-V battery. What is the capacitance?

A) 1.3×10^{-15} F

B) 2.6×10^{-15} F

C) 1.3×10^{-12} F

D) 2.6×10^{-12} F

Answer: C
Diff: 2 *Page Ref: Sec. 17.7-17.9*

39) A parallel-plate capacitor consists of plates of area 1.5×10^{-4} m^2 and separated by 1.0 mm. The capacitor is connected to a 12-V battery. What is the charge on the plates?

A) 1.6×10^{-11} C

B) 3.2×10^{-11} C

C) 1.6×10^{-14} C

D) 3.2×10^{-14} C

Answer: A
Diff: 2 *Page Ref: Sec. 17.7-17.9*

40) A parallel-plate capacitor consists of plates of area 1.5×10^{-4} m^2 and separated by 1.0 mm. The capacitor is connected to a 12-V battery. What is the electric field between the plates?

A) 12 V/m

B) 1.2×10^2 V/m

C) 1.2×10^3 V/m

D) 1.2×10^4 V/m

Answer: D
Diff: 2 *Page Ref: Sec. 17.7-17.9*

41) A parallel-plate capacitor is constructed with plate area of 0.40 m^2 and a plate separation of 0.10 mm. How much charge is stored on it when it is charged to a potential difference of 12 V?

A) 0.21 μC

B) 0.42 μC

C) 0.63 μC

D) 0.84 μC

Answer: B
Diff: 2 *Page Ref: Sec. 17.7-17.9*

42) A parallel-plate capacitor is constructed with plate area of 0.40 m^2 and a plate separation of 0.10 mm. How much energy is stored when it is charged to a potential difference of 12 V?

A) 2.5 μJ

B) 5.0 μJ

C) 7.5 μJ

D) 10 μJ

Answer: A
Diff: 2 *Page Ref: Sec. 17.7-17.9*

43) A 15-μF capacitor is connected to a 50-V battery and becomes fully charged. The battery is removed and a slab of dielectric that completely fills the space between the plates is inserted. If the dielectric has a dielectric constant of 5.0, what is the capacitance of the capacitor after the slab is inserted?

A) 75 μF

B) 20 μF

C) 3.0 μF

D) 1.0 μF

Answer: A
Diff: 2 *Page Ref: Sec. 17.7-17.9*

44) A 15-μF capacitor is connected to a 50-V battery and becomes fully charged. The battery is removed and a slab of dielectric that completely fills the space between the plates is inserted. If the dielectric has a dielectric constant of 5.0, what is the voltage across the capacitor's plates after the slab is inserted?

A) 250 V

B) 10 V

C) 2.0 V

D) 0.75 V

Answer: B
Diff: 2 *Page Ref: Sec. 17.7-17.9*

Chapter 18 Electric Currents

Conceptual Questions

1) A device that produces electricity by transforming chemical energy into electrical energy is called a

A) generator.

B) transformer.

C) battery.

D) none of the given answers

Answer: C
Diff: 2 *Page Ref: Sec. 18.1*

2) A car battery

A) has an emf of 6 V consisting of one 6-V cell.

B) has an emf of 6 V consisting of three 2-V cells connected in series.

C) has an emf of 6 V consisting of three 2-V cells connected in parallel.

D) has an emf of 12 V consisting of six 2-V cells connected in series.

Answer: D
Diff: 2 *Page Ref: Sec. 18.1*

3) The total amount of charge that passes through a wire's full cross section at any point per unit of time is referred to as

A) current.

B) electric potential.

C) voltage.

D) wattage.

Answer: A
Diff: 2 *Page Ref: Sec. 18.2*

4) The direction of convention current is taken to be the direction that

A) negative charges would flow.

B) positive charges would flow.

Answer: B
Diff: 2 *Page Ref: Sec. 18.2*

5) A coulomb per second is the same as

A) a watt.

B) an ampere.

C) a volt-second.

D) a volt per second.

Answer: B
Diff: 1 *Page Ref: Sec. 18.2*

6) Car batteries are rated in "amp-hours." This is a measure of their

A) charge.

B) current.

C) emf.

D) power.

Answer: A
Diff: 1 *Page Ref: Sec. 18.2*

7) The resistance of a wire is defined as

A) (current)*(voltage).

B) (current)/(voltage).

C) (voltage)/(current).

D) none of the given answers

Answer: C
Diff: 2 *Page Ref: Sec. 18.3*

8) What is 1 Ω equivalent to?

A) 1 J/s

B) 1 W/A

C) 1 V•A

D) 1 V/A

Answer: D
Diff: 1 *Page Ref: Sec. 18.3*

9) The resistance of a wire is

A) proportional to its length and its cross-sectional area.

B) proportional to its length and inversely proportional to its cross-sectional area.

C) inversely proportional to its length and proportional to its cross-sectional area.

D) inversely proportional to its length and its cross-sectional area.

Answer: B
Diff: 2 *Page Ref: Sec. 18.4*

10) The resistivity of a wire depends on

A) its length.

B) its cross-sectional area.

C) the material out of which it is composed.

D) all of the given answers

Answer: C
Diff: 2 *Page Ref: Sec. 18.4*

11) Which conducting material has the lowest resistivity value?

A) gold

B) silver

C) copper

D) aluminum

Answer: B
Diff: 2 *Page Ref: Sec. 18.4*

12) Consider two copper wires. One has twice the length of the other. How do the resistivities of these two wires compare?

A) Both wires have the same resistivity.

B) The longer wire has twice the resistivity of the shorter wire.

C) The longer wire has four times the resistivity of the shorter wire.

D) none of the given answers

Answer: A
Diff: 1 *Page Ref: Sec. 18.4*

13) Consider two copper wires. One has twice the length of the other. How do the resistances of these two wires compare?

A) Both wires have the same resistance.

B) The longer wire has half the resistance of the shorter wire.

C) The longer wire has twice the resistance of the shorter wire.

D) none of the given answers

Answer: C
Diff: 1 *Page Ref: Sec. 18.4*

14) Consider two copper wires. One has twice the cross-sectional area of the other. How do the resistances of these two wires compare?

A) Both wires have the same resistance.

B) The thicker wire has half the resistance of the shorter wire.

C) The thicker wire has twice the resistance of the shorter wire.

D) none of the given answers

Answer: B
Diff: 1 *Page Ref: Sec. 18.4*

15) Consider two copper wires. One has twice the length and twice the cross-sectional area of the other. How do the resistances of these two wires compare?

A) Both wires have the same resistance.

B) The longer wire has twice the resistance of the shorter wire.

C) The longer wire has four times the resistance of the shorter wire.

D) none of the given answers

Answer: A
Diff: 2 *Page Ref: Sec. 18.4*

16) The length of a wire is doubled and the radius is doubled. By what factor does the resistance change?

A) four times as large

B) twice as large

C) half as large

D) quarter as large

Answer: C
Diff: 2 *Page Ref: Sec. 18.4*

17) How much more resistance does a 1.0 cm diameter rod have compared to a 2.0 cm diameter rod of the same length and made of the same material?

A) 75%

B) 100%

C) 300%

D) 400%

Answer: C
Diff: 2 *Page Ref: Sec. 18.4*

18) The resistivity of most common metals

A) remains constant over wide temperature ranges.

B) increases as the temperature increases.

C) decreases as the temperature increases.

D) varies randomly as the temperature increases.

Answer: B
Diff: 1 *Page Ref: Sec. 18.4*

19) Negative temperature coefficients of resistivity

A) do not exist.

B) exist in conductors.

C) exist in semiconductors.

D) exist in superconductors.

Answer: C
Diff: 1 *Page Ref: Sec. 18.4*

20) What is 1 W equivalent to?

A) 1 V/A

B) 1 Ω•A

C) 1 V•A

D) 1 V/Ω

Answer: C
Diff: 2 *Page Ref: Sec. 18.5–18.6*

21) A kilowatt-hour is equivalent to

A) 1000 W.

B) 3600 s.

C) 3,600,000 J/s.

D) 3,600,000 J.

Answer: D
Diff: 1 *Page Ref: Sec. 18.5–18.6*

22) If the resistance in a constant voltage circuit is doubled, the power dissipated by that circuit will

A) increase by a factor of two.

B) increase by a factor of four.

C) decrease to one-half its original value.

D) decrease to one-fourth its original value.

Answer: C
Diff: 2 *Page Ref: Sec. 18.5–18.6*

23) If the voltage across a circuit of constant resistance is doubled, the power dissipated by that circuit will

A) quadruple.

B) double.

C) decrease to one half.

D) decrease to one fourth.

Answer: A
Diff: 1 *Page Ref: Sec. 18.5–18.6*

24) If the resistance in a circuit with constant current flowing is doubled, the power dissipated by that circuit will

A) quadruple.

B) double.

C) decrease to one half.

D) decrease to one fourth.

Answer: B
Diff: 1 *Page Ref: Sec. 18.5–18.6*

25) If the current flowing through a circuit of constant resistance is doubled, the power dissipated by that circuit will

A) quadruple.

B) double.

C) decrease to one half.

D) decrease to one fourth.

Answer: A
Diff: 1 *Page Ref: Sec. 18.5–18.6*

26) During a power demand, the voltage output is reduced by 5.0%. By what percentage is the power on a resistor affected?

A) 2.5% less

B) 5.0% less

C) 10% less

D) 90% less

Answer: C
Diff: 2 *Page Ref: Sec. 18.5–18.6*

27) A current that is sinusoidal with respect to time is referred to as

A) a direct current.

B) an alternating current.

Answer: B
Diff: 1 *Page Ref: Sec. 18.7*

28) Consider two copper wires each carrying a current of 3.0 A. One wire has twice the diameter of the other. The ratio of the drift velocity in the smaller diameter wire to that in the larger diameter wire is

A) 4:1.

B) 2:1.

C) 1:2.

D) 1:4.

Answer: A
Diff: 2 *Page Ref: Sec. 18.8*

29) Materials in which the resistivity becomes essentially zero at very low temperatures are referred to as

A) conductors.

B) insulators.

C) semiconductors.

D) superconductors.

Answer: D
Diff: 1 *Page Ref: Sec. 18.9*

Quantitative Problems

1) What current is flowing if 0.67 C of charge pass a point in 0.30 s?

A) 2.2 A

B) 0.67 A

C) 0.30 A

D) 0.20 A

Answer: A
Diff: 1 *Page Ref: Sec. 18.1*

2) A charge of 12 C passes through an electroplating apparatus in 2.0 min. What is the average current?

A) 0.10 A

B) 0.60 A

C) 1.0 A

D) 6.0 A

Answer: A
Diff: 1 *Page Ref: Sec. 18.2*

3) How much charge must pass by a point in 10 s for the current to be 0.50 A?

A) 20 C

B) 2.0 C

C) 5.0 C

D) 0.050 C

Answer: C
Diff: 1 *Page Ref: Sec. 18.2*

4) A total of 2.0×10^{13} protons pass a given point in 15 s. What is the current?

A) 1.3 mA

B) 1.3 A

C) 0.21 μA

D) 3.2 μA

Answer: C
Diff: 2 *Page Ref: Sec. 18.2*

5) What current is flowing if 4.0×10^{16} electrons pass a point in 0.50 s?

A) 0.013 A

B) 0.31 A

C) 6.3 A

D) 78 A

Answer: A
Diff: 2 *Page Ref: Sec. 18.2*

6) If 3.0×10^{15} electrons flow through a section of a wire of diameter 2.0 mm in 4.0 s, what is the current in the wire?

A) 0.12 mA

B) 0.24 mA

C) 7.5×10^{7} A

D) 7.5×10^{14} A

Answer: A
Diff: 2 *Page Ref: Sec. 18.2*

7) A coffee maker, which draws 13.5 A of current, has been left on for 10 min. What is the net number of electrons that have passed through the coffee maker?

A) 1.5×10^{22}

B) 5.1×10^{22}

C) 1.8×10^{3}

D) 8.1×10^{3}

Answer: B
Diff: 2 *Page Ref: Sec. 18.2*

8) In an electroplating process, it is desired to deposit 40 mg of silver on a metal part by using a current of 2.0 A. How long must the current be allowed to run to deposit this much silver? (The silver ions are singly charged, and the atomic weight of silver is 108.)

A) 16 s

B) 18 s

C) 20 s

D) 22 s

Answer: B
Diff: 2 *Page Ref: Sec. 18.2*

9) What potential difference is required to cause 4.00 A to flow through a resistance of 330 Ω?

A) 12.1 V

B) 82.5 V

C) 334 V

D) 1320 V

Answer: D
Diff: 1 *Page Ref: Sec. 18.3*

10) What is the voltage across a 5.0-Ω resistor if the current through it is 5.0 A?

A) 100 V

B) 25 V

C) 4.0 V

D) 1.0 V

Answer: B
Diff: 1 *Page Ref: Sec. 18.3*

11) A 4000-Ω resistor is connected across 220 V. What current will flow?

A) 0.055 A

B) 1.8 A

C) 5.5 A

D) 18 A

Answer: A
Diff: 1 *Page Ref: Sec. 18.3*

12) A light bulb operating at 110 V draws 1.40 A of current. What is its resistance?

A) 12.7 Ω

B) 78.6 Ω

C) 109 Ω

D) 154 Ω

Answer: B
Diff: 1 *Page Ref: Sec. 18.3*

13) A 12-V battery is connected to a 100-Ω resistor. How many electrons flow through the wire in 1.0 min?

A) 1.5×10^{19}

B) 2.5×10^{19}

C) 3.5×10^{19}

D) 4.5×10^{19}

Answer: D
Diff: 2 *Page Ref: Sec. 18.3*

14) What is the resistance of 1.0 m of no. 18 copper wire (diameter 0.40 in)? (The resistivity of copper is 1.68×10^{-8} Ω•m.)

A) 0.00012 Ω

B) 0.00021 Ω

C) 0.0012 Ω

D) 0.0021 Ω

Answer: B
Diff: 2 *Page Ref: Sec. 18.4*

15) What is the resistance of a circular rod 1.0 cm in diameter and 45 m long, if the resistivity is 1.4 $\times 10^{-8}$ Ω•m?

A) 0.0063 Ω

B) 0.0080 Ω

C) 0.80 Ω

D) 6.3 Ω

Answer: B
Diff: 2 *Page Ref: Sec. 18.4*

16) What length of copper wire (resistivity 1.68 $\times 10^{-8}$ Ω•m) of diameter 0.15 mm is needed for a total resistance of 15 Ω?

A) 16 mm

B) 16 cm

C) 1.6 m

D) 16 m

Answer: D
Diff: 2 *Page Ref: Sec. 18.4*

17) A 120-m long copper wire (resistivity 1.68 $\times 10^{-8}$ Ω•m) has resistance 6.0 Ω. What is the diameter of the wire?

A) 0.065 mm

B) 0.65 mm

C) 0.65 cm

D) 0.65 m

Answer: B
Diff: 3 *Page Ref: Sec. 18.4*

18) A 1.5-cm square rod, 4.0 m long, measures 0.040 ohms. What is its resistivity?

A) 0.023 Ω•m

B) 0.015 Ω•m

C) 1.5 $\times 10^{-4}$ Ω•m

D) 2.3 $\times 10^{-6}$ Ω•m

Answer: D
Diff: 2 *Page Ref: Sec. 18.4*

19) Calculate the current through a 10.0–m long 22 gauge (the radius is 0.321 mm) nichrome wire if it is connected to a 12.0–V battery. (The resistivity of nichrome is 100×10^{-8} Ω•m.)

A) 30.9 A

B) 61.8 A

C) 0.388 A

D) 0.776 A

Answer: C
Diff: 2 *Page Ref: Sec. 18.4*

20) A heavy bus bar is 20 cm long and of rectangular cross–section, 1.0 cm × 2.0 cm. What is the voltage drop along its length when it carries 4000 A? (The resistivity of copper is 1.68×10^{-8} Ω•m.)

A) 0.67 V

B) 0.34 V

C) 0.067 V

D) 0.034 V

Answer: C
Diff: 2 *Page Ref: Sec. 18.4*

21) A 1.0–m length of nichrome wire has a radius of 0.50 mm and a resistivity of 100×10^{-8} Ω•m. If the wire carries a current of 0.50 A, what is the voltage across the wire?

A) 0.0030 V

B) 0.32 V

C) 0.64 V

D) 1.6 V

Answer: C
Diff: 2 *Page Ref: Sec. 18.4*

22) A 1.0–mm diameter copper wire (resistivity 1.68×10^{-8} Ω•m) carries a current of 15 A. What is the potential difference between two points 100 m apart?

A) 12 V

B) 23 V

C) 32 V

D) 41 V

Answer: C
Diff: 2 *Page Ref: Sec. 18.4*

23) A carbon resistor has a resistance of 18 Ω at a temperature of 20°C. What is its resistance at a temperature of 120°C? (The temperature coefficient of resistivity for carbon is -5.0×10^{-4} /C°.)

A) 18 Ω

B) 17 Ω

C) 16 Ω

D) 15 Ω

Answer: B

Diff: 2 *Page Ref: Sec. 18.4*

24) The temperature coefficient of resistivity of platinum is 3.9×10^{-3}/C°. If a platinum wire has a resistance of R at room temperature (23°C), to what temperature must it be heated in order to double its resistance to 2R?

A) 279°C

B) 297°C

C) 729°C

D) 927°C

Answer: A

Diff: 2 *Page Ref: Sec. 18.4*

25) A platinum wire is used to determine the melting point of indium. The resistance of the platinum wire is 2.000 Ω at 20°C and increases to 3.072 Ω as indium starts to melt. What is the melting point of indium? (The temperature coefficient of resistivity for platinum is 3.9×10^{-3}/C°.)

A) 117°C

B) 137°C

C) 157°C

D) 351°C

Answer: C

Diff: 2 *Page Ref: Sec. 18.4*

26) 5.00 A is flowing through an 10.0 Ω resistor. How much power is being dissipated?

A) 50.0 W

B) 250 W

C) 500 W

D) 2.50 kW

Answer: B

Diff: 1 *Page Ref: Sec. 18.5–18.6*

27) A 110-V hair dryer is rated at 1200 W. What current will it draw?

A) 0.090 A

B) 1.0 A

C) 11 A

D) 12 A

Answer: C
Diff: 1 *Page Ref: Sec. 18.5-18.6*

28) A 150-W light bulb running on 110 V draws how much current?

A) 0.73 A

B) 1.4 A

C) 2.0 A

D) 15 A

Answer: B
Diff: 1 *Page Ref: Sec. 18.5-18.6*

29) What is the nominal resistance of a 100-W light bulb designed to be used in a 120-V circuit?

A) 12.0 Ω

B) 144 Ω

C) 1.2 Ω

D) 0.83 Ω

Answer: B
Diff: 2 *Page Ref: Sec. 18.5-18.6*

30) A toaster is rated 800 W at 120 V. What is the resistance of its heating element?

A) 16 Ω

B) 18 Ω

C) 6.7 Ω

D) 0.15 Ω

Answer: B
Diff: 1 *Page Ref: Sec. 18.5-18.6*

31) A 200-Ω resistor is rated at 1/4 W. What is the maximum current it can draw?

A) 0.035 A

B) 0.35 A

C) 50 A

D) 0.25 A

Answer: A
Diff: 2 *Page Ref: Sec. 18.5-18.6*

32) A 200-Ω resistor is rated at 1/4 W. What is the maximum voltage?

A) 0.71 V

B) 7.1 V

C) 50 V

D) 0.25 V

Answer: B
Diff: 2 *Page Ref: Sec. 18.5-18.6*

33) A lamp uses a 150-W bulb. If it is used at 120 V, what current does it draw?

A) 0.800 A

B) 1.25 A

C) 150 A

D) 8 kA

Answer: B
Diff: 1 *Page Ref: Sec. 18.5-18.6*

34) A lamp uses a 150-W bulb. If it is used at 120 V, what is its resistance?

A) 48 Ω

B) 96 Ω

C) 80 Ω

D) 150 Ω

Answer: B
Diff: 2 *Page Ref: Sec. 18.5-18.6*

35) A 25-W soldering iron runs on 110 V. What is its resistance?

A) 0.0020 Ω

B) 4.4 Ω

C) 0.48 kΩ

D) 2.8 kΩ

Answer: C
Diff: 1 *Page Ref: Sec. 18.5-18.6*

36) How much does it cost to operate a 25-W soldering iron for 8.0 hours, if energy costs $0.08/kWh?

A) $1.50

B) $0.25

C) $0.16

D) $0.016

Answer: D
Diff: 2 *Page Ref: Sec. 18.5-18.6*

37) How much energy does a 100-W light bulb use in 8.0 hours?

A) 0.0080 kWh

B) 0.80 kWh

C) 13 kWh

D) 800 kWh

Answer: B
Diff: 1 *Page Ref: Sec. 18.5-18.6*

38) A 1500-W heater is connected to a 120-V line for 2.0 hours. How much heat energy is produced?

A) 1.5 kJ

B) 3.0 kJ

C) 0.18 MJ

D) 11 MJ

Answer: D
Diff: 2 *Page Ref: Sec. 18.5-18.6*

39) A battery is rated at 12 V and 160 A-h. How much energy does the battery store?

A) 1.9 kJ

B) 6.0 kJ

C) 1.9 MJ

D) 6.9 MJ

Answer: D
Diff: 2 *Page Ref: Sec. 18.5-18.6*

40) How much energy does a 25-W soldering iron use in 8.0 hours?

A) 400 J

B) 11 kJ

C) 12 kJ

D) 0.72 MJ

Answer: D
Diff: 2 *Page Ref: Sec. 18.5-18.6*

41) A 100-W driveway light bulb is on 10 hours per day. Assuming the power company charges 10 cents for each kilowatt-hour of electricity used, estimate the annual cost to operate the bulb.

A) $3.65

B) $7.30

C) $36.50

D) $73.00

Answer: C
Diff: 2 *Page Ref: Sec. 18.5-18.6*

42) A 400-W computer (computer plus monitor) is turned on 8.0 hours per day. If electricity costs 10 cents per kWh, how much does it cost to run the computer annually?

A) $116.80

B) $1168.00

C) $14.60

D) $146.00

Answer: A
Diff: 2 *Page Ref: Sec. 18.5-18.6*

43) The monthly (30 days) electric bill included the cost of running a central air-conditioning unit for 2.0 hr/day at 5000 W, and a series connection of ten 60 W light bulbs for 5.0 hr/day. How much did these items contribute to the cost of the monthly electric bill if electricity costs 8.0¢ per kWh?

A) $21.30

B) $31.20

C) $13.20

D) $12.30

Answer: B
Diff: 2 *Page Ref: Sec. 18.5-18.6*

44) The heating element in an electric drier operates on 240 V and generates heat at the rate of 2.0 kW. The heating element shorts out and, in repairing it, the owner shortens the Nichrome wire by 10%. (Assume the temperature is unchanged. In reality, the resistivity of the wire will depend on its temperature.) What effect will the repair have on the power dissipated in the heating element?

A) Power is still 2.0 kW.

B) Power increases to 2.2 kW.

C) Power decreases to 1.8 kW.

D) none of the given answers

Answer: B
Diff: 2 *Page Ref: Sec. 18.5-18.6*

45) 14 A of current flows through 8.0 Ω for 24 hours. How much does this cost if energy costs $0.09/kWh?

A) $0.24

B) $1.04

C) $2.16

D) $3.39

Answer: D
Diff: 2 *Page Ref: Sec. 18.5-18.6*

46) A 9.0-V battery costs $1.49, and will run a portable CD player for 6.0 hours. Suppose the battery supplies a current of 25 mA to the player. What is the cost of energy in dollars per kWh?

A) $11/kWh

B) $110/kWh

C) $1100/kWh

D) 11,000/kWh

Answer: C
Diff: 3 *Page Ref: Sec. 18.5-18.6*

47) A motor that can do work at the rate of 2.0 hp has 60% efficiency. How much current does it draw from a 120-V line? (1 hp = 746 W.)

A) 12 A

B) 17 A

C) 21 A

D) 29 A

Answer: C
Diff: 2 *Page Ref: Sec. 18.5-18.6*

48) A 500-W device is connected to a 120-V ac power source. What rms current flows through this device?

A) 4.2 A

B) 5.9 A

C) 120 A

D) 170 A

Answer: A
Diff: 1 *Page Ref: Sec. 18.7*

49) A 500-W device is connected to a 120-V ac power source. What peak current flows through this device?

A) 4.2 A

B) 5.9 A

C) 120 A

D) 170 A

Answer: B
Diff: 1 *Page Ref: Sec. 18.7*

50) A 500-W device is connected to a 120-V ac power source. What is the peak voltage across this device?

A) 4.2 V

B) 5.9 V

C) 120 V

D) 170 V

Answer: D
Diff: 1 *Page Ref: Sec. 18.7*

51) The diameter of no. 12 copper wire is 0.081 in. The maximum safe current it can carry (in order to prevent fire danger in building construction) is 20 A. At this current, what is the drift velocity of the electrons? (The number of electron carriers in one cubic centimeter of copper is 8.5×10^{22}.)

A) 0.044 mm/s

B) 0.44 mm/s

C) 0.44 cm/s

D) 0.44 m/s

Answer: B
Diff: 3 *Page Ref: Sec. 18.8*

Chapter 19 DC Circuits

Conceptual Questions

1) The potential difference between the terminals of a battery, when no current flows to an external circuit, is referred to as the

A) emf.

B) terminal voltage.

Answer: A
Diff: 1 *Page Ref: Sec. 19.1*

2) The potential difference between the terminals of a battery, when current flows to an external circuit, is referred to as the

A) emf.

B) terminal voltage.

Answer: B
Diff: 1 *Page Ref: Sec. 19.1*

3) When two or more resistors are connected in series to a battery

A) the total voltage across the combination is the algebraic sum of the voltages across the individual resistors.

B) the same current flows through each resistor.

C) the equivalent resistance of the combination is equal to the sum of the resistances of each resistor.

D) all of the given answers

Answer: D
Diff: 1 *Page Ref: Sec. 19.2*

4) When resistors are connected in series,

A) the same power is dissipated in each one.

B) the potential difference across each is the same.

C) the current flowing in each is the same.

D) More than one of the given answers is true.

Answer: C
Diff: 1 *Page Ref: Sec. 19.2*

5) Three identical resistors are connected in series to a battery. If the current of 12 A flows from the battery, how much current flows through any one of the resistors?

A) 12 A

B) 4 A

C) 36 A

D) zero

Answer: A
Diff: 1 *Page Ref: Sec. 19.2*

6) Three identical resistors are connected in series to a 12–V battery. What is the voltage across any one of the resistors?

A) 36 V

B) 12 V

C) 4 V

D) zero

Answer: C
Diff: 1 *Page Ref: Sec. 19.2*

7) You obtain a 100–W light bulb and a 50–W light bulb. Instead of connecting them in the normal way, you devise a circuit that places them in series across normal household voltage. Which statement is correct?

A) Both bulbs glow at the same reduced brightness.

B) Both bulbs glow at the same increased brightness.

C) The 100–W bulb glows brighter than the 50–W bulb.

D) The 50–W bulb glows more brightly than the 100–W bulb.

Answer: D
Diff: 3 *Page Ref: Sec. 19.2*

8) As more resistors are added in series to a constant voltage source, the power supplied by the source

A) increases.

B) decreases.

C) does not change.

D) increases for a time and then starts to decrease.

Answer: B
Diff: 2 *Page Ref: Sec. 19.2*

9) When two or more resistors are connected in parallel to a battery,

A) the voltage across each resistor is the same.

B) the total current flowing from the battery equals the sum of the currents flowing through each resistor.

C) the equivalent resistance of the combination is less than the resistance of any one of the resistors.

D) all of the given answers

Answer: D
Diff: 1 *Page Ref: Sec. 19.2*

10) When resistors are connected in parallel, we can be certain that

A) the same current flows in each one.

B) the potential difference across each is the same.

C) the power dissipated in each is the same.

D) their equivalent resistance is greater than the resistance of any one of the individual resistances.

Answer: B
Diff: 1 *Page Ref: Sec. 19.2*

11) Three identical resistors are connected in parallel to a 12-V battery. What is the voltage of any one of the resistors?

A) 36 V

B) 12 V

C) 4 V

D) zero

Answer: B
Diff: 1 *Page Ref: Sec. 19.2*

12) Three identical resistors are connected in parallel to a battery. If the current of 12 A flows from the battery, how much current flows through any one of the resistors?

A) 12 A

B) 4 A

C) 36 A

D) zero

Answer: B
Diff: 1 *Page Ref: Sec. 19.2*

13) The lamps in a string of Christmas tree lights are connected in parallel. What happens if one lamp burns out? (Assume negligible resistance in the wires leading to the lamps.)

A) The brightness of the lamps will not change appreciably.

B) The other lamps get brighter equally.

C) The other lamps get brighter, but some get brighter than others.

D) The other lamps get dimmer equally.

E) The other lamps get dimmer, but some get dimmer than others.

Answer: A
Diff: 2 *Page Ref: Sec. 19.2*

14) As more resistors are added in parallel to a constant voltage source, the power supplied by the source

A) increases.

B) decreases.

C) does not change.

D) increases for a time and then starts to decrease.

Answer: A
Diff: 2 *Page Ref: Sec. 19.2*

15) Consider three identical resistors, each of resistance R. The maximum power each can dissipate is P. Two of the resistors are connected in series, and a third is connected in parallel with these two. What is the maximum power this network can dissipate?

A) 2P/3

B) 3P/2

C) 2P

D) 3P

Answer: B
Diff: 3 *Page Ref: Sec. 19.2*

16) State Kirchhoff's junction rule.

Answer: At any junction point, the sum of all the currents entering the junction must equal the sum of all the currents leaving the junction.
Diff: 1 *Page Ref: Sec. 19.3*

17) State Kirchhoff's loop rule.

Answer: The sum of the changes in potential around any closed path of a circuit must be zero.
Diff: 1 *Page Ref: Sec. 19.3*

18) Kirchhoff's loop rule is an example of

A) conservation of energy.

B) conservation of charge.

C) conservation of momentum.

D) none of the given answers

Answer: A
Diff: 1 *Page Ref: Sec. 19.3*

19) Kirchhoff's junction rule is an example of

A) conservation of energy.

B) conservation of charge.

C) conservation of momentum.

D) none of the given answers

Answer: B
Diff: 1 *Page Ref: Sec. 19.3*

20) Which of the equations here is valid for the circuit shown?

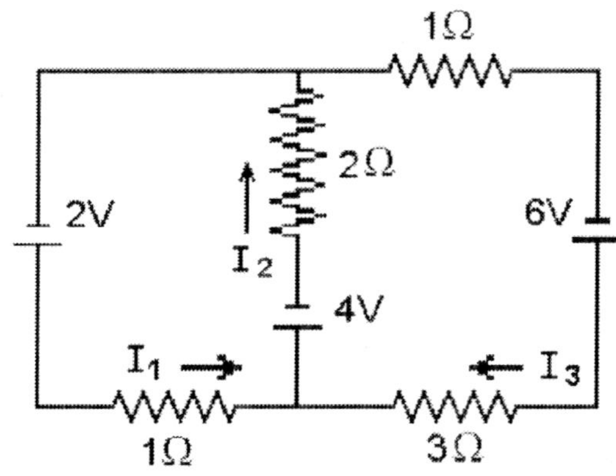

FIGURE 19–1

A) $2 - I_1 - 2I_2 = 0$

B) $2 - 2I_1 - 2I_2 - 4I_3 = 0$

C) $4 - I_1 + 4I_3 = 0$

D) $-2 - I_1 - 2I_2 = 0$

E) $6 - I_1 - 2I_2 = 0$

Answer: D
Diff: 2 *Page Ref: Sec. 19.3*

21) If you connect two identical storage batteries together in series ("+" to "-" to "+" to "-"), and place them in a circuit, the combination will provide

A) zero volts.

B) twice the voltage, and different currents will flow through each.

C) twice the voltage, and the same current will flow through each.

D) the same voltage, and different currents will flow through each.

Answer: C
Diff: 2 *Page Ref: Sec. 19.4*

22) If you connect two identical storage batteries together in series ("+" to "-" to "-" to "+"), and place them in a circuit, the combination will provide

A) zero volts.

B) twice the voltage, and different currents will flow through each.

C) twice the voltage, and the same current will flow through each.

D) the same voltage, and different currents will flow through each.

Answer: A
Diff: 2 *Page Ref: Sec. 19.4*

23) If you connect two identical storage batteries together in parallel, and place them in a circuit, the combination will provide

A) twice the voltage and twice the total charge that one battery would.

B) twice the voltage and the same total charge that one battery would.

C) the same voltage and twice the total charge that one battery would.

D) half the voltage and half the total charge that one battery would.

Answer: C
Diff: 2 *Page Ref: Sec. 19.4*

24) When two or more capacitors are connected in series to a battery,

A) the total voltage across the combination is the algebraic sum of the voltages across the individual capacitors.

B) each capacitor carries the same amount of charge.

C) the equivalent capacitance of the combination is less than the capacitance of any of the capacitors.

D) all of the given answers

Answer: D
Diff: 1 *Page Ref: Sec. 19.5*

25) As more and more capacitors are connected in series, the equivalent capacitance of the combination increases.

A) always true

B) Sometimes true; it depends on the voltage of the battery to which the combination is connected.

C) Sometimes true; it goes up only if the next capacitor is larger than the average of the existing combination.

D) never true

Answer: D
Diff: 2 *Page Ref: Sec. 19.5*

26) Three identical capacitors are connected in series to a battery. If a total charge of Q flows from the battery, how much charge does each capacitor carry?

A) 3Q

B) Q

C) Q/3

D) Q/9

Answer: B
Diff: 1 *Page Ref: Sec. 19.5*

27) When two or more capacitors are connected in parallel to a battery,

A) the voltage across each capacitor is the same.

B) each capacitor carries the same amount of charge.

C) the equivalent capacitance of the combination is less than the capacitance of any one of the capacitors.

D) all of the given answers

Answer: A
Diff: 1 *Page Ref: Sec. 19.5*

28) As more and more capacitors are connected in parallel, the equivalent capacitance of the combination increases.

A) always true

B) Sometimes true; it depends on the voltage of the battery to which the combination is connected.

C) Sometimes true; it goes up only if the next capacitor is larger than the average of the existing combination.

D) never true

Answer: A
Diff: 2 *Page Ref: Sec. 19.5*

29) Three identical capacitors are connected in parallel to a battery. If a total charge of Q flows from the battery, how much charge does each capacitor carry?

A) 3Q

B) Q

C) Q/3

D) Q/9

Answer: C
Diff: 1 *Page Ref: Sec. 19.5*

30) What is the unit for the quantity RC?

A) ohms

B) volt-ampere/ohm

C) seconds

D) meters

Answer: C
Diff: 1 *Page Ref: Sec. 19.6*

31) A resistor and a capacitor are connected in series to an ideal battery of constant terminal voltage. At the moment contact is made with the battery, the voltage across the capacitor is

A) greater than the battery's terminal voltage.

B) less than the battery's terminal voltage, but greater than zero.

C) equal to the battery's terminal voltage.

D) zero.

Answer: D
Diff: 1 *Page Ref: Sec. 19.6*

32) A resistor and a capacitor are connected in series to an ideal battery of constant terminal voltage. At the moment contact is made with the battery, the voltage across the resistor is

A) greater than the battery's terminal voltage.

B) less than the battery's terminal voltage, but greater than zero.

C) equal to the battery's terminal voltage.

D) zero.

Answer: C
Diff: 1 *Page Ref: Sec. 19.6*

33) A resistor and a capacitor are connected in series to an ideal battery of constant terminal voltage. When this system reaches its steady–state, the voltage across the resistor is

A) greater than the battery's terminal voltage.

B) less than the battery's terminal voltage, but greater than zero.

C) equal to the battery's terminal voltage.

D) zero.

Answer: D
Diff: 2 *Page Ref: Sec. 19.6*

34) An ideal ammeter should

A) have a high coil resistance.

B) introduce a very small series resistance into the circuit whose current is to be measured.

C) introduce a very large series resistance into the circuit whose current is to be measured.

D) consist of a galvanometer in series with a large resistor.

Answer: B
Diff: 1 *Page Ref: Sec. 19.8*

35) A galvanometer can be converted to an ammeter by the addition of a

A) small resistance in parallel.

B) large resistance in parallel.

C) small resistance in series.

D) large resistance in series.

Answer: A
Diff: 1 *Page Ref: Sec. 19.8*

36) A current reading is obtained by properly placing an ammeter in a circuit consisting of one resistor and one battery. As a result,

A) the voltage drop across the resistor increases.

B) the current flowing in the circuit increases.

C) the current flowing in the circuit decreases.

D) the current flowing in the circuit does not change.

Answer: C
Diff: 2 *Page Ref: Sec. 19.8*

37) Decreasing the resistance of an ammeter's shunt resistance

A) allows it to measure a larger current at full scale deflection.

B) allows it to measure a smaller current at full scale deflection.

C) enables more current to pass directly through the galvanometer.

D) converts it to a voltmeter.

Answer: A
Diff: 2 *Page Ref: Sec. 19.8*

38) In order to construct a voltmeter from a galvanometer, one normally would

A) use a very small shunt resistor.

B) use a very large shunt resistor.

C) use a very small series resistor.

D) use a very large series resistor.

Answer: D
Diff: 1 *Page Ref: Sec. 19.8*

39) Increasing the resistance of a voltmeter's series resistance

A) allows it to measure a larger voltage at full-scale deflection.

B) allows it to measure a smaller voltage at full-scale deflection.

C) enables more current to pass through the meter movement at full-scale deflection.

D) converts it to an ammeter.

Answer: A
Diff: 2 *Page Ref: Sec. 19.8*

40) A voltage reading is obtained by placing a voltmeter across a resistor. What happens to the total current flowing in the circuit as a result of this action?

A) The current increases.

B) The current decreases.

C) The current does not change.

D) The current increases if the meter's internal resistance is less than the original resistance in the circuit and decreases if its internal resistance is greater than the circuit's original resistance.

Answer: A
Diff: 2 *Page Ref: Sec. 19.8*

41) An unknown resistor is wired in series with an ammeter, and a voltmeter is placed in parallel across both the resistor and the ammeter. This network is then placed across a battery. If one computes the value of the resistance by dividing the voltmeter reading by the ammeter reading, the value obtained

A) is less than the true resistance.

B) is greater than the true resistance.

C) is the true resistance.

D) could be any of the given answers. It depends on other factors.

Answer: B
Diff: 3 *Page Ref: Sec. 19.8*

42) An unknown resistor is wired in series with an ammeter, and a voltmeter is placed in parallel across the resistor only. This network is then connected to a battery. If one computes the value of the resistance by dividing the voltmeter reading by the ammeter reading, the value obtained

A) is less than the true resistance.

B) is greater than the true resistance.

C) is the true resistance.

D) could be any of the given answers. It depends on other factors.

Answer: A
Diff: 3 *Page Ref: Sec. 19.8*

Quantitative Problems

1) Four 20-Ω resistors are connected in series. What is the equivalent resistance?

A) 80 Ω

B) 20 Ω

C) 10 Ω

D) 5.0 Ω

Answer: A
Diff: 1 *Page Ref: Sec. 19.2*

2) Four resistors of 12, 3.0, 5.0, and 4.0 Ω are connected in series. A 12-V battery is connected to the combination. What is the current through the battery?

A) 0.50 A

B) 1.0 A

C) 1.5 A

D) 2.0 A

Answer: A
Diff: 2 *Page Ref: Sec. 19.2*

3) Three resistors of 12, 12, and 6.0 Ω are connected in series. A 12-V battery is connected to the combination. What is the current through the battery?

A) 0.10 A

B) 0.20 A

C) 0.30 A

D) 0.40 A

Answer: D
Diff: 2 *Page Ref: Sec. 19.2*

4) Three resistors of 12, 12, and 6.0 Ω are connected in parallel. A 12-V battery is connected to the combination. What is the current through the 6.0-Ω resistor?

A) 1.0 A

B) 2.0 A

C) 3.0 A

D) 4.0 A

Answer: B
Diff: 2 *Page Ref: Sec. 19.2*

5) A 14-A current flows into a series combination of a 3.0-Ω and a 4.0-Ω resistor. What is the voltage drop across the 4.0-Ω resistor?

A) 38 V

B) 42 V

C) 56 V

D) 98 V

Answer: C
Diff: 2 *Page Ref: Sec. 19.2*

6) A 14-A current flows into a series combination of a 3.0-Ω and a 4.0-Ω resistor. What is the voltage drop across the 3.0-Ω resistor?

A) 42 V

B) 56 V

C) 98 V

D) 38 V

Answer: A
Diff: 2 *Page Ref: Sec. 19.2*

7) A 22-A current flows into a parallel combination of 4.0 Ω, 6.0 Ω, and 12 Ω resistors. What current flows through the 12-Ω resistor?

A) 18 A

B) 11 A

C) 7.3 A

D) 3.7 A

Answer: D
Diff: 2 *Page Ref: Sec. 19.2*

8) A 22-A current flows into a parallel combination of a 4.0-Ω, 6.0-Ω, and 12-Ω resistors. What current flows through the 6.0-Ω resistor?

A) 18 A

B) 11 A

C) 7.3 A

D) 3.7 A

Answer: C
Diff: 2 *Page Ref: Sec. 19.2*

9) A 22-A current flows into a parallel combination of a 4.0-Ω, 6.0-Ω, and 12-Ω resistor. What current flows through the 4.0-Ω resistor?

A) 18 A

B) 11 A

C) 7.3 A

D) 3.7 A

Answer: B
Diff: 2 *Page Ref: Sec. 19.2*

10) A 6.0-Ω and a 12-Ω resistor are connected in parallel to a 36-V battery. What power is dissipated by the 6.0-Ω resistor?

A) 220 W

B) 48 W

C) 490 W

D) 24 W

Answer: A
Diff: 2 *Page Ref: Sec. 19.2*

11) The following three appliances are connected to a 120-V circuit: 1200-W toaster, 650-W coffee pot, and 600-W microwave. If all were operated at the same time what total current would they draw?

A) 4.0 A

B) 5.0 A

C) 10 A

D) 20 A

Answer: D
Diff: 2 *Page Ref: Sec. 19.2*

12) What is the maximum number of 100-W light bulbs you can connect in parallel in a 120-V circuit without tripping a 20-A circuit breaker?

A) 11

B) 17

C) 24

D) 27

Answer: C
Diff: 2 *Page Ref: Sec. 19.2*

13) A combination of 2.0 Ω in series with 4.0 Ω is connected in parallel with 3.0 Ω. What is the equivalent resistance?

A) 2.0 Ω

B) 3.0 Ω

C) 4.0 Ω

D) 9.0 Ω

Answer: A
Diff: 2 *Page Ref: Sec. 19.2*

14) Two 4.0-Ω resistors are connected in parallel, and this combination is connected in series with 3.0 Ω. What is the effective resistance of this combination?

A) 1.2 Ω

B) 5.0 Ω

C) 7.0 Ω

D) 11 Ω

Answer: B
Diff: 2 *Page Ref: Sec. 19.2*

15) A 2.0-Ω resistor is in series with a parallel combination of 4.0 Ω, 6.0 Ω, and 12 Ω. What is the equivalent resistance of this combination?

A) 24 Ω

B) 4.0 Ω

C) 1.8 Ω

D) 2.7 Ω

Answer: B
Diff: 1 *Page Ref: Sec. 19.2*

16) Two resistors of 15 and 30 Ω are connected in parallel. If the combination is connected in series with a 9.0-V battery and a 20-Ω resistor, what is the current through the 15-Ω resistor?

A) 0.10 A

B) 0.13 A

C) 0.20 A

D) 0.26 A

Answer: C
Diff: 2 *Page Ref: Sec. 19.2*

17) Three resistors of 4.0, 6.0, and 10.0 Ω are connected in parallel. If the combination is connected in series with a 12.0-V battery and a 2.0-Ω resistor, what is the current through the 10.0-Ω resistor?

A) 0.59 A

B) 2.7 A

C) 11.2 A

D) 16.0 A

Answer: A
Diff: 2 *Page Ref: Sec. 19.2*

18) Two resistors of 5.0 and 9.0 Ω are connected in parallel. A 4.0-Ω resistor is then connected in series with the parallel combination. A 6.0-V battery is then connected to the series-parallel combination. What is the current through the 4.0-Ω resistor?

A) zero

B) 0.53 A

C) 0.83 A

D) 0.30 A

Answer: C
Diff: 2 *Page Ref: Sec. 19.2*

19) Two resistors of 5.0 and 9.0 Ω are connected in parallel. A 4.0-Ω resistor is then connected in series with the parallel combination. A 6.0-V battery is then connected to the series-parallel combination. What is the current through the 5.0-Ω resistor?

A) zero

B) 0.53 A

C) 0.83 A

D) 0.30 A

Answer: B
Diff: 2 *Page Ref: Sec. 19.2*

20) Two resistors of 5.0 and 9.0 Ω are connected in parallel. A 4.0-Ω resistor is then connected in series with the parallel combination. A 6.0-V battery is then connected to the series-parallel combination. What is the current through the 9.0-Ω resistor?

A) zero

B) 0.53 A

C) 0.83 A

D) 0.30 A

Answer: D
Diff: 2 *Page Ref: Sec. 19.2*

21) A 3.0-Ω resistor is connected in parallel with a 6.0-Ω resistor. This combination is connected in series with a 4.0-Ω resistor. The resistors are connected to a 12-volt battery. How much power is dissipated in the 3.0-Ω resistor?

A) 2.7 W

B) 5.3 W

C) 6.0 W

D) 12 W

Answer: B
Diff: 3 *Page Ref: Sec. 19.2*

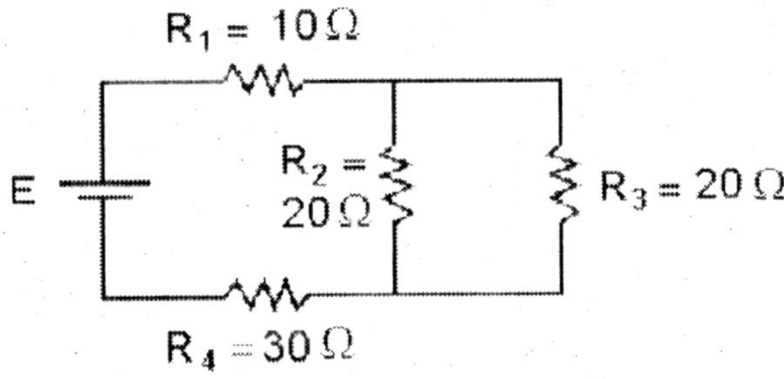

FIGURE 19-2

22) What is the total resistance of the circuit in Fig. 19-2?

A) 80 Ω

B) 55 Ω

C) 50 Ω

D) 35 Ω

Answer: C
Diff: 2 *Page Ref: Sec. 19.2*

23) If E = 40 V, what is the voltage on R_1 in Fig. 19-2?

A) 6.7 V

B) 8.0 V

C) 10 V

D) 20 V

Answer: B
Diff: 2 *Page Ref: Sec. 19.2*

24) If E = 20 V, what is the current through R_3 in Fig. 19-2?

A) 0.050 A

B) 0.20 A

C) 1.0 A

D) 4.0 A

Answer: B
Diff: 2 *Page Ref: Sec. 19.2*

25) If 1.5 A flows through R_2, what is E in Fig. 19-2?

A) 150 V

B) 75 V

C) 60 V

D) 30 V

Answer: A
Diff: 3 *Page Ref: Sec. 19.2*

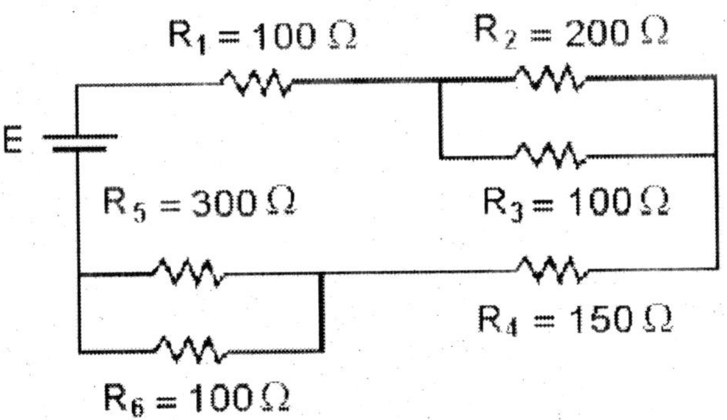

FIGURE 19–3

26) What is the total resistance of the circuit in Fig. 19–3?

A) 950 Ω

B) 450 Ω

C) 392 Ω

D) 257 Ω

Answer: C

Diff: 2 *Page Ref: Sec. 19.2*

27) If E = 100 V, what is the voltage across R_5 in Fig. 19–3?

A) 19 V

B) 40 V

C) 75 V

D) 77 V

Answer: A

Diff: 3 *Page Ref: Sec. 19.2*

28) If E = 4.0 V, what is the current through R_6 in Fig. 19–3?

A) 0.0077 A

B) 0.017 A

C) 0.040 A

D) 4.0 A

Answer: A

Diff: 3 *Page Ref: Sec. 19.2*

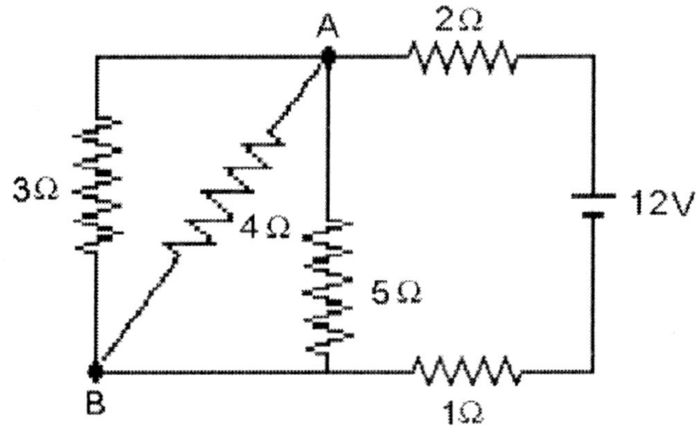

FIGURE 19-4

29) For the circuit in Fig. 19-4, determine the current in the 1-Ω resistor.

A) 0.90 A

B) 1.2 A

C) 2.8 A

D) 3.2 A

Answer: C

Diff: 3 *Page Ref: Sec. 19.2*

30) For the circuit in Fig. 19-4, determine the current in the 3-Ω resistor.

A) 0.90 A

B) 1.2 A

C) 2.8 A

D) 3.2 A

Answer: B

Diff: 3 *Page Ref: Sec 19.2*

31) For the circuit in Fig. 19-4, determine the current in the 4-Ω resistor.

A) 0.90 A

B) 1.2 A

C) 2.8 A

D) 3.2 A

Answer: A

Diff: 3 *Page Ref: Sec. 19.2*

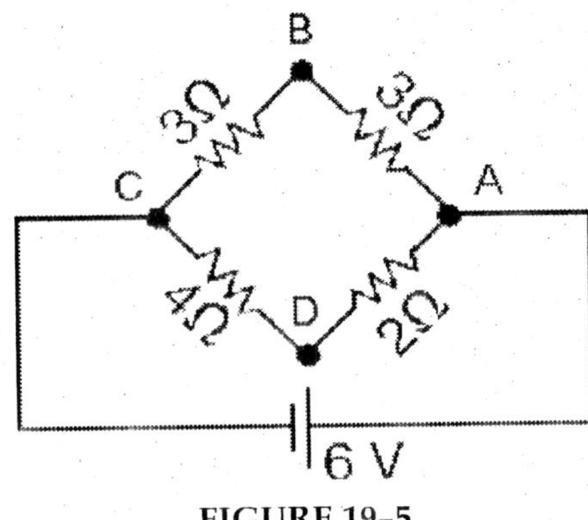

FIGURE 19-5

32) What is the potential of point A relative to point C in Fig. 19-5?

A) +6.0 V

B) +4.0 V

C) +3.0 V

D) +2.0 V

Answer: A

Diff: 1 *Page Ref: Sec. 19.2*

33) What is the potential of point B relative to point C in Fig. 19-5?

A) +6.0 V

B) +4.0 V

C) +3.0 V

D) +2.0 V

Answer: C

Diff: 2 *Page Ref: Sec. 19.2*

34) What is the potential of point D relative to point C in Fig. 19-5?

A) +6.0 V

B) +4.0 V

C) +3.0 V

D) +2.0 V

Answer: B

Diff: 2 *Page Ref: Sec. 19.2*

35) What current flows from the battery in Fig. 19-5?

A) 0.35 A

B) 2.0 A

C) 2.5 A

D) 3.0 A

Answer: B
Diff: 3 *Page Ref: Sec. 19.2*

36) What is the potential drop from point A to point B in Fig. 19-5?

A) 0.35 V

B) 2.0 V

C) 2.5 V

D) 3.0 V

Answer: D
Diff: 3 *Page Ref: Sec. 19.2*

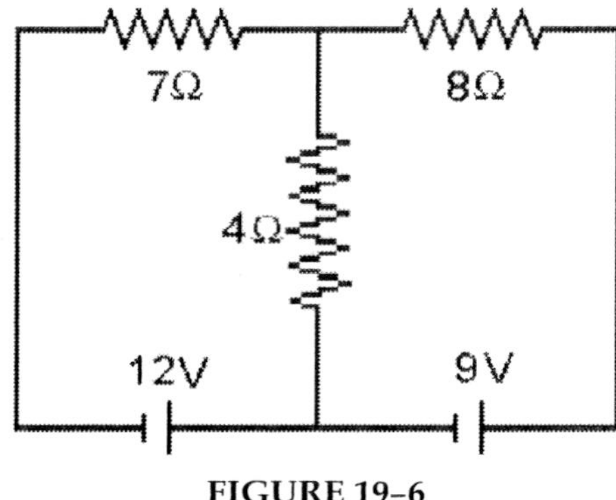

FIGURE 19-6

37) Determine the current in the 7-Ω resistor in Fig. 19-6.

A) 0.28 A

B) 1.3 A

C) 1.6 A

D) 2.1 A

Answer: C
Diff: 2 *Page Ref: Sec. 19.3*

38) Determine the current in the 8-Ω resistor in Fig. 19-6.

A) 0.28 A

B) 1.3 A

C) 1.6 A

D) 2.1 A

Answer: B
Diff: 2 *Page Ref: Sec. 19.3*

39) Determine the current in the 4-Ω resistor in Fig. 19-6.

A) 0.28 A

B) 1.3 A

C) 1.6 A

D) 2.1 A

Answer: A
Diff: 2 *Page Ref: Sec. 19.3*

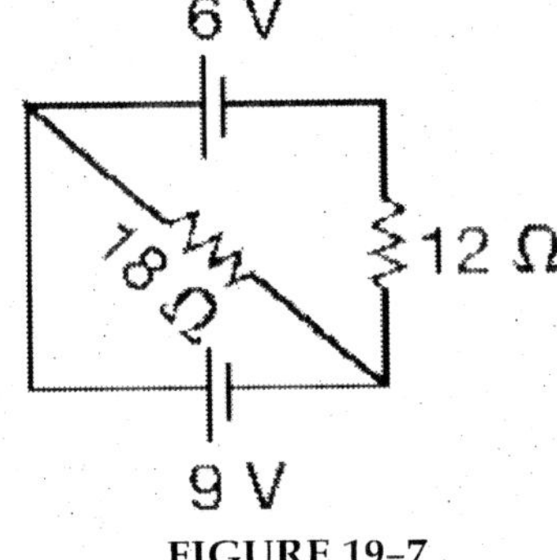

FIGURE 19-7

40) What current flows in the 12-Ω resistor in Fig. 19-7?

A) 0.25 A

B) 0.50 A

C) 0.75 A

D) 1.0 A

Answer: A
Diff: 3 *Page Ref: Sec. 19.3*

41) What current flows in the 18-Ω resistor in Fig. 19-7?

A) 0.25 A

B) 0.50 A

C) 0.75 A

D) 1.0 A

Answer: B
Diff: 3 *Page Ref: Sec. 19.3*

42) What current flows in the solid wire connecting the upper left and lower left corners?

A) 0.25 A

B) 0.50 A

C) 0.75 A

D) 1.0 A

Answer: C
Diff: 3 *Page Ref: Sec. 19.3*

43) Four 16 μF capacitors are connected in series. The equivalent capacitance of this combination is

A) 64 μF.

B) 16 μF.

C) 8.0 μF.

D) 4.0 μF.

Answer: D
Diff: 1 *Page Ref: Sec. 19.5*

44) 5.00 μF, 10.0 μF, and 50.0 μF capacitors are connected in series across a 12.0-V battery. How much charge is stored in the 5.00-μF capacitor?

A) 12.5 μC

B) 25.0 μC

C) 37.5 μC

D) 50.0 μC

Answer: C
Diff: 2 *Page Ref: Sec. 19.5*

45) 5.00 μF, 10.0 μF, and 50.0 μF capacitors are connected in series across a 12.0-V battery. What is the potential difference across the 10.0-μF capacitor?

A) 1.25 V

B) 2.50 V

C) 3.75 V

D) 5.00 V

Answer: C
Diff: 2 *Page Ref: Sec. 19.5*

46) A 1.0-μF and a 2.0-μF capacitor are connected in series across a 3.0-V battery. What is the voltage across the 1.0-μF capacitor?

A) 3.0 V

B) 2.0 V

C) 1.0 V

D) zero

Answer: B
Diff: 2 *Page Ref: Sec. 19.5*

47) A 1.0-μF and a 2.0-μF capacitor are connected in series across a 3.0-V battery. What is the voltage across the 2.0-μF capacitor?

A) 3.0 V

B) 2.0 V

C) 1.0 V

D) zero

Answer: C
Diff: 2 *Page Ref: Sec. 19.5*

48) 1.0 μF, 2.0 μF, and 3.0 μF capacitors are connected in parallel across a 24-V battery. How much energy is stored in this combination when the capacitors are fully charged?

A) 1.7 mJ

B) 2.1 mJ

C) 4.8 mJ

D) 7.1 mJ

Answer: A
Diff: 2 *Page Ref: Sec. 19.5*

49) Capacitances of 10 μF and 20 μF are connected in parallel, and this pair is then connected in series with a 30-μF capacitor. What is the equivalent capacitance of this arrangement?

A) 10 μF

B) 15 μF

C) 25 μF

D) 60 μF

Answer: B
Diff: 2 *Page Ref: Sec. 19.5*

50) Two capacitors of 6.00 μF and 8.00 μF are connected in parallel. The combination is then connected in series with a 12.0-V battery and a 14.0-μF capacitor. What is the equivalent capacitance?

A) 6.00 μF

B) 7.00 μF

C) 8.00 μF

D) 14.0 μF

Answer: B

Diff: 2 *Page Ref: Sec. 19.5*

51) Two capacitors of 6.00 μF and 8.00 μF are connected in parallel. The combination is then connected in series with a 12.0-V battery and a 14.0-μF capacitor. What is the charge on the 6.00-μF capacitor?

A) 12.0 μC

B) 36.0 μC

C) 48.0 μC

D) 84.0 μC

Answer: B

Diff: 2 *Page Ref: Sec. 19.5*

52) Two capacitors of 6.00 μF and 8.00 μF are connected in parallel. The combination is then connected in series with a 12.0-V battery and a 14.0-μF capacitor. What is the voltage across the 6.00-μF capacitor?

A) 4.00 V

B) 5.00 V

C) 6.00 V

D) 12.0 V

Answer: C

Diff: 2 *Page Ref: Sec. 19.5*

53) A 2.0-μF capacitor is charged through a 50-kΩ resistor. How long does it take for the capacitor to reach 90% of full charge?

A) 0.90 s

B) 0.23 s

C) 2.2 s

D) 2.3 s

Answer: B

Diff: 2 *Page Ref: Sec. 19.6*

54) A 2.0-μF capacitor is charged to 12 V and then discharged through a $4.0 \times 10^6\ \Omega$ resistor. How long will it take for the voltage across the capacitor to drop to 3.0 V?

A) 8.0 s

B) 11 s

C) 22 s

D) 24 s

Answer: B
Diff: 2 *Page Ref: Sec. 19.6*

55) A 4.0-MΩ resistor is connected in series with a 0.50-μF capacitor. The capacitor is initially uncharged. The RC combination is charged by a 9.0-V battery. What is the change in voltage between t = RC and t = 3RC?

A) 11 V

B) 7.6 V

C) 5.7 V

D) 2.9 V

Answer: D
Diff: 2 *Page Ref: Sec. 19.6*

56) A 4.0-μF capacitor is charged to 6.0-V. It is then connected in series with a 3.0-MΩ resistor and connected to a 12-V battery. How long after being connected to the battery will the voltage across the capacitor be 9.0 V?

A) 5.5 s

B) 8.3 s

C) 12 s

D) 17 s

Answer: B
Diff: 3 *Page Ref: Sec. 19.6*

57) A galvanometer has an internal resistance of 100 Ω and deflects full-scale at 2.00 mA. What size resistor should be added to it to convert it to a milliammeter capable of reading up to 4.00 mA?

A) 50.0 Ω in series

B) 50.0 Ω in parallel

C) 100 Ω in series

D) 100 Ω in parallel

Answer: D
Diff: 2 *Page Ref: Sec. 19.8*

58) A galvanometer has a coil with a resistance of 24.0 Ω. A current of 180 μA causes full-scale deflection. If the galvanometer is to be used to construct an ammeter that deflects full scale for 10.0 A, what shunt resistor is required?

A) 234 μΩ

B) 342 μΩ

C) 432 μΩ

D) 423 μΩ

Answer: C
Diff: 2 *Page Ref: Sec. 19.8*

59) A galvanometer has an internal resistance of 100 Ω and deflects full-scale at 2.00 mA. What size resistor should be added to it to convert it to a millivoltmeter capable of reading up to 400 mV?

A) 50.0 Ω in series

B) 50.0 Ω in parallel

C) 100 Ω in series

D) 100 Ω in parallel

Answer: C
Diff: 2 *Page Ref: Sec. 19.8*

60) A galvanometer with a coil resistance of 40.0 Ω deflects full scale for a current of 2.0 mA. What series resistance should be used with this galvanometer in order to construct a voltmeter that deflects full scale for 50 V?

A) 25 kΩ

B) 27 kΩ

C) 29 kΩ

D) 31 kΩ

Answer: A
Diff: 2 *Page Ref: Sec. 19.8*

Chapter 20 Magnetism

Conceptual Questions

1) If the north poles of two bar magnets are brought close to each other, the magnets will

A) attract.

B) repel.

Answer: B
Diff: 1 *Page Ref: Sec. 20.1*

2) If the south pole of one bar magnet is brought near the north pole of a second bar magnet, the two magnets will

A) attract.

B) repel.

Answer: A
Diff: 1 *Page Ref: Sec. 20.1*

3) If a bar magnet is divided into two equal pieces,

A) the north and south poles are separated.

B) two magnets result.

C) the magnet properties are destroyed.

D) an electric field is created.

Answer: B
Diff: 1 *Page Ref: Sec. 20.1*

4) The Earth's geographic North Pole is magnetically a

A) north pole.

B) south pole.

Answer: B
Diff: 1 *Page Ref: Sec. 20.1*

5) The south pole of a magnet points toward the Earth's

A) South Pole.

B) North Pole.

C) center.

D) middle latitudes.

Answer: A
Diff: 1 *Page Ref: Sec. 20.1*

6) An electric current produces
   A) a gravitational field.
   B) an electric field.
   C) a magnetic field.
   D) an electromagnetic field.

Answer: C
Diff: 1 *Page Ref: Sec. 20.2*

7) Which of the following is correct?
   A) When a current carrying wire is in your right hand, thumb in the direction of the magnetic field lines, your fingers point in the direction of the current.
   B) When a current carrying wire is in your left hand, thumb in the direction of the magnetic field lines, your fingers point in the direction of the current.
   C) When a current carrying wire is in your right hand, thumb in the direction of the current, your fingers point in the direction of the magnetic field lines.
   D) When a current carrying wire is in your left hand, thumb in the direction of the current, your fingers point in the direction of the magnetic field lines.

Answer: C
Diff: 1 *Page Ref: Sec. 20.2*

8) A vertical wire carries a current straight down. To the east of this wire, the magnetic field points
   A) north.
   B) east.
   C) south.
   D) down.

Answer: C
Diff: 1 *Page Ref: Sec. 20.2*

9) A horizontal wire carries a current straight toward you. From your point of view, the magnetic field caused by this current
   A) points directly away from you.
   B) points to the left.
   C) circles the wire in a clockwise direction.
   D) circles the wire in a counter-clockwise direction.

Answer: D
Diff: 1 *Page Ref: Sec. 20.2*

10) A current carrying loop of wire lies flat on a table top. When viewed from above, the current moves around the loop in a counterclockwise sense. What is the direction of the magnetic field caused by this current, outside the loop? The magnetic field

A) circles the loop in a clockwise direction.

B) circles the loop in a counterclockwise direction.

C) points straight up.

D) points straight down.

Answer: D
Diff: 1 *Page Ref: Sec. 20.2*

11) A current carrying circular loop of wire lies flat on a table top. When viewed from above, the current moves around the loop in a counterclockwise sense. What is the direction of the magnetic field caused by this current, inside the loop? The magnetic field

A) circles the loop in a clockwise direction.

B) circles the loop in a counterclockwise direction.

C) points straight up.

D) points straight down.

Answer: C
Diff: 1 *Page Ref: Sec. 20.2*

12) The SI unit of magnetic field is the

A) weber.

B) gauss.

C) tesla.

D) lorentz.

Answer: C
Diff: 1 *Page Ref: Sec. 20.3*

13) 1 T is equivalent to

A) 1 N•m / A.

B) 1 N•A / m.

C) V•m / A.

D) N / A•m.

Answer: D
Diff: 1 *Page Ref: Sec. 20.3*

14) The direction of the force on a current–carrying wire in a magnetic field is described by which of the following?

A) perpendicular to the current only

B) perpendicular to the magnetic field only

C) perpendicular to both the current and the magnetic field

D) perpendicular to neither the current or the magnetic field

Answer: C
Diff: 1 *Page Ref: Sec. 20.3*

15) The force on a current–carrying wire in a magnetic field is the strongest when

A) the current is parallel to the field lines.

B) the current is at a 30° angle with respect to the field lines.

C) the current is at a 60° angle with respect to the field lines.

D) the current is perpendicular to the field lines.

Answer: D
Diff: 1 *Page Ref: Sec. 20.3*

16) The force on a current–carrying wire in a magnetic field is equal to zero when

A) the current is parallel to the field lines.

B) the current is at a 30° angle with respect to the field lines.

C) the current is at a 60° angle with respect to the field lines.

D) the current is perpendicular to the field lines.

Answer: A
Diff: 1 *Page Ref: Sec. 20.3*

17) A vertical wire carries a current straight up in a region where the magnetic field vector points due north. What is the direction of the resulting force on this current?

A) down

B) north

C) east

D) west

Answer: D
Diff: 1 *Page Ref: Sec. 20.3*

18) A charged particle moves and experiences no magnetic force. From this we can conclude that

A) no magnetic field exists in that region of space.

B) the particle is moving parallel to the magnetic field.

C) the particle is moving at right angles to the magnetic field.

D) either no magnetic field exists or the particle is moving parallel to the field.

Answer: D
Diff: 2 *Page Ref: Sec. 20.4*

19) A charged particle moves with a constant speed through a region where a uniform magnetic field is present. If the magnetic field points straight upward, the magnetic force acting on this particle will be maximum when the particle moves

A) straight upward.

B) straight downward.

C) in a plane parallel to the Earth's surface.

D) upward at an angle of 45° above the horizontal.

Answer: C
Diff: 2 *Page Ref: Sec. 20.4*

20) A charged particle moves across a constant magnetic field. The magnetic force on this particle

A) changes the particle's speed.

B) causes the particle to accelerate.

C) is in the direction of the particle's motion.

D) changes the particle's speed causing the particle to accelerate.

Answer: B
Diff: 2 *Page Ref: Sec. 20.4*

21) A charged particle is injected into a uniform magnetic field such that its velocity vector is perpendicular to the magnetic field vector. Ignoring the particle's weight, the particle will

A) move in a straight line.

B) follow a spiral path.

C) move along a parabolic path.

D) follow a circular path.

Answer: D
Diff: 1 *Page Ref: Sec. 20.4*

22) A charged particle is observed traveling in a circular path in a uniform magnetic field. If the particle had been traveling twice as fast, the radius of the circular path would be

A) twice the original radius.

B) four times the original radius.

C) one-half the original radius.

D) one-fourth the original radius.

Answer: A
Diff: 1 *Page Ref: Sec. 20.4*

23) A particle carrying a charge of +e travels in a circular path in a uniform magnetic field. If instead the particle carried a charge of +2e, the radius of the circular path would have been

A) twice the original radius.

B) four times the original radius.

C) one-half the original radius.

D) one-fourth the original radius.

Answer: C
Diff: 1 *Page Ref: Sec. 20.4*

24) At a particular instant, an electron moves eastward at speed V in a uniform magnetic field that is directed straight downward. The magnetic force that acts on it is

A) zero.

B) directed upward.

C) directed to the south.

D) directed to the north.

Answer: C
Diff: 2 *Page Ref: Sec. 20.4*

25) An electron has an initial velocity to the south but is observed to curve upward as the result of a magnetic field. The direction of the magnetic field is

A) to the west.

B) to the east.

C) upward.

D) downward.

Answer: A
Diff: 2 *Page Ref: Sec. 20.4*

26) An electron moving along the +x axis enters a region where there is a uniform magnetic field in the +y direction. What is the direction of the magnetic force on the electron? (+x to right, +y up, and +z out of the page.)

A) +z direction

B) -z direction

C) -y direction

D) -x direction

Answer: B
Diff: 2 *Page Ref: Sec. 20.4*

27) The magnetic field produced by a long straight current–carrying wire is

A) proportional to both the current in the wire and the distance from the wire

B) proportional to the current in the wire and inversely proportional to the distance from the wire.

C) inversely proportional to the current in the wire and proportional to the distance from the wire.

D) inversely proportional to both the current in the wire and the distance from the wire.

Answer: B
Diff: 2 *Page Ref: Sec. 20.5*

28) At double the distance from a long current–carrying wire, the strength of the magnetic field produced by that wire decreases to

A) 1/8 of its original value.

B) 1/4 of its original value.

C) 1/2 of its original value.

D) none of the given answers

Answer: C
Diff: 1 *Page Ref: Sec. 20.5*

29) Two long parallel wires placed side–by–side on a horizontal table carry identical size currents in opposite directions. The wire on your right carries current toward you, and the wire on your left carries current away from you. From your point of view, the magnetic field at the point exactly midway between the two wires

A) points up.

B) points down.

C) points toward you.

D) is zero.

Answer: B
Diff: 2 *Page Ref: Sec. 20.5*

30) Two long parallel wires placed side–by–side on a horizontal table carry identical current straight toward you. From your point of view, the magnetic field at the point exactly between the two wires

A) points up.

B) points down.

C) points toward you.

D) is zero.

Answer: D
Diff: 2 *Page Ref: Sec. 20.5*

31) Two long parallel wires carry equal currents. The magnitude of the force between the wires is F. The current in each wire is now doubled. What is the magnitude of the new force between the two wires?

A) 4F

B) 2F

C) F/4

D) F/2

Answer: A
Diff: 2 *Page Ref: Sec. 20.6*

32) A long straight wire carries current toward the east. A proton moves toward the east alongside and just south of the wire. What is the direction of the force on the proton?

A) north

B) south

C) up

D) down

Answer: A
Diff: 2 *Page Ref: Sec. 20.6*

33) A wire lying in the plane of the page carries a current toward the bottom of the page. What is the direction of the magnetic force it produces on an electron that is moving perpendicularly toward the wire, also in the plane of the page, from your right?

A) zero

B) perpendicular to the page and towards you

C) perpendicular to the page and away from you

D) toward the top of the page

E) toward the bottom of the page

Answer: E
Diff: 2 *Page Ref: Sec. 20.6*

34) Two long parallel wires are placed side-by-side on a horizontal table. If the wires carry current in the same direction,

A) one wire is lifted slightly as the other wire is forced against the table's surface.

B) both wires are lifted slightly.

C) the wires attract each other.

D) the wires repel each other.

Answer: C
Diff: 1 *Page Ref: Sec. 20.6*

35) Two long parallel wires are placed side-by-side on a horizontal table. If the wires carry current in opposite directions,

A) one wire is lifted slightly as the other is forced against the table's surface.

B) both wires are lifted slightly.

C) the wires attract each other.

D) the wires repel each other.

Answer: D
Diff: 1 *Page Ref: Sec. 20.6*

36) Consider two current-carrying circular loops. Both are made from one strand of wire and both carry the same current, but one has twice the radius of the other. Compared to the magnetic field at the center of the smaller loop, the magnetic field at the center of the larger loop is

A) 8 times stronger.

B) 4 times stronger.

C) 2 times stronger.

D) none of the given answers

Answer: D
Diff: 2 *Page Ref: Sec. 20.7*

37) Consider two current-carrying circular loops. Both are made from one strand of wire and both carry the same current, but one has twice the radius of the other. Compared to the magnetic moment of the smaller loop, the magnetic moment of the larger loop is

A) 16 times stronger.

B) 8 times stronger.

C) 4 times stronger.

D) 2 times stronger.

Answer: C
Diff: 2 *Page Ref: Sec. 20.9-20.10*

38) The maximum torque on a current carrying loop occurs when the angle between the loop's magnetic moment and the magnetic field vector is

A) $0°$

B) $90°$

C) $180°$

D) none of the given answers

Answer: B
Diff: 2 *Page Ref: Sec. 20.9-20.10*

39) When placed askew in a magnetic field, a current carrying loop that is free to rotate in any direction will experience a torque until its magnetic moment vector

A) is at right angles to the magnetic field vector.

B) makes a 45° angle with the magnetic field vector.

C) makes an angle of 270° with the magnetic field vector.

D) is aligned with the magnetic field vector.

Answer: D
Diff: 2 *Page Ref: Sec. 20.9–20.10*

40) What fundamental fact underlies the operation of essentially all electric motors?

A) Opposite electric charges attract and like charges repel.

B) A current–carrying conductor placed perpendicular to a magnetic field will experience a force.

C) Alternating current and direct current are both capable of doing work.

D) Iron is the only element that is magnetic.

E) A magnetic north pole carries a positive electric charge, and a magnetic south pole carries a negative electric charge.

Answer: B
Diff: 1 *Page Ref: Sec. 20.9–20.10*

41) A circular wire loop lies in a horizontal plane on a table and carries current in a counterclockwise direction when viewed from above. At this point, the Earth's magnetic field points to the north and dips below the horizontal. Which side of the coil tends to lift off of the table because of the torque caused by the currents interaction with the magnetic field?

A) the north side

B) the east side

C) the south side

D) the west side

Answer: C
Diff: 2 *Page Ref: Sec. 20.9–20.10*

42) In a mass spectrometer a particle of mass m and charge q is accelerated through a potential difference V and allowed to enter a magnetic field B, where it is deflected in a semi–circular path of radius R. The magnetic field is uniform and oriented perpendicular to the velocity of the particle. Derive an expression for the mass of the particle in terms of B, q, V, and R.

A) qB^2R^2/V

B) $qB^2R^2/(2V)$

C) $q^2B^2R^2/V$

D) $q^2B^2R^2/(2V)$

Answer: B
Diff: 3 *Page Ref: Sec. 20.11*

43) A velocity selector consists of a charged particle passing through crossed electric and magnetic fields. The forces exerted by these fields are in opposite directions, and only particles of a certain velocity will move in a straight line. In the following, disregard the magnitudes of the fields. In a velocity selector, the particles move toward the east, and the magnetic field is directed to the north. What direction should the electric field point?

A) east

B) west

C) up

D) down

Answer: D
Diff: 2 *Page Ref: Sec. 20.11*

Quantitative Problems

1) A 2.0-m wire carrying a current of 0.60 A is oriented parallel to a uniform magnetic field of 0.50 T. What is the magnitude of the force it experiences?

A) zero

B) 0.15 N

C) 0.30 N

D) 0.60 N

Answer: A
Diff: 1 *Page Ref: Sec. 20.3*

2) A wire carries a current of 10 A in a direction of 30° with respect to the direction of a 0.30-T magnetic field. Find the magnitude of the magnetic force on a 0.50-m length of the wire.

A) 0.75 N

B) 1.5 N

C) 3.0 N

D) 6.0 N

Answer: A
Diff: 1 *Page Ref: Sec. 20.3*

3) What is the force per meter on a straight wire carrying 5.0 A when it is placed in a magnetic field of 0.020 T? The wire makes an angle of 27° with respect to the magnetic field lines.

A) 0.022 N/m

B) 0.045 N/m

C) 0.17 N/m

D) 0.26 N/m

Answer: B
Diff: 1 *Page Ref: Sec. 20.3*

4) A thin copper rod 1.0 m long has a mass of 0.050 kg and is in a magnetic field of 0.10 T. What minimum current in the rod is needed in order for the magnetic force to cancel the weight of the rod?

A) 1.2 A

B) 2.5 A

C) 4.9 A

D) 9.8 A

Answer: C
Diff: 2 *Page Ref: Sec. 20.3*

5) A stationary proton is in a uniform magnetic field of 0.20 T. What is the magnitude of the magnetic force on the proton?

A) zero

B) 1.6×10^{-20} N

C) 3.2×10^{-20} N

D) 1.6×10^{-21} N

Answer: A
Diff: 1 *Page Ref: Sec. 20.4*

6) A proton moving at 4.0×10^4 m/s horizontally enters a region where a magnetic field of 0.13 T is present, directed vertically downward. What force acts on the proton?

A) zero

B) 1.4×10^{-16} N

C) 5.2×10^{-16} N

D) 8.3×10^{-16} N

Answer: D
Diff: 1 *Page Ref: Sec. 20.4*

7) An electron moves with a speed of 5.0×10^4 m/s perpendicular to a uniform magnetic field of 0.20 T. What is the magnitude of the magnetic force on the electron?

A) 4.4×10^{-14} N

B) 1.6×10^{-15} N

C) 2.6×10^{-24} N

D) zero

Answer: B
Diff: 1 *Page Ref: Sec. 20.4*

8) A proton travels at a speed of 5.0×10^7 m/s through a 1.0-T magnetic field. What is the magnitude of the magnetic force which acts on the proton if the angle between the proton's velocity and the magnetic field vector is 30°?

A) 2.0×10^{-14} N

B) 4.0×10^{-14} N

C) 2.0×10^{-12} N

D) 4.0×10^{-12} N

Answer: D
Diff: 1 *Page Ref: Sec. 20.4*

9) An electron traveling due north with speed 4.0×10^5 m/s enters a region where the Earth's magnetic field has the magnitude 5.0×10^{-5} T and is directed downward at 45° below horizontal. What force acts on the electron?

A) 2.3×10^{-18} N

B) 3.2×10^{-18} N

C) 2.3×10^{-19} N

D) 3.2×10^{-19} N

Answer: A
Diff: 2 *Page Ref: Sec. 20.4*

10) An electron moves with a speed of 8.0×10^6 m/s along the +x axis. It enters a region where there is a magnetic field of 2.5 T, directed at an angle of 60° to the +x axis and lying in the xy plane. Calculate the magnetic force of the electron.

A) 2.8×10^{-10} N

B) 3.2×10^{-10} N

C) 2.8×10^{-12} N

D) 3.2×10^{-12} N

Answer: C
Diff: 2 *Page Ref: Sec. 20.4*

11) An electron moves with a speed of 8.0×10^6 m/s along the +x axis. It enters a region where there is a magnetic field of 2.5 T, directed at an angle of 60° to the +x axis and lying in the xy plane. Calculate the acceleration of the electron.

A) 1.3×10^{18} m/s2

B) 3.1×10^{18} m/s2

C) 1.3×10^{-18} m/s2

D) 3.1×10^{-18} m/s2

Answer: B
Diff: 2 *Page Ref: Sec. 20.4*

12) A proton has a speed of 3.0×10^6 m/s in a direction perpendicular to a uniform magnetic field, and the proton moves in a circle of radius 0.20 m. What is the magnitude of the magnetic field?

A) 0.080 T

B) 0.16 T

C) 0.24 T

D) 0.32 T

Answer: B
Diff: 2 *Page Ref: Sec. 20.4*

13) What is the strength of a magnetic field 5.0 cm from a long straight wire carrying 4.0 A of current?

A) 3.8×10^{-6} T

B) 4.9×10^{-6} T

C) 1.6×10^{-5} T

D) 4.7×10^{-5} T

Answer: C
Diff: 1 *Page Ref: Sec. 20.5*

14) A very long straight wire carries a current of 25 A. What is the magnitude of the magnetic field at a distance of 0.15 m from the wire?

A) 3.3×10^{-5} T

B) 6.6×10^{-5} T

C) 3.3×10^{-6} T

D) 6.6×10^{-6} T

Answer: A
Diff: 1 *Page Ref: Sec. 20.5*

15) A high power line carrying 1000 A generates what magnetic field at the ground, 10 m away?

A) 4.7×10^{-6} T

B) 6.4×10^{-6} T

C) 2.0×10^{-5} T

D) 5.6×10^{-5} T

Answer: C
Diff: 1 *Page Ref: Sec. 20.5*

16) How much current must flow for 1.0×10^{-3} T of magnetic field to be present 1.0 cm from a wire?

A) 0.050 A

B) 9.2 A

C) 16 A

D) 50 A

Answer: D
Diff: 2 *Page Ref: Sec. 20.5*

17) At what distance from a long straight wire carrying a current of 5.0 A is the magnitude of the magnetic field due to the wire equal to the strength of the Earth's magnetic field of about 5.0×10^{-5} T?

A) 1.0 cm

B) 2.0 cm

C) 3.0 cm

D) 4.0 cm

Answer: B
Diff: 2 *Page Ref: Sec. 20.5*

18) Two long parallel wires carry currents of 10 A in opposite directions. They are separated by 40 cm. What is the magnetic field in the plane of the wires at a point that is 20 cm from one wire and 60 cm from the other?

A) 3.3×10^{-6} T

B) 6.7×10^{-6} T

C) 3.3×10^{-5} T

D) 6.7×10^{-5} T

Answer: B
Diff: 2 *Page Ref: Sec. 20.5*

19) Two long parallel wires carry currents of 20 A and 5.0 A in opposite directions. The wires are separated by 0.20 m. What is the magnetic field midway between the two wires?

A) 1.0×10^{-5} T

B) 3.0×10^{-5} T

C) 4.0×10^{-5} T

D) 5.0×10^{-5} T

Answer: D
Diff: 2 *Page Ref: Sec. 20.5*

20) Two long parallel wires carry currents of 20 A and 5.0 A in opposite directions. The wires are separated by 0.20 m. At what point between the two wires are the contributions from the two wires the same?

A) 0.040 m from the 20 A wire

B) 0.080 m from the 20 A wire

C) 0.12 m from the 20 A wire

D) 0.16 m from the 20 A wire

Answer: D
Diff: 2 *Page Ref: Sec. 20.5*

21) Four long parallel wires each carry 2.0 A in the same direction. They are parallel to the z-axis, and they pass through the corners of a square of side 4.0 cm positioned in the x-y plane. What magnetic field does one of the wires experience due to the other wires?

A) 1.2×10^{-6} T

B) 2.1×10^{-6} T

C) 1.2×10^{-5} T

D) 2.1×10^{-5} T

Answer: D
Diff: 3 *Page Ref: Sec. 20.5*

22) Two long parallel wires carry currents of 5.0 A and 8.0 A in the opposite direction. The wires are separated by 0.30 m. Find the magnetic force per unit length between the two wires.

A) 2.7×10^{-5} N repulsive

B) 7.2×10^{-5} N repulsive

C) 2.7×10^{-5} N attractive

D) 7.2×10^{-5} N attractive

Answer: A
Diff: 2 *Page Ref: Sec. 20.6*

23) What is the magnetic field at the center of a circular loop of wire of radius 4.0 cm when a current of 2.0 A flows in the wire?

A) 1.3×10^{-6} T

B) 3.1×10^{-6} T

C) 1.3×10^{-5} T

D) 3.1×10^{-5} T

Answer: D
Diff: 2 *Page Ref: Sec. 20.7*

24) A solenoid 20 cm long is wound with 5000 turns of wire. What magnetic field is produced at the center of the solenoid when a current of 10 A flows?

A) 0.0063 T

B) 0.20 T

C) 3.2 T

D) 4.8 T

Answer: A
Diff: 2 *Page Ref: Sec. 20.7*

25) A solenoid with 500 turns is 0.10 m long and carries a current of 4.0 A. What strength of magnetic field will it have at its center?

A) 3.1 mT

B) 6.2 mT

C) 13 mT

D) 25 mT

Answer: D
Diff: 2 *Page Ref: Sec. 20.7*

26) How much current must pass through a 400 turn coil 4.0 cm long to generate a 1.0-T magnetic field at the center?

A) 0.013 A

B) 13 A

C) 40 A

D) 80 A

Answer: D
Diff: 2 *Page Ref: Sec. 20.7*

27) How many turns should a 10-cm long solenoid have if it is to generate a 1.5×10^{-3} T magnetic field on 1.0 A of current?

A) 12

B) 15

C) 119

D) 1194

Answer: C
Diff: 2 *Page Ref: Sec. 20.7*

28) What is the magnetic moment of a rectangular loop of 120 turns that carries 6.0 A if its dimensions are 4.0 cm × 8.0 cm?

A) 0.23 A•m2

B) 2.3 A•m2

C) 23 A•m2

D) 230 A•m2

Answer: B
Diff: 1 *Page Ref: Sec. 20.9–20.10*

29) A circular loop of wire of radius 0.50 m is in a uniform magnetic field of 0.30 T. The current in the loop is 2.0 A. What is the magnetic torque when the plane of the loop is perpendicular to the magnetic field?

A) zero

B) 0.41 m•N

C) 0.47 m•N

D) 0.52 m•N

Answer: A
Diff: 2 *Page Ref: Sec. 20.9–20.10*

30) A circular loop of wire of cross-sectional area 0.12 m2 consists of 200 turns, each carrying 0.50 A. It is placed in a magnetic field of 0.050 T oriented at 30° to the plane of the loop. What torque acts on the loop?

A) 0.25 m•N

B) 0.52 m•N

C) 2.5 m•N

D) 5.2 m•N

Answer: B
Diff: 2 *Page Ref: 20.9–20.10*

31) A circular loop carrying a current of 2.0 A is in a magnetic field of 3.5 T. The loop has an area of 0.12 m2 and its plane is oriented at a 37° angle to the field. What is the magnitude of the magnetic torque on the loop?

A) 0.10 m•N

B) 0.51 m•N

C) 0.67 m•N

D) 46 m•N

Answer: C
Diff: 2 *Page Ref: Sec. 20.9–20.10*

32) A circular loop of wire of radius 0.50 m is in a uniform magnetic field of 0.30 T. The current in the loop is 2.0 A. What is the magnetic torque when the plane of the loop is parallel to the magnetic field?

A) zero

B) 0.41 m•N

C) 0.47 m•N

D) 0.52 m•N

Answer: C
Diff: 2 *Page Ref: Sec. 20.9–20.10*

33) A circular loop of wire of radius 0.50 m is in a uniform magnetic field of 0.30 T. The current in the loop is 2.0 A. What is the magnetic torque when the plane of the loop is parallel to the magnetic field?

A) zero

B) 0.41 m•N

C) 0.47 m•N

D) 0.52 m•N

Answer: C
Diff: 2 *Page Ref: Sec. 20.9–20.10*

34) A circular wire loop of area 0.25 m^2 carries a current of 5.0 A. The coil lies in a horizontal plane with the current flowing in the counterclockwise direction when viewed from above. At this point, the Earth's magnetic field is 1.2×10^{-4} T directed 60° below the horizontal. What is the magnitude of the torque which acts on the loop?

A) 2.5×10^{-5} m•N

B) 5.0×10^{-5} m•N

C) 7.5×10^{-5} m•N

D) 1.0×10^{-4} m•N

Answer: C
Diff: 2 *Page Ref: Sec. 20.9–20.10*

35) In a mass spectrometer, a single-charged particle (charge e) has a speed of 1.0×10^6 m/s and enters a uniform magnetic field of 0.20 T. The radius of the circular orbit is 0.020 m. What is the mass of the particle?

A) 3.2×10^{-28} kg

B) 6.4×10^{-28} kg

C) 1.7×10^{-27} kg

D) 3.1×10^{-31} kg

Answer: B
Diff: 2 *Page Ref: Sec. 20.11*

36) A doubly charged ion with velocity 6.9×10^6 m/s moves in a path of radius 30 cm in a magnetic field of 0.80 T in a mass spectrometer. What is the mass of this ion?

A) 11×10^{-27} kg

B) 6.7×10^{-27} kg

C) 3.3×10^{-27} kg

D) 8.2×10^{-27} kg

Answer: A
Diff: 2 *Page Ref: Sec. 20.11*

37) A proton travels through a potential of 1.0 kV and then moves into a magnetic field of 0.040 T. What is the radius of the proton's resulting orbit?

A) 0.080 m

B) 0.11 m

C) 0.14 m

D) 0.17 m

Answer: B
Diff: 2 *Page Ref: Sec. 20.11*

38) A proton is accelerated from rest through 500 V. It enters a magnetic field of 0.30 T oriented perpendicular to its direction of motion. Determine the radius of the path it follows.

A) 1.1 mm

B) 1.1 cm

C) 11 cm

D) 1.1 m

Answer: B
Diff: 2 *Page Ref: Sec. 20.11*

39) A beam of electrons is accelerated through a potential difference of 10 kV before entering a velocity selector. If the B-field of the velocity selector has a value of 0.010 T, what value of the E-field is required if the particles are to be undeflected?

A) 2.3×10^3 V/m

B) 5.9×10^5 V/m

C) 6.0×10^5 V/m

D) 7.2×10^6 V/m

Answer: B
Diff: 2 *Page Ref: Sec. 20.11*

Chapter 21 Electromagnetic Induction and Faraday's Law

Conceptual Questions

1) All of the following are units of magnetic flux except

A) T•m2.

B) T/V•m.

C) weber.

D) V•s.

Answer: B
Diff: 2 *Page Ref: Sec. 21.1–21.2*

2) Faraday's law of induction states that the emf induced in a loop of wire is proportional to

A) the magnetic flux.

B) the magnetic flux density times the loop's area.

C) the time variation of the magnetic flux.

D) current divided by time.

Answer: C
Diff: 1 *Page Ref: Sec. 21.1–21.2*

3) Doubling the number of loops of wire in a coil produces what kind of change on the induced emf, assuming all other factors remain constant?

A) The induced emf is 4 times as much.

B) The induced emf is twice times as much.

C) The induced emf is half as much.

D) There is no change in the induced emf.

Answer: B
Diff: 1 *Page Ref: Sec. 21.1–21.2*

4) Doubling the strength of the magnetic field through a loop of wire produces what kind of change on the induced emf, assuming all other factors remain constant?

A) The induced emf is 4 times as much.

B) The induced emf is twice as much.

C) The induced emf is half as much.

D) There is no change in the induced emf.

Answer: B
Diff: 1 *Page Ref: Sec. 21.1–21.2*

5) Doubling the diameter of a loop of wire produces what kind of change on the induced emf, assuming all other factors remain constant?

A) The induced emf is 4 times as much.

B) The induced emf is twice times as much.

C) The induced emf is half as much.

D) There is no change in the induced emf.

Answer: A
Diff: 1 *Page Ref: Sec. 21.1–21.2*

6) As a coil is removed from a magnetic field an emf is induced in the coil causing a current to flow within the coil. This current interacts with the magnetic field producing a force which

A) acts at right angles to the coil's motion.

B) acts in the direction of the coil's motion.

C) causes the coil to tend to flip over.

D) acts in the direction opposite to the coil's motion.

Answer: D
Diff: 1 *Page Ref: Sec. 21.1–21.2*

7) According to Lenz's law, the direction of an induced current in a conductor will be that which tends to produce which of the following effects?

A) enhance the effect which produces it

B) produce a greater heating effect

C) produce the greatest voltage

D) oppose the effect which produces it

Answer: D
Diff: 2 *Page Ref: Sec. 21.1–21.2*

8) A circular coil lies flat on a horizontal table. A bar magnet is held above its center with its north pole pointing down. The stationary magnet induces (when viewed from above)

A) no current in the coil.

B) a clockwise current in the coil.

C) a counterclockwise current in the coil.

D) a current whose direction cannot be determined from the information given.

Answer: A
Diff: 2 *Page Ref: Sec. 21.1–21.2*

9) A circular coil lies flat on a horizontal table. A bar magnet is held above its center with its north pole pointing down, and released. As it approaches the coil, the falling magnet induces (when viewed from above)

A) no current in the coil.

B) a clockwise current in the coil.

C) a counterclockwise current in the coil.

D) a current whose direction cannot be determined from the information provided.

Answer: C
Diff: 2 *Page Ref: Sec. 21.1-21.2*

10) A coil lies flat on a table top in a region where the magnetic field vector points straight up. The magnetic field vanishes suddenly. When viewed from above, what is the sense of the induced current in this coil as the field fades?

A) The induced current flows counterclockwise.

B) The induced current flows clockwise.

C) There is no induced current in this coil.

D) The current flows clockwise initially, and then it flows counterclockwise before stopping.

Answer: A
Diff: 2 *Page Ref: Sec. 21.1-21.2*

11) A coil lies flat on a level table top in a region where the magnetic field vector points straight up. The magnetic field suddenly grows stronger. When viewed from above, what is the direction of the induced current in this coil as the field increases?

A) counterclockwise

B) clockwise

C) clockwise initially, then counterclockwise before stopping

D) There is no induced current in this coil.

Answer: B
Diff: 2 *Page Ref: Sec. 21.1-21.2*

12) A coil lies flat on a horizontal table top in a region where the magnetic field points straight down. The magnetic field disappears suddenly. When viewed from above, what is the direction of the induced current in this coil as the field disappears?

A) counterclockwise

B) clockwise

C) clockwise initially, then counterclockwise before stopping

D) There is no induced current in this coil.

Answer: B
Diff: 2 *Page Ref: Sec. 21.1-21.2*

13) A long straight wire lies on a horizontal table and carries an ever-increasing current northward. Two coils of wire lie flat on the table, one on either side of the wire. When viewed from above, the induced current circles

A) clockwise in both coils.

B) counterclockwise in both coils.

C) clockwise in the east coil and counterclockwise in the west coil.

D) counterclockwise in the east coil and clockwise in the west coil.

Answer: D
Diff: 2 *Page Ref: Sec. 21.1–21.2*

14) A bar magnet falls through a loop of wire with the north pole entering first. As the north pole enters the wire, the induced current will be (as viewed from above)

A) zero.

B) clockwise.

C) counterclockwise.

D) to top of loop.

Answer: C
Diff: 2 *Page Ref: Sec. 21.1–21.2*

15) A circular loop of wire is rotated at constant angular speed about an axis whose direction can be varied. In a region where a uniform magnetic field points straight down, what must be the orientation of the loop's axis of rotation if the induced emf is to be zero?

A) Any horizontal orientation will do.

B) It must make an angle of 45° to the vertical.

C) It must be vertical.

D) none of the given answers

Answer: C
Diff: 2 *Page Ref: Sec. 21.1–21.2*

16) A circular loop of wire is rotated at constant angular speed about an axis whose direction can be varied. In a region where a uniform magnetic field points straight down, what must be the orientation of the loop's axis of rotation if the induced emf is to be a maximum?

A) Any horizontal orientation will do.

B) It must make an angle of 45° to the vertical.

C) It must be vertical.

D) none of the given answers

Answer: A
Diff: 2 *Page Ref: Sec. 21.1–21.2*

17) State Faraday's law.

Answer: A changing magnetic field induces an emf.
Diff: 1 *Page Ref: Sec. 21.1–21.2*

18) State Lenz's law.

Answer: A current produced by an induced emf moves in a direction so that its magnetic field opposes the original change in flux.
Diff: 1 *Page Ref: Sec. 21.1-21.2*

19) List the three ways that an emf can be induced in a loop of wire.

Answer: 1. by changing the magnetic field
2. by changing the area of the loop in the field
3. by changing the loop's orientation with respect to the field
Diff: 1 *Page Ref: Sec. 21.1-21.2*

20) A wire moves across a magnetic field. The emf produced in the wire depends on

A) the strength of the magnetic field.

B) the length of the wire.

C) the orientation of the wire with respect to the magnetic field vector.

D) all of the given answers

Answer: D
Diff: 1 *Page Ref: Sec. 21.3*

21) A horizontal rod (oriented in the east-west direction) is moved northward at constant velocity through a magnetic field that points straight down. Make a statement concerning the potential induced across the rod.

A) The west end of the rod is at higher potential than the east end.

B) The east end of the rod is at higher potential than the west end.

C) The top surface of the rod is at higher potential than the bottom surface.

D) The bottom surface of the rod is at higher potential than the top surface.

Answer: A
Diff: 2 *Page Ref: Sec. 21.3*

22) A horizontal metal bar rotates at a constant angular velocity ω about a vertical axis through one of its ends while in a constant magnetic field B that is directed down. The emf induced between the two ends of the bar is

A) constant and proportional to the product B ω.

B) constant and proportional to the product B $\omega 2$.

C) constant and proportional to the product B2 $\omega 2$.

D) none of the given answers

Answer: A
Diff: 2 *Page Ref: Sec. 21.3*

23) An electric generator transforms
   A) electrical energy into mechanical energy.
   B) mechanical energy into electrical energy.
   C) direct current into alternating current.
   D) alternating current into direct current.

Answer: B
Diff: 2 *Page Ref: Sec. 21.5*

24) A generator coil rotates through 60 revolutions each second. The frequency of the emf is
   A) 30 Hz.
   B) 60 Hz.
   C) 120 Hz.
   D) cannot be determined from the information given.

Answer: B
Diff: 1 *Page Ref: Sec. 21.5*

25) A transformer is a device used to
   A) transform an alternating current into a direct current.
   B) transform a direct current into an alternating current.
   C) increase or decrease an ac voltage.
   D) increase or decrease a dc voltage.

Answer: C
Diff: 1 *Page Ref: Sec. 21.7*

26) A transformer is a device that
   A) operates on either DC or AC.
   B) operates only on AC.
   C) operates only on DC.

Answer: B
Diff: 1 *Page Ref: Sec. 21.7*

27) In a transformer, if the secondary coil contains more loops than the primary coil then it is a
   A) step-up transformer.
   B) step-down transformer.

Answer: A
Diff: 1 *Page Ref: Sec. 21.7*

28) In a transformer, if the primary coil contains more loops than the secondary coil then it is a
   A) step-up transformer.
   B) step-down transformer.

Answer: B
Diff: 1 *Page Ref: Sec. 21.7*

29) In a transformer, the power input

A) is larger than the power output.

B) is equal to the power output.

C) is smaller than the power output.

D) can be either larger or smaller than the power output.

Answer: B
Diff: 1 *Page Ref: Sec. 21.7*

30) In a given LC resonant circuit,

A) the stored electric field energy is greater than the stored magnetic field energy.

B) the stored electric field energy is less than the stored magnetic field energy.

C) the stored electric field energy is equal to the stored magnetic field energy.

D) all of the given answers are possible.

Answer: D
Diff: 2 *Page Ref: Sec. 21.11*

31) A resistor and an inductor are connected in series to an ideal battery of constant terminal voltage. At the moment contact is made with the battery, the voltage across the resistor is

A) greater than the battery's terminal voltage.

B) equal to the battery's terminal voltage.

C) less than the battery's terminal voltage, but not zero.

D) zero.

Answer: D
Diff: 2 *Page Ref: Sec. 21.11*

32) A resistor and an inductor are connected in series to an ideal battery of constant terminal voltage. At the moment contact is made with the battery, the voltage across the inductor is

A) greater than the battery's terminal voltage.

B) equal to the battery's terminal voltage.

C) less than the battery's terminal voltage, but not zero.

D) zero.

Answer: B
Diff: 2 *Page Ref: Sec. 21.11*

33) A series RL circuit with inductance L and resistance R is connected to an emf V. After a period of time, the current reaches a final value of 2.0 A. A second series circuit is identical except that the inductance is 2L. When it is connected to the same emf V, what will be the final value of the current?

A) 0.50 A

B) 1.0 A

C) 2.0 A

D) 4.0 A

Answer: C
Diff: 2 *Page Ref: Sec. 21.11*

34) A resistor and an inductor are connected in series to a battery. The time constant for the circuit represents the time required for the current to reach

A) 25% of the maximum current.

B) 37% of the maximum current.

C) 63% of the maximum current.

D) 75% of the maximum current.

Answer: C
Diff: 2 *Page Ref: Sec. 21.11*

35) A resistor and an inductor are connected in series to a battery. The battery is suddenly removed from the circuit. The time constant for of the circuit represents the time required for the current to decrease to

A) 25% of the original value.

B) 37% of the original value.

C) 63% of the original value.

D) 75% of the original value.

Answer: B
Diff: 2 *Page Ref: Sec. 21.11*

36) All of the following have the same units except:

A) inductance.

B) capacitive reactance.

C) impedance.

D) resistance.

Answer: A
Diff: 1 *Page Ref: Sec. 21.12*

37) A resistor is connected to an AC power supply. On this circuit, the current

A) leads the voltage by 90°.

B) lags the voltage by 90°.

C) is in phase with the voltage.

D) none of the given answers

Answer: C
Diff: 1 *Page Ref: Sec. 21.12*

38) A pure inductor is connected to an AC power supply. In this circuit, the current

A) leads the voltage by 90°.

B) lags the voltage by 90°.

C) is in phase with the voltage.

D) none of the given answers

Answer: B
Diff: 2 *Page Ref: Sec. 21.12*

39) The inductive reactance in an ac circuit changes by what factor when the frequency is tripled?

A) 1/3

B) 1/9

C) 3

D) 9

Answer: C
Diff: 2 *Page Ref: Sec. 21.12*

40) If the frequency of the AC voltage across an inductor is doubled, the inductive reactance of that inductor

A) increases to 4 times its original value.

B) increases to twice its original value.

C) decreases to one-half its original value.

D) decreases to one-fourth its original value.

Answer: B
Diff: 1 *Page Ref: Sec. 21.12*

41) As the frequency of the AC voltage across an inductor approaches zero, the inductive reactance of that coil

A) approaches zero.

B) approaches infinity.

C) approaches unity.

D) none of the given answers

Answer: A
Diff: 1 *Page Ref: Sec. 21.12*

42) A pure capacitor is connected to an AC power supply. In this circuit, the current

A) leads the voltage by 90°.

B) lags the voltage by 90°.

C) is in phase with the voltage.

D) none of the given answers

Answer: A
Diff: 1 *Page Ref: Sec. 21.12*

43) The capacitive reactance in an ac circuit changes by what factor when the frequency is tripled?

A) 1/3

B) 1/9

C) 3

D) 9

Answer: A
Diff: 2 *Page Ref: Sec. 21.12*

44) As the frequency of the AC voltage across a capacitor approaches zero, the capacitive reactance of that capacitor

A) approaches zero.

B) approaches infinity.

C) approaches unity.

D) none of the given answers

Answer: B
Diff: 1 *Page Ref: Sec. 21.12*

45) What is the phase angle between the voltages of the inductor and capacitor in a RLC series circuit?

A) zero

B) 90°

C) 180°

D) 270°

Answer: C
Diff: 2 *Page Ref: Sec. 21.13*

46) The power factor of an RLC circuit is defined as cos $\phi = R/Z$, but the phase angle can also be calculated from ________.

A) sin $\phi = (X_L - X_C)/Z$

B) sin $\phi = (X_L - X_C)/RZ$

C) sin $\phi = Z/(X_L - X_C)$

D) sin $\phi = RZ/(X_L - X_C)$

Answer: A
Diff: 2 *Page Ref: Sec. 21.13*

47) Consider an RLC circuit. The impedance of the circuit increases if R increases. When is this statement true?

A) always true

B) true only if X_L is less than or equal to X_C

C) true only if X_L is greater than or equal to X_C

D) never true

Answer: A
Diff: 1 *Page Ref: Sec. 21.13*

48) Consider an RLC circuit. The impedance of the circuit increases if X_L increases. When is this statement true?

A) always true

B) true only if X_L is less than or equal to X_C

C) true only if X_L is greater than or equal to X_C

D) never true

Answer: C
Diff: 2 *Page Ref: Sec. 21.13*

49) Consider an RLC series circuit. The impedance of the circuit increases if X_C increases. When is this statement true?

A) always true

B) true only if X_L is less than or equal to X_C

C) true only if X_L is greater than or equal to X_C

D) never true

Answer: B
Diff: 2 *Page Ref: Sec. 21.13*

50) If the inductance and the capacitance both double in an LRC series circuit, the resonant frequency of that circuit will

A) decrease to one-half its original value.

B) decrease to one-fourth its original value.

C) decrease to one-eighth its original value.

D) none of the given answers

Answer: A
Diff: 2 *Page Ref: Sec. 21.13*

51) Consider an RLC circuit that is driven by an AC applied voltage. At resonance,

A) the peak voltage across the capacitor is greater than the peak voltage across the inductor.

B) the peak voltage across the inductor is greater than the peak voltage across the capacitor.

C) the current is in phase with the driving voltage.

D) the peak voltage across the resistor is equal to the peak voltage across the inductor.

Answer: C
Diff: 1 *Page Ref: Sec. 21.14*

52) Resonance in a series RLC circuit occurs when

A) X_L is greater than X_C.

B) X_C is greater than X_L.

C) $(X_L - X_C)^2$ is equal to R^2.

D) X_C equals X_L.

Answer: D
Diff: 1 *Page Ref: Sec. 21.14*

Quantitative Problems

1) A flux of 4.0×10^{-5} Wb is maintained through a coil for 0.50 s. What emf is induced in this coil by this flux?

A) 8.0×10^{-5} V

B) 4.0×10^{-5} V

C) 2.0×10^{-5} V

D) No emf is induced in this coil.

Answer: D
Diff: 2 *Page Ref: Sec. 21.1–21.2*

2) A circular loop of radius 0.10 m is rotating in a uniform magnetic field of 0.20 T. Find the magnetic flux through the loop when the plane of the loop and the magnetic field vector are parallel.

A) zero

B) 3.1×10^{-3} T·m^2

C) 5.5×10^{-3} T·m^2

D) 6.3×10^{-3} T·m^2

Answer: A
Diff: 1 *Page Ref: Sec. 21.1–21.2*

3) A circular loop of radius 0.10 m is rotating in a uniform magnetic field of 0.20 T. Find the magnetic flux through the loop when the plane of the loop and the magnetic field vector are perpendicular.

A) zero

B) 3.1×10^{-3} T•m^2

C) 5.5×10^{-3} T•m^2

D) 6.3×10^{-3} T•m^2

Answer: D

Diff: 1 *Page Ref: Sec. 21.1–21.2*

4) A circular loop of radius 0.10 m is rotating in a uniform magnetic field of 0.20 T. Find the magnetic flux through the loop when the plane of the loop and the magnetic field vector are at an angle of 30°.

A) zero

B) 3.1×10^{-3} T•m^2

C) 5.5×10^{-3} T•m^2

D) 6.3×10^{-3} T•m^2

Answer: B

Diff: 1 *Page Ref: Sec. 21.1–21.2*

5) The cross-sectional area of an adjustable single loop is reduced from 1.0 m^2 to 0.50 m^2 in 0.10 s. What is the average emf that is induced in this coil if it is in a region where B = 2.0 T upward, and the coil's plane is perpendicular to B?

A) 5 V

B) 10 V

C) 15 V

D) 20 V

Answer: B

Diff: 1 *Page Ref: Sec. 21.1–21.2*

6) The flux through a coil changes from 4.0×10^{-5} Wb to 5.0×10^{-5} Wb in 0.10 s. What emf is induced in this coil?

A) 5.0×10^{-4} V

B) 4.0×10^{-4} V

C) 1.0×10^{-4} V

D) none of the given answers

Answer: C

Diff: 1 *Page Ref: Sec. 21.1–21.2*

7) A coil is wrapped with 200 turns of wire on a square frame with sides 18 cm. A uniform magnetic field is applied perpendicular to the plane of the coil. If the field changes uniformly from 0.50 T to 0 in 8.0 s, find the average value of the induced emf.

A) 2.1 mV

B) 4.1 mV

C) 0.21 V

D) 0.41 V

Answer: D
Diff: 2 *Page Ref: Sec. 21.1-21.2*

8) A square coil of wire with 15 turns and an area of 0.40 m^2 is placed parallel to a magnetic field of 0.75 T. The coil is flipped so its plane is perpendicular to the magnetic field in 0.050 s. What is the magnitude of the average induced emf?

A) 6.0 V

B) 36 V

C) 45 V

D) 90 V

Answer: D
Diff: 2 *Page Ref: Sec. 21.1-21.2*

9) A coil of 160 turns and area 0.20 m^2 is placed with its axis parallel to a magnetic field of 0.40 T. The magnetic field changes from 0.40 T in the x-direction to 0.40 T in the negative x-direction in 2.0 s. If the resistance of the coil is 16 Ω, at what rate is power generated in the coil?

A) 5.0 W

B) 10 W

C) 15 W

D) 20 W

Answer: B
Diff: 2 *Page Ref: Sec. 21.1-21.2*

10) An airplane with a wing span of 60 m flies horizontally at a location where the downward component of the Earth's magnetic field is 6.0×10^{-5} T. Find the magnitude of the induced emf between the tips of the wings when the speed of the plane is 225 m/s.

A) 0.41 V

B) 0.61 V

C) 0.81 V

D) 1.2 V

Answer: C
Diff: 2 *Page Ref: Sec. 21.3*

11) A horizontal metal bar that is 2.0 m long rotates at a constant angular velocity of 2.0 rad/s about a vertical axis through one of its ends while in a constant magnetic field of 5.0×10^{-5} T. If the magnetic field vector points straight down, what emf is induced between the two ends of the bar?

A) 5.6×10^{-3} V

B) 3.0×10^{-3} V

C) 2.0×10^{-4} V

D) 1.6×10^{-4} V

Answer: C
Diff: 2 *Page Ref: Sec. 21.3*

12) The coil of a generator has 50 loops and a cross-sectional area of 0.25 m^2. What is the maximum emf generated by this generator if it is spinning with an angular velocity of 4.0 rad/s in a 2.0 T magnetic field?

A) 50 V

B) 100 V

C) 200 V

D) 400 V

Answer: B
Diff: 1 *Page Ref: Sec. 21.5*

13) An AC generator consists of 100 turns of wire of area 0.090 m^2 and total resistance 12 Ω. The loops rotate in a magnetic field of 0.50 T at a constant angular speed of 60 revolutions per second. Find the maximum induced emf.

A) 0.27 kV

B) 0.54 kV

C) 1.7 kV

D) 3.4 kV

Answer: C
Diff: 2 *Page Ref: Sec. 21.5*

14) An AC generator has 80 rectangular loops on its armature. Each loop is 12 cm long and 8 cm wide. The armature rotates at 1200 rpm about an axis parallel to the long side. If the loop rotates in a uniform magnetic field of 0.30 T, which is perpendicular to the axis of rotation, what will be the maximum output voltage of this generator?

A) 20 V

B) 27 V

C) 29 V

D) 35 V

Answer: C
Diff: 2 *Page Ref: Sec. 21.5*

15) An AC generator consists of 100 turns of wire of area 0.090 m^2 and total resistance 12 Ω. The loops rotate in a magnetic field of 0.50 T at a constant angular speed of 60 revolutions per second. Find the maximum induced current.

A) 23 A

B) 46 A

C) 0.14 kA

D) 0.28 kA

Answer: C
Diff: 2 *Page Ref: Sec. 21.5*

16) Suppose that you wish to construct a simple AC generator with an output of 12 V maximum when rotated at 60 Hz. A magnetic field of 0.050 T is available. If the area of the rotating coil is 100 cm^2, how many turns are needed?

A) 16

B) 32

C) 64

D) 128

Answer: C
Diff: 2 *Page Ref: Sec. 21.5*

17) You are designing a generator with a maximum emf 8.0 V. If the generator coil has 200 turns and a cross-sectional area of 0.030 m^2, what would be the frequency of the generator in a magnetic field of 0.030 T?

A) 7.1 Hz

B) 7.5 Hz

C) 8.0 Hz

D) 44 Hz

Answer: A
Diff: 2 *Page Ref: Sec. 21.5*

18) The windings of a DC motor have a resistance of 6.00 Ω. The motor operates on 120 V AC, and when running at full speed it generates a back emf of 105 V. What is the starting current of the motor?

A) 2.50 A

B) 17.5 A

C) 20.0 A

D) 37.5 A

Answer: C
Diff: 2 *Page Ref: Sec. 21.6*

19) The windings of a DC motor have a resistance of 6.00 Ω. The motor operates on 120 V AC, and when running at full speed it generates a back emf of 105 V. What current does the motor draw when operating at full speed?

A) 2.50 A

B) 17.5 A

C) 20.0 A

D) 37.5 A

Answer: A
Diff: 2 *Page Ref: Sec. 21.6*

20) A DC motor of internal resistance 6.0 Ω is connected to a 24-V power supply. The operating current is 1.0 A. What is the start-up current?

A) 1.0 A

B) 2.0 A

C) 3.0 A

D) 4.0 A

Answer: D
Diff: 2 *Page Ref: Sec. 21.6*

21) A DC motor of internal resistance 6.0 Ω is connected to a 24-V power supply. The operating current is 1.0 A at full speed. What is the back emf when the motor is running at full speed?

A) zero

B) 6.0 V

C) 18 V

D) 24 V

Answer: C
Diff: 2 *Page Ref: Sec. 21.6*

22) A DC motor of internal resistance 6.0 Ω is connected to a 24-V power supply. The operating current is 1.0 A at full speed. What is the back emf when the motor is running at half speed?

A) 6.0 V

B) 9.0 V

C) 18 V

D) 24 V

Answer: B
Diff: 2 *Page Ref: Sec. 21.6*

23) A step-down transformer is needed to reduce a primary voltage of 120 V AC to 6.0V AC. What turns ratio is required?

A) 10:1

B) 1:10

C) 20:1

D) 1:20

Answer: C
Diff: 1 *Page Ref: Sec. 21.7*

24) 2.0 A in the 100-turn primary of a transformer causes 14 A to flow in the secondary. How many turns are in the secondary?

A) 700

B) 114

C) 14

D) 4

Answer: C
Diff: 1 *Page Ref: Sec. 21.7*

25) In a transformer, how many turns are necessary in a 110-V primary if the 24-V secondary has 100 turns?

A) 458

B) 240

C) 110

D) 22

Answer: A
Diff: 1 *Page Ref: Sec. 21.7*

26) An transformer consists of a 500-turn primary coil and a 2000-turn secondary coil. If the current in the secondary is 3.0 A, what is the current in the primary?

A) 0.75 A

B) 1.3 A

C) 12 A

D) 48 A

Answer: C
Diff: 1 *Page Ref: Sec. 21.7*

27) 5.0 A at 110 V flows in the primary of a transformer. Assuming 100% efficiency, how many amps at 24 V can flow in the secondary?

A) 1.1 A

B) 4.6 A

C) 5.0 A

D) 23 A

Answer: D
Diff: 1 *Page Ref: Sec. 21.7*

28) The secondary coil of a neon sign transformer provides 7500 V at 10.0 mA. The primary coil operates on 120 V. What does the primary draw?

A) 0.625 A

B) 0.625 mA

C) 0.160 A

D) 1.66 A

Answer: A
Diff: 2 *Page Ref: Sec. 21.7*

29) An ideal transformer has 60 turns on its primary coil and 300 turns on its secondary coil. If 120 V at 2.0 A is applied to the primary, what voltage is present in the secondary?

A) 24 V

B) 120 V

C) 240 V

D) 600 V

Answer: D
Diff: 1 *Page Ref: Sec. 21.7*

30) An ideal transformer has 60 turns on its primary coil and 300 turns on its secondary coil. If 120 V at 2.0 A is applied to the primary, what current is present in the secondary?

A) 0.40 A

B) 2.0 A

C) 4.0 A

D) 10 A

Answer: A
Diff: 1 *Page Ref: Sec. 21.7*

31) The primary of a transformer has 100 turns and its secondary has 200 turns. If the input current at the primary is 100 A, we can expect the output current at the secondary to be

A) 50 A.

B) 100 A.

C) 200 A.

D) none of the given answers

Answer: A
Diff: 1 *Page Ref: Sec. 21.7*

32) The primary of a transformer has 100 turns and its secondary has 200 turns. If the input voltage to the primary is 100 V, we can expect the output voltage of the secondary to be

A) 50 V.

B) 100 V.

C) 200 V.

D) none of the given answers

Answer: C
Diff: 1 *Page Ref: Sec. 21.7*

33) The primary of a transformer has 100 turns and its secondary has 200 turns. If the power input to the primary is 100 W, we can expect the power output of the secondary to be (neglecting frictional losses)

A) 50 W.

B) 100 W.

C) 200 W.

D) none of the given answers

Answer: B
Diff: 1 *Page Ref: Sec. 21.7*

34) A generator produces 60 A of current at 120 V. The voltage is usually stepped up to 4500 V by a transformer and transmitted through a power line of total resistance 1.0 Ω. Find the number of turns in the secondary if the primary has 200 turns.

A) 5

B) 200

C) 4500

D) 7500

Answer: D
Diff: 2 *Page Ref: Sec. 21.7*

35) A generator produces 60 A of current at 120 V. The voltage is usually stepped up to 4500 V by a transformer and transmitted through a power line of total resistance 1.0 Ω. Find the percentage power lost in the transmission line.

A) 0.012%

B) 0.024%

C) 0.036%

D) 0.048%

Answer: C
Diff: 3 *Page Ref: Sec. 21.7*

36) A generator produces 60 A of current at 120 V. The voltage is usually stepped up to 4500 V by a transformer and transmitted through a power line of total resistance 1.0 Ω. Find the percentage power lost in the transmission line if the voltage is not stepped up.

A) 0.018%

B) 0.036%

C) 25%

D) 50%

Answer: D
Diff: 3 *Page Ref: Sec. 21.7*

37) A power transmission line 50 km long has a total resistance of 0.60 Ω. A generator produces 100 V at 70 A. In order to reduce energy loss due to heating of the transmission line, the voltage is stepped up with a transformer with a turns ratio of 100:1. What percentage of the original energy would be lost if the transformer were not used?

A) 0.0042%

B) 0.042%

C) 4.2%

D) 42%

Answer: D
Diff: 3 *Page Ref: Sec. 21.7*

38) A power transmission line 50 km long has a total resistance of 0.60 Ω. A generator produces 100 V at 70 A. In order to reduce energy loss due to heating of the transmission line, the voltage is stepped up with a transformer with a turns ratio of 100:1. What percentage of the original energy is lost when the transformer is used?

A) 0.0042%

B) 0.042%

C) 4.2%

D) 42%

Answer: A
Diff: 3 *Page Ref: Sec. 21.7*

39) 100 kW is transmitted down a 6-Ω line at 1000 V. How much less power would be lost if the power were transmitted at 3000 V instead of at 1000 V?

A) 1.0 kW

B) 10 kW

C) 30 kW

D) 53 kW

Answer: D
Diff: 3 *Page Ref: Sec. 21.7*

40) The output of a generator is 440 V at 20 A. It is to be transmitted on a line with resistance of 0.60 Ω. To what voltage must the generator output be stepped up with a transformer if the power loss in transmission is not to exceed 0.010% of the original power?

A) 4.4 kV

B) 7.3 kV

C) 22 kV

D) 45 kV

Answer: B
Diff: 3 *Page Ref: Sec. 21.7*

41) A 4.0-mH coil carries a current of 5.0 A. How much energy is stored in the coil's magnetic field?

A) 2.0 mJ

B) 10 mJ

C) 20 mJ

D) none of the given answers

Answer: D
Diff: 1 *Page Ref: Sec. 21.10*

42) A simple RL circuit contains a 6.0-Ω resistor and an 18-H inductor. What is this circuit's time constant?

A) 108 s

B) 3.0 s

C) 0.33 s

D) none of the given answers

Answer: B
Diff: 1 *Page Ref: Sec. 21.11*

43) What is the peak voltage in an AC circuit where the rms voltage is 120 V?

A) 84.8 V

B) 120 V

C) 170 V

D) none of the given answers

Answer: C
Diff: 1 *Page Ref: Sec. 21.12*

44) A 150-W lamp is placed into a 120-V AC outlet. What is the peak current?

A) 0.80 A

B) 0.88 A

C) 1.25 A

D) 1.77 A

Answer: D
Diff: 2 *Page Ref: Sec. 21.12*

45) A 150-W lamp is placed into a 120-V AC outlet. What is the resistance of the lamp?

A) 1.25 Ω

B) 0.80 Ω

C) 48 Ω

D) 96 Ω

Answer: D
Diff: 2 *Page Ref: Sec. 21.12*

46) A 10-Ω resistor is connected to a 120-V ac power supply. What is the peak current through the resistor?

A) 12 A

B) 17 A

C) 0.083 A

D) 0.12 A

Answer: B
Diff: 2 *Page Ref: Sec. 21.12*

47) A 10-Ω resistor is connected to a 120-V ac power supply. What is the power dissipated in the resistor?

A) 1.0 kW

B) 1.4 kW

C) 2.0 kW

D) 2.9 kW

Answer: B
Diff: 2 *Page Ref: Sec. 21.12*

48) The current through a 50-Ω resistor is I = 0.80 sin (240 t). What is the rms current?

A) 0.57 A

B) 0.80 A

C) 1.1 A

D) 1.6 A

Answer: A
Diff: 2 *Page Ref: Sec. 21.12*

49) The current through a 50-Ω resistor is I = 0.80 sin (240 t). At what frequency does the current vary?

A) 38 Hz

B) 76 Hz

C) 120 Hz

D) 240 Hz

Answer: A
Diff: 2 *Page Ref: Sec. 21.12*

50) The current through a 50-Ω resistor is I = 0.80 sin (240 t). How much power on average is dissipated in the resistor?

A) 16 W

B) 32 W

C) 45 W

D) 64 W

Answer: A
Diff: 2 *Page Ref: Sec. 21.12*

51) What is the reactance of a 1.0-mH inductor at 60 Hz?

A) 0.19 Ω

B) 0.38 Ω

C) 2.7 Ω

D) 5.3 Ω

Answer: B
Diff: 1 *Page Ref: Sec. 21.12*

52) What is the inductive reactance of a 2.50-mH coil at 1000 Hz?

A) 2500 Ω

B) 796 Ω

C) 15.7 Ω

D) 2.50 Ω

Answer: C
Diff: 1 *Page Ref: Sec. 21.12*

53) At what frequency will a 14.0-mH coil have 14.0 Ω of inductive reactance?

A) 1000 Hz

B) 505 Hz

C) 257 Hz

D) 159 Hz

Answer: D
Diff: 1 *Page Ref: Sec. 21.12*

54) What inductance is necessary for 157 Ω of inductive reactance at 1000 Hz?

A) 25.0 mH

B) 157 mH

C) 2.40 H

D) 6.40 H

Answer: A
Diff: 1 *Page Ref: Sec. 21.12*

55) What current flows in a 60-mH inductor when 120 V AC at a frequency of 20 kHz is applied to it?

A) 8.0 mA

B) 16 mA

C) 24 mA

D) 32 mA

Answer: B
Diff: 2 *Page Ref: Sec. 21.12*

56) What is the current through a 2.50-mH coil due to a 110-V, 60.0 Hz source?

A) 0.94 A

B) 2.5 A

C) 104 A

D) 117 A

Answer: D
Diff: 2 *Page Ref: Sec. 21.12*

57) What is the capacitive reactance of a 4.7-μF capacitor at 10 kHz?

A) 0.047 Ω

B) 3.4 Ω

C) 14 Ω

D) 47 Ω

Answer: B
Diff: 1 *Page Ref: Sec. 21.12*

58) What size capacitor is needed to have 50 Ω of capacitive reactance at 10 kHz?

A) 16 μF

B) 5.0 μF

C) 3.2 μF

D) 0.32 μF

Answer: D
Diff: 1 *Page Ref: Sec. 21.12*

59) At what frequency does a 10-μF capacitor have a reactance of 1200 Ω?

A) 13 Hz

B) 42 Hz

C) 60 Hz

D) 83 Hz

Answer: A
Diff: 2 *Page Ref: Sec. 21.12*

60) At what frequency will the capacitive reactance of a 0.010-μF capacitor be 100 Ω?

A) 1.0 kHz

B) 16 kHz

C) 0.16 MHz

D) 0.31 MHz

Answer: C
Diff: 1 *Page Ref: Sec. 21.12*

61) What is the current through a 0.0010-μF capacitor at 1000 Hz and 5.0 V?

A) 5.4 μA

B) 31 μA

C) 3.1 mA

D) 10 mA

Answer: B
Diff: 2 *Page Ref: Sec. 21.12*

62) What is the impedance of an ac series circuit with 12.0 Ω resistance, 15.0 Ω inductive reactance, and 10.0 Ω capacitive reactance?

A) 11.6 Ω

B) 13.0 Ω

C) 21.9 Ω

D) 27.7 Ω

Answer: B
Diff: 2 *Page Ref: Sec. 21.13*

63) What is the total impedance at 1500 Hz if a 100-Ω resistor, 20-mH coil, and 1.0-μF capacitor are connected in series?

A) 0.19 kΩ

B) 0.13 kΩ

C) 0.11 kΩ

D) 82 Ω

Answer: B
Diff: 1   *Page Ref: Sec. 21.13*

64) What is the phase angle at 1500 Hz if a 100-Ω resistor, 20-mH coil, and 1.0-μF capacitor are connected in series?

A) 0.014°

B) 40°

C) 45°

D) 70°

Answer: B
Diff: 1   *Page Ref: Sec. 21.13*

65) If a 1000-Ω resistor is connected in series with a 20-mH inductor, what is the impedance at 1000 Hz?

A) 0.13 kΩ

B) 1.0 kΩ

C) 1.1 kΩ

D) 0.13 MΩ

Answer: B
Diff: 1   *Page Ref: Sec. 21.13*

66) If a 1000-Ω resistor is connected in series with a 20-mH inductor, what is the phase angle at 1000 Hz?

A) 2.9°

B) 7.2°

C) 45°

D) 90°

Answer: B
Diff: 2   *Page Ref: Sec. 21.13*

67) What resistance is needed in a series circuit with a 20-mH coil and 1.0-μF capacitor for a total impedance of 100 Ω at 1500 Hz?

A) 0.16 kΩ

B) 82 Ω

C) 57 Ω

D) 18 Ω

Answer: C
Diff: 2 *Page Ref: Sec. 21.13*

68) Which of the following capacitances is needed in series with a 100-Ω resistor and 15-mH coil to get a total impedance of 110 Ω at 2000 Hz?

A) 0.14 mF

B) 46 μF

C) 10 μF

D) 0.56 μF

Answer: D
Diff: 3 *Page Ref: Sec. 21.13*

69) What resistance must be put in series with a 450-mH inductor at 5000 Hz for a total impedance of 40000 Ω?

A) 45 kΩ

B) 40 kΩ

C) 37 kΩ

D) 26 kΩ

Answer: C
Diff: 2 *Page Ref: Sec. 21.12*

70) What inductance must be put in series with a 100-kΩ resistor at 1.0-MHz for a total impedance of 150 kΩ?

A) 18 mH

B) 0.15 H

C) 0.17 H

D) 1.5 H

Answer: A
Diff: 3 *Page Ref: Sec. 21.13*

71) A 10-Ω resistor is connected in series with a 20-μF capacitor. What is the impedance at 1000 Hz?

A) 8.0 Ω

B) 10 Ω

C) 13 Ω

D) 15 Ω

Answer: C
Diff: 1 *Page Ref: Sec. 21.13*

72) What resistance is needed in series with a 10-μF capacitor at 1.0 kHz for a total impedance of 45 Ω?

A) 29 Ω

B) 42 Ω

C) 61 Ω

D) 1.8 Ω

Answer: B
Diff: 2 *Page Ref: Sec. 21.13*

73) What resistance is needed in series with a 10-μF capacitor at 1.0 kHz for a phase angle of 40°?

A) 0.40 Ω

B) 2.5 Ω

C) 16 Ω

D) 19 Ω

Answer: D
Diff: 3 *Page Ref: Sec. 21.13*

74) What capacitance is needed in series with a 30-Ω resistor at 1.0 kHz for a total impedance of 45 Ω?

A) 34 μF

B) 15 μF

C) 4.7 μF

D) 0.015 μF

Answer: C
Diff: 3 *Page Ref: Sec. 21.13*

75) A 10-Ω resistor is in series with a 100-μF capacitor at 120 Hz. What is the phase angle?

A) -82°

B) -53°

C) -37°

D) -4.7°

Answer: B
Diff: 2 *Page Ref: Sec. 21.13*

76) What current flows at 5.0 V and 1500 Hz if a 100-Ω resistor, 20-mH coil, and 1.0-μF capacitor are connected in series?

A) 0.13 A

B) 45 mA

C) 39 mA

D) 11 mA

Answer: C
Diff: 2 *Page Ref: Sec. 21.13*

77) A series RLC circuit consists of a 100-Ω resistor, a 10.0-μF capacitor, and a 0.350-H inductor. The circuit is connected to a 120-V, 60-Hz power supply. What is the rms current in the circuit?

A) 0.42 A

B) 0.52 A

C) 0.62 A

D) 0.72 A

Answer: D
Diff: 2 *Page Ref: Sec. 21.13*

78) A resistance of 55 Ω, a capacitor of capacitive reactance 30 Ω, and an inductor of inductive reactance 30 Ω are connected in series to a 110-V, 60-Hz power source. What current flows in this circuit?

A) 2.0 A

B) less than 2.0 A

C) more than 2.0 A

D) none of the given answers

Answer: A
Diff: 2 *Page Ref: Sec. 21.13*

79) What is the phase angle for a series RLC circuit containing a 50-Ω resistor, a 10-μF capacitor, and a 0.45-H inductor, when connected to a 60-Hz power supply?

A) 38°

B) -38°

C) 62°

D) -62°

Answer: D
Diff: 2 *Page Ref: Sec. 21.13*

80) What inductance is necessary in series with a 500-Ω resistor for a phase angle of 40° at 10 kHz?

A) 84 mH

B) 46 mH

C) 20 mH

D) 6.7 mH

Answer: D
Diff: 2 *Page Ref: Sec. 21.13*

81) A series RLC circuit has R = 20.0 Ω, L = 200-mH, C = 10.0 μF. At what frequency should the circuit be driven in order to have maximum power transferred from the driving source?

A) 113 Hz

B) 167 Hz

C) 277 Hz

D) 960 Hz

Answer: A
Diff: 2 *Page Ref: Sec. 21.13*

82) What is the power output in an ac series circuit with 12.0 Ω resistance, 15.0 Ω inductive reactance, and 10.0 Ω capacitive reactance, when the circuit is connected to a 120-V power supply?

A) 0.60 kW

B) 0.10 kW

C) 0.11 kW

D) 0.12 kW

Answer: C
Diff: 2 *Page Ref: Sec. 21.13*

83) The phase angle of an AC circuit is 63°. What is the power factor?

A) 0.89

B) 0.55

C) 0.45

D) 0.11

Answer: C
Diff: 1 *Page Ref: Sec. 21.13*

84) An ac series circuit has an impedance of 60 Ω and a resistance of 30 Ω. What is the power factor?

A) 0.50

B) 0.71

C) 1.0

D) 1.4

Answer: A
Diff: 2 *Page Ref: Sec. 21.13*

85) What is the power factor for a series RLC circuit containing a 50-Ω resistor, a 10-μF capacitor, and a 0.45-H inductor, when connected to a 60-Hz power supply?

A) zero

B) 0.47

C) 0.79

D) 1.0

Answer: B
Diff: 2 *Page Ref: Sec. 21.13*

86) What is the resonant frequency of a 1.0-μF capacitor and a 15-mH coil in series?

A) 15 kHz

B) 1.3 kHz

C) 0.77 kHz

D) 67 Hz

Answer: B
Diff: 1 *Page Ref: Sec. 21.14*

87) What inductance is needed in series with a 4.7-μF capacitor for a resonant frequency of 10 kHz?

A) 21 μH

B) 54 μH

C) 4.7 mH

D) 5.4 mH

Answer: B
Diff: 2 *Page Ref: Sec. 21.14*

88) What capacitance is needed in series with a 3.7-mH inductor for a resonant frequency of 1000 Hz?

A) 0.15 mF

B) 15 μF

C) 6.8 μF

D) 0.015 μF

Answer: C
Diff: 2 *Page Ref: Sec. 21.14*

89) What size capacitor must be placed in series with a 30-Ω resistor and a 40-mH coil if the resonant frequency of the circuit is to be 1000 Hz?

A) 0.63 μF

B) 0.50 μF

C) 0.22 μF

D) 0.17 μF

Answer: A
Diff: 2 *Page Ref: Sec. 21.14*

Chapter 22 Electromagnetic Waves

Conceptual Questions

1) The basic equations for all electromagnetism were developed by

A) Newton.

B) Gauss.

C) Maxwell.

D) Hertz.

Answer: C
Diff: 1 *Page Ref: Sec. 22.1-22.2*

2) An electric field is produced by a

A) constant magnetic field.

B) changing magnetic field.

C) either a constant or a changing magnetic field.

D) none of the given answers

Answer: B
Diff: 1 *Page Ref: Sec. 22.1-22.1*

3) A changing electric field will produce a

A) current.

B) gravitational field.

C) magnetic field.

D) none of the given answers

Answer: C
Diff: 1 *Page Ref: Sec. 22.1-22.2*

4) All electromagnetic waves travel through a vacuum at

A) the same speed.

B) speeds that are proportional to their frequency.

C) speeds that are inversely proportional to their frequency.

D) none of the given answers

Answer: A
Diff: 1 *Page Ref: Sec. 22.1-22.1*

5) In a vacuum, the velocity of all electromagnetic waves

A) is zero.

B) is nearly 3×10^8 m/s.

C) depends on the frequency.

D) depends on their amplitude.

Answer: B
Diff: 1 *Page Ref: Sec. 22.1–22.2*

6) Electromagnetic waves can travel through

A) glass.

B) iron.

C) water.

D) none of the given answers

Answer: D
Diff: 1 *Page Ref: Sec. 22.1–22.2*

7) The strength of both the electric and magnetic fields in the radiation field are found to decrease with distance as

A) $1/r$.

B) $1/r^2$.

C) $1/r^3$.

D) $1/r^4$.

Answer: A
Diff: 2 *Page Ref: Sec. 22.1–22.2*

8) The **E** and **B** fields in electromagnetic waves are oriented

A) parallel to the wave's direction of travel, as well as to each other.

B) parallel to the waves direction of travel, and perpendicular to each other.

C) perpendicular to the wave's direction of travel, and parallel to each other.

D) perpendicular to the wave's direction of travel, and also to each other.

Answer: D
Diff: 2 *Page Ref: Sec. 22.1–22.2*

9) An electromagnetic wave is traveling to the east. At one instant at a given point its **E** vector points straight up. What is the direction of its **B** vector?

A) north

B) down

C) east

D) south

Answer: D
Diff: 2 *Page Ref: Sec. 22.1–22.2*

10) An electromagnetic wave is radiated by a straight wire antenna that is oriented vertically. What should be the orientation of a straight wire receiving antenna? It should be placed

A) vertically.

B) horizontally and in a direction parallel to the wave's direction of motion.

C) horizontally and in a direction perpendicular to the wave's direction of motion.

D) none of the given answers

Answer: A
Diff: 2 *Page Ref: Sec. 22.1–22.2*

11) Electromagnetic waves are

A) longitudinal.

B) transverse.

C) both longitudinal and transverse.

D) neither longitudinal or transverse.

Answer: B
Diff: 1 *Page Ref: Sec. 22.1–22.2*

12) Of the following, which is not electromagnetic in nature?

A) microwaves

B) gamma rays

C) sound waves

D) radio waves

Answer: C
Diff: 1 *Page Ref: Sec. 22.3*

13) Visible light ranges in wavelength from

A) 400 μm to 750 μm.

B) 400 nm to 750 nm.

C) 500 μm to 850 μm.

D) 500 nm to 850 nm.

Answer: B
Diff: 1 *Page Ref: Sec. 22.3*

14) The energy an electromagnetic wave transports per unit time per unit area is the

A) energy density.

B) power.

C) intensity.

D) radiation pressure.

Answer: C
Diff: 1 *Page Ref: Sec. 22.5*

15) The force per unit area exerted by an electromagnetic wave is called the

A) energy density.

B) power.

C) intensity.

D) radiation pressure.

Answer: D
Diff: 1 *Page Ref: Sec. 22.6*

16) Which of the following correctly lists electromagnetic waves in order from longest to shortest wavelength?

A) gamma rays, ultraviolet, infrared, microwaves

B) microwaves, ultraviolet, visible light, gamma rays

C) radio waves, infrared, gamma rays, ultraviolet

D) television, infrared, visible light, X-rays

Answer: D
Diff: 2 *Page Ref: Sec. 22.3*

Quantitative Problems

1) If the electric field in an EM wave has a peak value of 2.0 V/m, what is the peak value of the magnetic field?

A) 6.7 nT

B) 2.0 T

C) 3.0×10^8 T

D) none of the given answers

Answer: A
Diff: 1 *Page Ref: Sec. 22.2*

2) What is the wavelength of light waves if their frequency is 5.0×10^{14} Hz?

A) 0.60 m

B) 6.0 mm

C) 0.060 mm

D) 0.60 μm

Answer: D
Diff: 1 *Page Ref: Sec. 22.3–22.4*

3) What is the wavelength of a 92.9-MHz radio wave?

A) 32 mm

B) 32 cm

C) 3.2 m

D) 32 m

Answer: C
Diff: 1 *Page Ref: Sec. 22.3-22.4*

4) What is the wavelength of a radio wave signal transmitted at a frequency of 7.2 MHz?

A) 42 m

B) 4.2 m

C) 29 m

D) 0.024 m

Answer: A
Diff: 1 *Page Ref: Sec. 22.3-22.4*

5) What is the wavelength for the carrier wave in the station WBRN 1460?

A) 2.05 m

B) 20.5 m

C) 205 m

D) 2.05 km

Answer: C
Diff: 2 *Page Ref: Sec. 22.3-22.4*

6) What is the frequency of 20 mm microwaves?

A) 100 MHz

B) 400 MHz

C) 15 GHz

D) 73 GHz

Answer: C
Diff: 1 *Page Ref: Sec. 22.3-22.4*

7) How far does light travel in 1.0 μs?

A) 3.0×10^{14} m

B) 0.30 km

C) 3.0 m

D) 30 cm

Answer: B
Diff: 1 *Page Ref: Sec. 22.3-22.4*

8) How long does it take light to travel 1.0 m?

A) 3.3 ns

B) 3.3 μs

C) 3.3 ms

D) 3.3 s

Answer: A
Diff: 1 *Page Ref: Sec. 22.3–22.4*

9) How long does it take the signal from a local radio station to travel 20 miles?

A) 2.8 s

B) 108 ms

C) 38 ms

D) 108 μs

Answer: D
Diff: 1 *Page Ref: Sec, 22.3–22.4*

10) How far is a light year (the distance light travels in a year)?

A) 186,000 m

B) 3.0×10^8 m

C) 8.7×10^{13} m

D) 9.5×10^{15} m

Answer: D
Diff: 2 *Page Ref: Sec. 22.3–22.4*

11) A radar receiver indicates that a transmitted pulse return as an echo in 20 μs after transmission. How far away is the reflecting object?

A) 1.5 km

B) 3.0 km

C) 6.0 km

D) 9.0 km

Answer: B
Diff: 2 *Page Ref: Sec. 22.3–22.4*

12) Radiation from the Sun reaches the Earth (above the atmosphere) at a rate of about 1350 W/m^2. Assume that this is a single EM wave and calculate the maximum value of the electric field.

A) 0.71 kV/m

B) 1.0 kV/m

C) 1.4 kV/m

D) 2.0 kV/m

Answer: B
Diff: 2 *Page Ref: Sec. 22.5*

13) Radiation from the Sun reaches the Earth (above the atmosphere) at a rate of about 1350 W/m^2. Assume that this is a single EM wave and calculate the maximum value of the magnetic field.

A) 6.7 μT

B) 4.8 μT

C) 3.4 μT

D) 2.4 μT

Answer: C
Diff: 2 *Page Ref: Sec. 22.5*

14) What is the maximum value of the electric field at a distance 2.5 m from a 100-W light bulb?

A) 22 V/m

B) 31 V/m

C) 44 V/m

D) 62 V/m

Answer: B
Diff: 2 *Page Ref: Sec. 22.5*

15) What is the maximum value of the magnetic field at a distance 2.5 m from a 100-W light bulb?

A) 0.20 μT

B) 0.14 μT

C) 0.10 μT

D) 0.071 μT

Answer: C
Diff: 2 *Page Ref: Sec. 22.5*

16) A 15.0-mW laser puts out a narrow beam 2.00 mm in diameter. What is the average (rms) value of the electric field?

A) 0.95 kV/m

B) 1.3 kV/m

C) 1.9 kV/m

D) 2.7 kV/m

Answer: B
Diff: 2 *Page Ref: Sec. 22.5*

17) A 15.0-mW laser puts out a narrow beam 2.00 mm in diameter. What is the average (rms) value of the magnetic field?

A) 4.5 μT

B) 6.4 μT

C) 9.0 μT

D) none of the given answers

Answer: A
Diff: 2 *Page Ref: Sec. 22.5*

18) How much energy is transported across a 1.00-cm^2 area per hour by an EM wave whose electric field has an rms strength of 21.5 V/m?

A) 0.44 nJ

B) 0.44 μJ

C) 0.44 mJ

D) 0.44 J

Answer: D
Diff: 2 *Page Ref: Sec. 22.5*

19) Estimate the average power output of the Sun, given that about 1350 W/m^2 reaches the upper atmosphere of the Earth. The distance from the Sun to the Earth is 1.5×10^{11} m.

A) 1×10^{26} W

B) 2×10^{26} W

C) 3×10^{26} W

D) 4×10^{26} W

Answer: D
Diff: 2 *Page Ref: Sec. 22.5*

Chapter 23 Light: Geometric Optics

Conceptual Questions

1) Reflection, refraction, and the formation of images by mirrors and lenses has been successful described by the

A) wave model of light.

B) ray model of light.

C) particle model of light.

D) none of the given answers

Answer: B
Diff: 1 *Page Ref: Sec. 23.1*

2) The angle of incidence

A) must equal the angle of reflection.

B) is always less than the angle of reflection.

C) is always greater than the angle of reflection.

D) may be greater than, less than, or equal to the angle of reflection.

Answer: A
Diff: 1 *Page Ref: Sec. 23.2*

3) The principle on which mirrors work is

A) refraction.

B) polarization.

C) dispersion.

D) reflection.

Answer: D
Diff: 1 *Page Ref: Sec. 23.2*

4) A plane mirror forms an image that is

A) real and upright.

B) virtual and upright.

C) real and upside down.

D) virtual and upside down.

Answer: B
Diff: 1 *Page Ref: Sec. 23.2*

5) Plane mirrors produce images which

A) are always smaller than the actual object.

B) are always larger than the actual object.

C) are always the same size as the actual object.

D) could be smaller, larger, or the same size as the actual object, depending on the placement of the object.

Answer: C
Diff: 1 *Page Ref: Sec. 23.2*

6) An image formed when the light rays do not actually pass through the image location, and would not appear on paper or film placed at that location is referred to as a

A) real image.

B) virtual image.

Answer: B
Diff: 1 *Page Ref: Sec. 23.2*

7) An image formed when the light rays pass through the image location, and could appear on paper or film placed at the that location is referred to as a

A) real image.

B) virtual image.

Answer: A
Diff: 1 *Page Ref: Sec. 23.2*

8) Is it possible to see a virtual image?

A) No, since the rays that seem to emanate from a virtual image do not in fact emanate from the image.

B) No, since virtual images do not really exist.

C) Yes, the rays that appear to emanate from a virtual image can be focused on the retina just like those from an illuminated object.

D) Yes, since almost everything we see is virtual because most things do not themselves give off light, but only reflect light coming from some other source.

E) Yes, but only indirectly in the sense that if the virtual image is formed on a sheet of photographic film, one could later look at the picture formed.

Answer: C
Diff: 2 *Page Ref: Sec. 23.2*

9) A spherical mirror on which reflection takes place on the outer surface of the spherical shape is referred to as a

A) convex mirror.

B) concave mirror.

Answer: A
Diff: 1 *Page Ref: Sec. 23.3*

10) A spherical mirror on which reflection takes place on the inner surface of the sphere is referred to as a

A) convex mirror.

B) concave mirror.

Answer: B
Diff: 1 *Page Ref: Sec. 23.3*

11) If the radius of curvature of the concave mirror is r, the focal length is

A) 2r.

B) r.

C) r/2.

D) cannot be determined from the information given

Answer: C
Diff: 1 *Page Ref: Sec. 23.3*

12) A light ray, traveling parallel to a concave mirror's axis, strikes the mirror's surface near its midpoint. After reflection, this ray

A) again travels parallel to the mirror's axis.

B) travels at right angles to the mirror's axis.

C) passes through the mirror's center of curvature.

D) passes through the mirror's focal point.

Answer: D
Diff: 2 *Page Ref: Sec. 23.3*

13) Light arriving at a concave mirror on a path parallel to the axis is reflected

A) back parallel to the axis.

B) back on itself.

C) through the focal point.

D) through the center of curvature.

Answer: C
Diff: 2 *Page Ref: Sec. 23.3*

14) A light ray, traveling obliquely to a concave mirror's axis, crosses the axis at the mirror's center of curvature before striking the mirror's surface. After reflection, this ray

A) travels parallel to the mirror's axis.

B) travels at right angles to the mirror's axis.

C) passes through the mirror's center of curvature.

D) passes through the mirror's focal point.

Answer: C
Diff: 2 *Page Ref: Sec. 23.3*

15) Light arriving at a concave mirror on a path through the center of curvature is reflected

A) back parallel to the axis.

B) back on itself.

C) through the focal point.

D) midway between the focal point and the center of curvature.

Answer: B
Diff: 2 *Page Ref: Sec. 23.3*

16) A light ray, traveling obliquely to a concave mirror's surface, crosses the axis at the mirror's focal point before striking the mirror's surface. After reflection, this ray

A) travels parallel to the mirror's axis.

B) travels at right angles to the mirror's axis.

C) passes through the mirror's center of curvature.

D) passes through the mirror's focal point.

Answer: A
Diff: 2 *Page Ref: Sec. 23.3*

17) Light arriving at a concave mirror on a path through the focal point is reflected

A) back parallel to the axis.

B) back on itself.

C) through the focal point.

D) through the center of curvature.

Answer: A
Diff: 2 *Page Ref: Sec. 23.3*

18) State how to draw the three rays for finding the image position due to a curved mirror.

Answer: Ray 1 leaves the top of the object and is drawn such that it is parallel to the axis; therefore after reflection it must pass along a line through the focal point.
Ray 2 leaves the top of the object and is made to pass through the focal point; therefore it must reflect so it is parallel to the axis.
Ray 3 leaves the top of the object and is made to pass through the center of curvature; therefore it must reflect back on itself.
Diff: 2 *Page Ref: Sec. 23.3*

19) If you stand in front of a concave mirror, exactly at its focal point,

A) you won't see your image because there is none.

B) you won't see your image because it's focused at a different distance.

C) you will see your image, and you will appear smaller.

D) you will see your image and you will appear larger.

E) you will see your image at your same height.

Answer: A
Diff: 2 *Page Ref: Sec. 23.3*

20) An object is placed at a concave mirror's center of curvature. The image produced by the mirror is located

A) out beyond the center of curvature.

B) at the center of curvature.

C) between the center of curvature and the focal point.

D) at the focal point.

Answer: B
Diff: 2 *Page Ref: Sec. 23.3*

21) An object is positioned between a concave mirror's center of curvature and its focal point. The image produced by the mirror is located

A) out past the center of curvature.

B) at the center of curvature.

C) between the center of curvature and the focal point.

D) at the focal point.

Answer: A
Diff: 2 *Page Ref: Sec. 23.3*

22) An object is situated between a concave mirror's surface and its focal point. The image formed in this case is

A) real and inverted.

B) real and erect.

C) virtual and erect.

D) virtual and inverted.

Answer: C
Diff: 2 *Page Ref: Sec. 23.3*

23) If you stand in front of a convex mirror, at the same distance from it as its radius of curvature,

A) you won't see your image because there is none.

B) you won't see your image because it's focused at a different distance.

C) you will see your image and you will appear smaller.

D) you will see your image and you will appear larger.

E) you will see your image at your same height.

Answer: C
Diff: 2 *Page Ref: Sec. 23.3*

24) If you stand in front of a convex mirror, at the same distance from it as its focal length,

A) you won't see your image because there is none.

B) you won't see your image because it's focused at a different distance.

C) you will see your image and you will appear smaller.

D) you will see your image and you will appear larger.

E) you will see your image at your same height.

Answer: C
Diff: 2 *Page Ref: Sec. 23.3*

25) Sometimes when you look into a curved mirror you see a magnified image (a great big you) and sometimes you see a diminished image (a little you). If you look at the bottom (convex) side of a shiny spoon, what will you see?

A) You won't see an image of yourself because no image will be formed.

B) You will see a little you, upside down.

C) You will see a little you, right side up.

D) You will see a little you, but whether you are right side up or upside down depends on how near you are to the spoon.

E) You will either see a little you or a great big you, depending on how near you are to the spoon.

Answer: C
Diff: 2 *Page Ref: Sec. 23.3*

26) Concave spherical mirrors produce images which

A) are always smaller than the actual object.

B) are always larger than the actual object.

C) are always the same size as the actual object.

D) could be smaller than, larger than, or the same size as the actual object, depending on the placement of the object.

Answer: D
Diff: 2 *Page Ref: Sec. 23.3*

27) Convex spherical mirrors produce images which

A) are always smaller than the actual object.

B) are always larger than the actual object.

C) are always the same size as the actual object.

D) could be larger than, smaller than, or the same size as the actual object, depending on the placement of the object.

Answer: A
Diff: 2 *Page Ref: Sec. 23.3*

28) A single concave spherical mirror produces an image which is

A) always virtual.

B) always real.

C) real only if the object distance is less than f.

D) real only if the object distance is greater than f.

Answer: D
Diff: 2 *Page Ref: Sec. 23.3*

29) A single convex spherical mirror produces an image which is

A) always virtual.

B) always real.

C) real only if the object distance is less than f.

D) real only if the object distance is greater than f.

Answer: A
Diff: 2 *Page Ref: Sec. 23.3*

30) A negative magnification for a mirror means

A) the image is inverted, and the mirror is concave.

B) the image is inverted, and the mirror is convex.

C) the image is inverted, and the mirror may be concave or convex.

D) the image is upright, and the mirror is convex.

E) the image is upright, and the mirror may be concave or convex.

Answer: A
Diff: 2 *Page Ref: Sec. 23.3*

31) If the image distance is positive, the image formed is a

A) real image.

B) virtual image.

Answer: A
Diff: 2 *Page Ref: Sec. 23.3*

32) If the image distance is negative, the image formed is a

A) real image.

B) virtual image.

Answer: B
Diff: 2 *Page Ref: Sec. 23.3*

33) If the magnification is a positive value, the image is

A) upright.

B) inverted.

Answer: A
Diff: 2 *Page Ref: Sec. 23.3*

34) If the magnification is a negative value, the image is

A) upright.

B) inverted.

Answer: B
Diff: 2 *Page Ref: Sec. 23.3*

35) If the absolute value of the magnification is larger than one, then the image is

A) larger than the object.

B) the same size as the object.

C) smaller than the object.

Answer: A
Diff: 2 *Page Ref: Sec. 23.3*

36) If the absolute value of the magnification is smaller than one, then the image is

A) larger than the object.

B) the same size as the object.

C) smaller than the object.

Answer: C
Diff: 2 *Page Ref: Sec. 23.3*

37) If the absolute value of the magnification is equal to one, then the image is

A) larger than the object.

B) the same size as the object.

C) smaller than the object.

Answer: B
Diff: 2 *Page Ref: Sec. 23.3*

38) Light travels fastest

A) in a vacuum.

B) through water.

C) through glass.

D) through diamond.

Answer: A
Diff: 1 *Page Ref: Sec. 23.4*

39) For all transparent material substances, the index of refraction

A) is less than 1.

B) is greater than 1.

C) is equal to 1.

D) could be any of the given answers; it all depends on optical density.

Answer: B
Diff: 1 *Page Ref: Sec. 23.4*

40) An index of refraction less than one for a medium would imply

A) that the speed of light in the medium is the same as the speed of light in vacuum.

B) that the speed of light in the medium is greater than the speed of light in vacuum.

C) refraction is not possible.

D) reflection is not possible.

Answer: B
Diff: 1 *Page Ref: Sec. 23.4*

41) The index of refraction of diamond is 2.42. This means that a given frequency of light travels

A) 2.42 times faster in air than it does in diamond.

B) 2.42 times faster in diamond than it does in air.

C) 2.42 times faster in vacuum than it does in diamond.

D) 2.42 times faster in diamond than it does in vacuum.

Answer: C
Diff: 1 *Page Ref: Sec. 24.4*

42) The angle of incidence

A) must equal the angle of refraction.

B) is always less than the angle of refraction.

C) is always greater than the angle of refraction.

D) may be greater than, less than, or equal to the angle of refraction.

Answer: D
Diff: 1 *Page Ref: Sec. 23.5*

43) Light traveling at an angle into a denser medium is refracted

A) toward the normal.

B) away from the normal.

C) parallel to the normal.

D) equally.

Answer: A
Diff: 1 *Page Ref: Sec. 23.5*

44) Light enters air from water. The angle of refraction will be

A) greater than the angle of incidence.

B) equal to the angle of incidence.

C) less than the angle of incidence.

Answer: A
Diff: 2 *Page Ref: Sec. 23.5*

45) A ray of light, which is traveling in air, is incident on a glass plate at a 45° angle. The angle of refraction in the glass

A) is less than 45°.

B) is greater than 45°.

C) is equal to 45°.

D) could be any of the above; it all depends on the index of refraction of glass.

Answer: A
Diff: 1 *Page Ref: Sec. 23.5*

46) The principle on which fiber optics is based is

A) refraction.

B) polarization.

C) dispersion.

D) total internal reflection.

Answer: D
Diff: 1 *Page Ref: Sec. 23.6*

47) The critical angle for a beam of light passing from water into air is 48.8°. This means that all light rays with an angle of incidence greater than this angle will be

A) absorbed.

B) totally reflected.

C) partially reflected and partially transmitted.

D) totally transmitted.

Answer: B
Diff: 2 *Page Ref: Sec. 23.6*

48) The principle on which lenses work is

A) refraction.

B) polarization.

C) dispersion.

D) total internal reflection.

Answer: A
Diff: 1 *Page Ref: Sec. 23.7-23.8*

49) Lenses that are thickest at the center called

A) converging lenses.

B) diverging lenses.

Answer: A
Diff: 1 *Page Ref: Sec. 23.7-23.8*

50) Lenses that are thinner at the center than the edges are called

A) converging lenses.

B) diverging lenses.

Answer: B
Diff: 1 *Page Ref: Sec. 23.7–23.8*

51) Lenses that are thicker at the center

A) spread out light rays.

B) bend light rays to a point beyond the lens.

C) have no effect on light rays.

D) reflect light rays back.

Answer: B
Diff: 1 *Page Ref: Sec. 23.7–23.8*

52) Two diverging lenses are similar except that lens B is rated at 20 diopters, whereas lens A is rated at 10 diopters. The focal length of lens B is

A) one-fourth of the focal length of lens A.

B) one-half of the focal length of lens A.

C) twice the focal length of lens A.

D) four times the focal length of lens A.

Answer: B
Diff: 1 *Page Ref: Sec. 23.7–23.8*

53) A light ray, traveling parallel to the axis of a thin concave lens, strikes the lens near its midpoint. After traveling though the lens, this ray emerges traveling obliquely to the axis of the lens

A) such that it never crosses the axis.

B) crossing the axis at a point equal to twice the focal length.

C) passing between the lens and its focal point.

D) passing through the focal point.

Answer: A
Diff: 2 *Page Ref: Sec. 23.7–23.8*

54) A light ray, traveling parallel to the axis of a convex thin lens, strikes the lens near its midpoint. After traveling through the lens, this ray emerges traveling obliquely to the axis of the lens

A) such that it never crosses the axis.

B) crossing the axis at a point equal to twice the focal length.

C) passing between the lens and its focal point.

D) passing through its focal point.

Answer: D
Diff: 2 *Page Ref: Sec. 23.7–23.8*

55) State how to draw the three rays for finding the image position due to a thin lens.

Answer: Ray 1 leaves the top of the object and is drawn such that it is parallel to the axis; therefore it emerges from the lens along a line through the focal point on the back side of the lens.
Ray 2 leaves the top of the object and is made to pass through the *other* focal point; therefore it emerges from the lens parallel to the axis.
Ray 3 leaves the top of the object and is directed toward the very center of the lens; therefore it emerges from the lens a the same angle as it entered.
Diff: 2 *Page Ref: Sec. 23.3*

56) A convex lens has focal length f. An object is located at infinity. The image formed is located

A) at 2f.

B) between f and 2f.

C) at f.

D) between the lens and f.

Answer: C
Diff: 1 *Page Ref: Sec. 23.7–23.8*

57) A convex lens has a focal length f. An object is placed at f on the axis. The image formed is located

A) at infinity.

B) between 2f and infinity.

C) at 2f.

D) between f and 2f.

Answer: A
Diff: 1 *Page Ref: Sec. 23.7–23.8*

58) A convex lens has focal length f. An object is placed at 2f on the axis. The image formed is located

A) at 2f.

B) between f and 2f.

C) at f.

D) between the lens and f.

Answer: A
Diff: 1 *Page Ref: Sec. 23.7–23.8*

59) A convex lens has a focal length f. An object is placed between f and 2f on the axis. The image formed is located

A) at 2f.

B) between f and 2f.

C) at f.

D) at a distance greater than 2f from the lens.

Answer: D
Diff: 2 Page Ref: Sec. 23.7–23.8

60) A convex lens has a focal length f. An object is placed between infinity and 2f from the lens on its axis. The image formed is located

A) at 2f.

B) between f and 2f.

C) at f.

D) between the lens and f.

Answer: B
Diff: 2 Page Ref: Sec. 23.7–23.8

61) A object is placed between a convex lens and its focal point. The image formed is

A) virtual and erect.

B) virtual and inverted.

C) real and erect.

D) real and inverted.

Answer: A
Diff: 2 Page Ref: Sec. 23.7–23.8

62) The images formed by concave lenses

A) are always real.

B) are always virtual.

C) could be real or virtual; it depends on whether the object distance is smaller or greater than the focal length.

D) could be real or virtual, but always real when the object is placed at the focal point.

Answer: B
Diff: 1 Page Ref: Sec. 23.7–23.8

63) The image of the rare stamp you see through a magnifying glass is

A) always the same orientation as the stamp.

B) always upside-down compared to the stamp.

C) either the same orientation or upside-down, depending on how close the stamp is to the glass.

D) either the same orientation or upside-down, depending on the thickness of the glass used.

Answer: C
Diff: 2 Page Ref: Sec. 23.7-23.8

64) A lamp is placed 1 m from a screen. Between the lamp and the screen is placed a converging lens of focal length 24 cm. The filament of the lamp can be imaged on the screen. As the lens position is varied with respect to the lamp,

A) no sharp image will be seen for any lens position.

B) a sharp image will be seen when the lens is halfway between the lamp and the screen.

C) a sharp image will be seen when the lens is 40 cm from the lamp.

D) a sharp image will be seen when the lens is 60 cm from the lamp.

E) a sharp image will be seen when the lens is either 40 cm from the lamp or 60 cm from the lamp, but not otherwise.

Answer: E
Diff: 2 Page Ref: Sec. 23.7-23.8

65) Two thin lenses, of focal lengths f_1 and f_2 placed in contact with each other are equivalent to a single lens of focal length of

A) $f_1 + f_2$.

B) $1/(f_1 + f_2)$.

C) $(f_1 + f_2)/f_1f_2$.

D) $f_1f_2/(f_1 + f_2)$.

Answer: D
Diff: 2 Page Ref: Sec. 23.9

66) Two thin double-convex (convex-convex) lenses are placed in contact. If each has a focal length of 20 cm, how would you expect the combination to function?

A) about like a single lens of focal length 20 cm

B) about like a single lens of focal length 40 cm

C) about like a single lens of focal length slightly greater than 20 cm

D) about like a single lens of focal length less than 20 cm

Answer: D
Diff: 2 Page Ref: Sec. 23.9

67) A diverging lens (f = –4.0 cm) is positioned 2.0 cm to the left of a converging lens f = +6.0 cm). A 1.0-mm diameter beam of parallel light rays is incident on the diverging lens from the left. After leaving the converging lens, the outgoing rays

A) converge.

B) diverge.

C) form a parallel beam of diameter D > 1.0 mm.

D) form a parallel beam of diameter D < 1.0 mm.

E) will travel back toward the light source.

Answer: C
Diff: 3 *Page Ref: Sec. 23.9*

Quantitative Problems

1) A laser beam strikes a plane's reflecting surface with an angle of incidence of 52°. What is the angle between the incident ray and the reflected ray?

A) 52°

B) 105°

C) 45°

D) 90°

Answer: B
Diff: 1 *Page Ref: Sec. 23.2*

2) An object is located 2.6 m in front of a plane mirror. The image formed by the mirror appears to be

A) 1.3 m in front of the mirror.

B) on the mirror's surface.

C) 1.3 m behind the mirror's surface.

D) 2.6 m behind the mirror's surface.

Answer: D
Diff: 1 *Page Ref: Sec. 23.2*

3) How far are you from your image when you stand 0.75 m in front of a vertical plane mirror?

A) 0.75 m

B) 1.5 m

C) 3.0 m

D) none of the given answers

Answer: B
Diff: 1 *Page Ref: Sec. 23.2*

4) How fast do you approach your image when you approach a vertical plane mirror at a speed of 2 m/s?

A) 1 m/s

B) 2 m/s

C) 4 m/s

D) none of the given answers

Answer: C
Diff: 1 *Page Ref: Sec. 23.2*

5) A spherical concave mirror has a radius of curvature of 20 cm. How far from the mirror is the focal point located?

A) 10 cm

B) 20 cm

C) 30 cm

D) 40 cm

Answer: A
Diff: 1 *Page Ref: Sec. 23.3*

6) A concave mirror with a radius of 20 cm creates a real image 30 cm from the mirror. What is the object distance?

A) 20 cm

B) 15 cm

C) 7.5 cm

D) 5.0 cm

Answer: B
Diff: 1 *Page Ref: Sec. 23.3*

7) A object is 12 cm in front of a concave mirror, and the image is 3.0 cm in front of the mirror. What is the focal length of the mirror?

A) 15 cm

B) 4.0 cm

C) 2.4 cm

D) 1.3 cm

Answer: C
Diff: 1 *Page Ref: Sec. 23.3*

8) An object is 10 cm in front of a concave mirror with focal length 3 cm. Where is the image?

A) 13 cm from the mirror

B) 7.0 cm from the mirror

C) 4.3 cm from the mirror

D) 3.3 cm from the mirror

Answer: C
Diff: 1 Page Ref: Sec. 23.3

9) A concave spherical mirror has a focal length of 20 cm. An object is placed 10 cm in front of the mirror on the mirror's axis. Where is the image located?

A) 20 cm behind the mirror

B) 20 cm in front of the mirror

C) 6.7 cm behind the mirror

D) 6.7 cm in front of the mirror

Answer: A
Diff: 1 Page Ref: Sec. 23.3

10) A concave spherical mirror has a focal length of 20 cm. An object is placed 30 cm in front of the mirror on the mirror's axis. Where is the image located?

A) 12 cm behind the mirror

B) 12 cm in front of the mirror

C) 60 cm behind the mirror

D) 60 cm in front of the mirror

Answer: D
Diff: 1 Page Ref: Sec. 23.3

11) An object is 5.7 cm from a concave mirror. The image is 4.7 cm tall, and 10 cm from the mirror. How tall is the object?

A) 12 cm

B) 11 cm

C) 8.2 cm

D) 2.7 cm

Answer: D
Diff: 2 Page Ref: Sec. 23.3

12) An object is placed 15 cm from a concave mirror of focal length 20 cm. The object is 4.0 cm tall. How tall is the image?

A) 1.0 cm

B) 2.0 cm

C) 8.0 cm

D) 16 cm

Answer: D
Diff: 2 *Page Ref: Sec. 23.3*

13) An object is 47.5 cm tall. The image is 38.6 cm tall, and 14.8 cm from the mirror. How far is the object from the mirror?

A) 124 cm

B) 47.6 cm

C) 18.2 cm

D) 12.0 cm

Answer: C
Diff: 2 *Page Ref: Sec. 23.3*

14) A 1.4 cm tall object is 4.0 cm from a concave mirror. If the image is 4.0 cm tall, how far is it from the mirror?

A) 11 cm

B) 9.4 cm

C) 1.4 cm

D) 0.090 cm

Answer: A
Diff: 1 *Page Ref: Sec. 23.3*

15) An object is placed 15 cm from a concave mirror of focal length 20 cm. The object is 4.0 cm tall. Where is the image located?

A) 12 cm behind the mirror

B) 12 cm in front of the mirror

C) 60 cm behind the mirror

D) 60 cm in front of the mirror

Answer: C
Diff: 2 *Page Ref: Sec. 23.3*

16) When a person stands 40 cm in front of a cosmetic mirror (concave mirror), the erect image is twice the size of the object. What is the focal length of the mirror?

A) 27 cm

B) 40 cm

C) 80 cm

D) 160 cm

Answer: C
Diff: 2 *Page Ref: Sec. 23.3*

17) A person's face is 30 cm in front of a concave shaving mirror. If the image is an erect image 1.5 times as large as the object, what is the mirror's focal length?

A) 20 cm

B) 50 cm

C) 70 cm

D) 90 cm

Answer: D
Diff: 2 *Page Ref: Sec. 23.3*

18) An image is 4.0 cm behind a concave mirror with focal length 5.0 cm. Where is the object?

A) 2.2 cm in front of the mirror

B) 2.2 cm behind the mirror

C) 9.0 cm in front of the mirror

D) 1.0 cm behind the mirror

Answer: A
Diff: 2 *Page Ref: Sec. 23.3*

19) A convex spherical mirror has a focal length of -20 cm. An object is placed 10 cm in front of the mirror on the mirror's axis. Where is the image located?

A) 20 cm behind the mirror

B) 20 cm in front of the mirror

C) 6.7 cm behind the mirror

D) 6.7 cm in front of the mirror

Answer: C
Diff: 1 *Page Ref: Sec. 23.3*

20) A convex spherical mirror has a focal length of –20 cm. An object is placed 30 cm in front of the mirror on the mirror's axis. Where is the image located?

A) 12 cm in front of the mirror

B) 60 cm behind the mirror

C) 60 cm in front of the mirror

D) none of the given answers

Answer: D
Diff: 1 *Page Ref: Sec. 23.3*

21) An object is 14 cm in front of a convex mirror. The image is 5.8 cm behind the mirror. What is the focal length of the mirror?

A) –4.1 cm

B) –8.2 cm

C) –9.9 cm

D) –20 cm

Answer: C
Diff: 2 *Page Ref: Sec. 23.3*

22) An object is 8.90 cm tall. The image is 7.80 cm tall, and 14.8 cm from a convex mirror. What is the mirror's focal length?

A) –120 cm

B) –105 cm

C) –16.9 cm

D) –13.0 cm

Answer: A
Diff: 3 *Page Ref: Sec. 23.3*

23) If a material has an index of refraction of 1.50, what is the speed of light through it?

A) 2.00×10^8 m/s

B) 3.00×10^8 m/s

C) 4.50×10^8 m/s

D) 6.00×10^8 m/s

Answer: A
Diff: 1 *Page Ref: Sec. 23.4*

24) A light ray in air is incident on an air to glass interface at an angle of 45° and is refracted at an angle of 30° to the normal. What is the index of refraction of the glass?

A) 1.23

B) 1.31

C) 1.41

D) 1.74

Answer: C
Diff: 1 *Page Ref: Sec. 23.5*

25) Light enters a substance from air at an angle of 32.0°, and continues at an angle of 23.0°. What is the index of refraction of the substance?

A) 0.74

B) 1.11

C) 1.28

D) 1.36

Answer: D
Diff: 1 *Page Ref: Sec. 23.5*

26) Light passes from air to water. The incoming ray is at an angle of 17.0° to the normal. The index of refraction is 1.33. What is the angle in the water?

A) 22.9°

B) 22.6°

C) 18.3°

D) 12.7°

Answer: D
Diff: 1 *Page Ref: Sec. 23.5*

27) An oil layer that is 5.0 cm thick is spread smoothly and evenly over the surface of water on a windless day. What is the angle of refraction in the water for a ray of light that has an angle of incidence of 45° as it enters the oil from the air above? (The index of refraction for oil is 1.15, and for water it is 1.33.)

A) 27°

B) 32°

C) 36°

D) 39°

Answer: B
Diff: 2 *Page Ref: Sec. 23.5*

28) A diver is 1.2 m beneath the surface of a still pond of water. At what angle must the diver shine a beam of light toward the surface in order for a person on a distant bank to see it? (The index of refraction for water is 1.33.)

A) 41°

B) 49°

C) 59°

D) 90°

Answer: B
Diff: 2 *Page Ref: Sec. 23.5*

29) A beam of light, traveling in air, strikes a plate of transparent material at an angle of incidence of 56.0°. It is observed that the reflected and refracted beams form an angle of 90.0°. What is the index of refraction of this material?

A) 1.40

B) 1.43

C) 1.44

D) 1.48

Answer: D
Diff: 1 *Page Ref: Sec. 23.5*

30) A beam of light traveling in air is incident on a slab of transparent material. The incident beam and the refracted beam make angles of 40° and 26° to the normal. What is the speed of light in the transparent material?

A) 1.0×10^8 m/s

B) 2.0×10^8 m/s

C) 2.3×10^8 m/s

D) 3.0×10^8 m/s

Answer: B
Diff: 2 *Page Ref: Sec. 23.5*

31) A substance has an index of refraction of 1.46. Light is passing through it at 53.0°. At what angle will it leave into the air?

A) It will not leave.

B) 59.1°

C) 43.2°

D) 33.2°

Answer: A
Diff: 1 *Page Ref: Sec. 23.6*

32) What is the critical angle for light traveling from crown glass (n = 1.52) into water (n = 1.33)?

A) 42°

B) 48°

C) 57°

D) 61°

Answer: D

Diff: 1 *Page Ref: Sec. 23.6*

33) Lucite has an index of refraction of 1.50. What is its critical angle of incidence?

A) 1.16°

B) 15°

C) 41.8°

D) 87.4°

Answer: C

Diff: 1 *Page Ref: Sec. 23.6*

34) An optic fiber is made of clear plastic with index of refraction of 1.50. For what angle of incidence will light remain within the plastic "guide"?

A) >23.4°

B) >38.3°

C) >40.3°

D) >41.8°

Answer: D

Diff: 1 *Page Ref: Sec. 23.6*

35) The critical angle for a substance is measured at 53.7°. Light enters from air at 45.0°. At what angle will it continue?

A) 34.7°

B) 45.0°

C) 53.7°

D) It will not continue, but be totally reflected.

Answer: A

Diff: 2 *Page Ref: Sec. 23.6*

36) Light enters a substance from air at 30.0° to the normal. It continues through the substance at 23.0° to the normal. What would be the critical angle for this substance?

A) 53°

B) 51.4°

C) 36.7°

D) 12.6°

Answer: B

Diff: 2 *Page Ref: Sec. 23.6*

37) An optical fiber is 1.0 meter long and has a diameter of 20 μm. Its ends are perpendicular to its axis. Its index of refraction is 1.30. What is the maximum number of reflections a light ray entering one end will make before it emerges from the other end?

A) 42,000

B) 26,000

C) 24,000

D) 18,000

Answer: A
Diff: 3 *Page Ref: Sec. 23.6*

38) An object is placed 40 cm in front of a 20 cm focal length converging lens. How far is the image of this object from the lens?

A) 40 cm

B) 20 cm

C) 13 cm

D) none of the given answers

Answer: A
Diff: 1 *Page Ref: Sec. 23.7–23.8*

39) An object is 12 cm in front of a converging lens with focal length 4 cm. Where is the image?

A) 8.0 cm behind the lens

B) 6.0 cm in front of the lens

C) 6.0 cm behind the lens

D) 4.0 cm in front of the lens

Answer: C
Diff: 1 *Page Ref: Sec. 23.7–23.8*

40) An object is 15 mm in front of a converging lens, and the image is 4.0 mm behind the lens. What is the focal length of the lens?

A) 11 mm

B) 5.5 mm

C) 3.8 mm

D) 3.2 mm

Answer: B
Diff: 1 *Page Ref: Sec. 23.7–23.8*

41) A 14-mm tall object is 4.0 mm from a converging lens. If the image is 4.0 mm tall, how far is it from the lens?

A) 14 mm

B) 8.7 mm

C) 1.4 mm

D) 1.1 mm

Answer: D
Diff: 1 *Page Ref: Sec. 23.7-23.8*

42) When an object is 40 m in front of a converging lens the inverted image is half the size of the object. What is the focal length of this lens?

A) 13 cm

B) 20 cm

C) 40 cm

D) 53 cm

Answer: A
Diff: 2 *Page Ref: Sec. 23.7-23.8*

43) An image is 4.0 mm in front of a converging lens with focal length 5.0 mm. Where is the object?

A) 2.2 mm in front of the lens

B) 2.2 mm behind the lens

C) 9.0 mm behind the lens

D) 20 mm in front of the lens

Answer: A
Diff: 2 *Page Ref: Sec. 23.7-23.8*

44) An object is 4.1 cm tall, and 10.3 cm from a converging lens. The image is virtual and 6.2 cm tall. What is the focal length of the lens?

A) 6.8 cm

B) 10 cm

C) 16 cm

D) 30 cm

Answer: D
Diff: 3 *Page Ref: Sec. 23.7-23.8*

45) An object is 15.2 mm from a converging lens. The image is 4.0 mm tall, and 9.0 cm from the lens. How tall is the object?

A) 6.8 mm

B) 5.4 mm

C) 1.7 mm

D) 0.68 mm

Answer: D
Diff: 2 *Page Ref: Sec. 23.7–23.8*

46) When an object is placed 60 cm from a converging lens, it forms a real image. When the object is moved to 40 cm from the lens, the image moves 10 cm farther from the lens. What is the focal length of the lens?

A) 20 cm

B) 30 cm

C) 40 cm

D) 42 cm

Answer: A
Diff: 3 *Page Ref: Sec. 23.7–23.8*

47) An object is placed at a distance of 30 cm from a thin convex lens. The lens has a focal length of 10 cm. What are the values, respectively, of the image distance and lateral magnification?

A) 15 cm, 2.0

B) 25 cm, 1.0

C) 60 cm, -0.50

D) 15 cm, -0.50

Answer: D
Diff: 2 *Page Ref: Sec. 23.7–23.8*

48) An object is placed at 30 cm in front of a diverging lens with a focal length of 10 cm. What is the image distance?

A) 7.5 cm

B) -7.5 cm

C) 15 cm

D) -15 cm

Answer: B
Diff: 2 *Page Ref: Sec. 23.7–23.8*

49) An object is placed at 30 cm in front of a diverging lens with a focal length of 10 cm. What is the magnification?

A) 0.25

B) -0.25

C) 0.67

D) -0.67

Answer: A
Diff: 2 *Page Ref: Sec. 23.7-23.8*

50) An object is 10.4 cm tall, and 4.8 cm in front of a diverging lens. The image is 4.0 cm from the lens. How tall is the image?

A) 13 cm

B) 8.7 cm

C) 5.4 cm

D) 1.8 cm

Answer: B
Diff: 2 *Page Ref: Sec. 23.7-23.8*

51) An object is 6.0 cm tall, and is in front of a diverging lens. The image is 2.5 cm tall, and 7.5 cm from the lens. What is the focal length of the lens?

A) -6.0 cm

B) -7.5 cm

C) -13 cm

D) -18 cm

Answer: C
Diff: 3 *Page Ref: Sec. 23.7-23.8*

52) An object is placed at a distance of 40 cm from a thin lens. If a virtual image forms at a distance of 50 cm from the lens, on the same side as the object, what is the focal length of the lens?

A) 45 cm

B) 75 cm

C) 90 cm

D) 200 cm

Answer: D
Diff: 2 *Page Ref: Sec. 23.7-23.8*

53) How far from a lens of focal length 50 mm must the object be placed if it is to form a virtual image magnified in size by a factor of three?

A) 33 mm

B) 42 mm

C) 48 mm

D) 54 mm

Answer: A
Diff: 3 *Page Ref: Sec. 23.7–23.8*

54) How far from a 50–mm focal length lens, such as is used in many 35–mm cameras, must an object be positioned if it is to form a real image magnified in size by a factor of three?

A) 46 mm

B) 52 mm

C) 58 mm

D) 67 mm

Answer: D
Diff: 3 *Page Ref: Sec. 23.7–23.8*

55) Two very thin lenses, each with focal length 20 cm, are placed in contact. What is the focal length of this compound lens?

A) 40 cm

B) 20 cm

C) 15 cm

D) 10 cm

Answer: D
Diff: 2 *Page Ref: Sec. 23.9*

56) A double convex (convex–convex) thin lens has radii of curvature 46 cm, and is made of glass of index of refraction $n = 1.60$. What is the focal length?

A) infinite

B) 38 cm

C) 30 cm

D) 18 cm

Answer: B
Diff: 1 *Page Ref: Sec. 23.10*

57) A double convex lens made of glass ($n = 1.50$) has a radius of 40 cm on the front side and 30 cm on the back side. What is the focal length of the lens?

A) 11 cm

B) 34 cm

C) 80 cm

D) 240 cm

Answer: B
Diff: 2 *Page Ref: Sec. 23.10*

58) A biconvex lens is formed by using a piece of plastic ($n = 1.70$). The radius of the front surface is 20 cm and the radius of the back surface is 30 cm. What is the focal length of the lens?

A) 17 cm

B) 86 cm

C) -86 cm

D) -17 cm

Answer: A
Diff: 2 *Page Ref: Sec. 23.10*

59) A plano-convex lens is to have a focal length of 40 cm. It is made of glass of index of refraction 1.65. What radius of curvature is required?

A) 13 cm

B) 26 cm

C) 32 cm

D) 36 cm

Answer: B
Diff: 2 *Page Ref: Sec. 23.10*

Chapter 24 The Wave Nature of Light

Conceptual Questions

1) State Huygen's principle.

Answer: Every point on a wave front can be considered as a source of tiny wavelets that spread out in the forward direction at the speed of the wave itself. The new wave front is the envelope of all the wavelets – that is, tangent to all of them.

Diff: 1 *Page Ref: Sec. 24.2–24.2*

2) Which of the following is a false statement?

A) All points on a given wave front have the same phase.

B) Rays are always perpendicular to wave fronts.

C) All wave fronts have the same amplitude.

D) The spacing between adjacent wave fronts is one-half wavelength.

Answer: C

Diff: 1 *Page Ref: Sec. 24.1–24.2*

3) The wave theory of light is attributed to

A) Christian Huygens.

B) Isaac Newton.

C) Max Planck.

D) Albert Einstein.

Answer: A

Diff: 1 *Page Ref: Sec. 24.1–24.2*

4) The particle theory of light is attributed to

A) Christian Huygens.

B) Isaac Newton.

C) Max Planck.

D) Albert Einstein.

Answer: B

Diff: 1 *Page Ref: Sec. 24.1–24.2*

5) When a light wave enters into a medium of different optical density,

A) its speed and frequency change.

B) its speed and wavelength change.

C) its frequency and wavelength change.

D) its speed, frequency, and wavelength change.

Answer: B
Diff: 1 *Page Ref: Sec. 24.1–24.2*

6) When a beam of light (wavelength = 590 nm), originally traveling in air, enters a piece of glass (index of refraction 1.50), its frequency

A) increases by a factor of 1.50.

B) is reduced to 2/3 its original value.

C) is unaffected.

D) none of the given answers

Answer: C
Diff: 1 *Page Ref: Sec. 24.1–24.2*

7) When a beam of light (wavelength = 590 nm), originally traveling in air, enters a piece of glass (index of refraction 1.50), its wavelength

A) increases by a factor of 1.50.

B) is reduced to 2/3 its original value.

C) is unaffected.

D) none of the given answers

Answer: B
Diff: 1 *Page Ref: Sec. 24.1–24.2*

8) What principle is responsible for light spreading as it passes through a narrow slit?

A) refraction

B) polarization

C) diffraction

D) interference

Answer: C
Diff: 1 *Page Ref: Sec. 24.1–24.2*

9) Radio waves are diffracted by large objects such as buildings, whereas light is not noticeably diffracted. Why is this?

A) Radio waves are unpolarized, whereas light is plane polarized.

B) The wavelength of light is much smaller than the wavelength of radio waves.

C) The wavelength of light is much greater than the wavelength of radio waves.

D) Radio waves are coherent and light is usually not coherent.

Answer: B
Diff: 1 *Page Ref: Sec. 24.1–24.2*

10) What principle is responsible for alternating light and dark bands when light passes through two or more narrow slits?

A) refraction

B) polarization

C) dispersion

D) interference

Answer: D
Diff: 1 *Page Ref: Sec. 24.3*

11) Two light sources are said to be coherent if they

A) are of the same frequency.

B) are of the same frequency, and maintain a constant phase difference.

C) are of the same amplitude, and maintain a constant phase difference.

D) are of the same frequency and amplitude.

Answer: B
Diff: 1 *Page Ref: Sec. 24.3*

12) What do we mean when we say that two light rays striking a screen are in phase with each other?

A) When the electric field due to one is a maximum, the electric field due to the other is also a maximum, and this relation is maintained as time passes.

B) They are traveling at the same speed.

C) They have the same wavelength.

D) They alternately reinforce and cancel each other.

Answer: A
Diff: 1 *Page Ref: Sec. 24.3*

13) Two beams of coherent light travel different paths arriving at point P. If the maximum constructive interference is to occur at point P, the two beams must

A) travel paths that differ by a whole number of wavelengths.

B) travel paths that differ by an odd number of half-wavelengths.

Answer: A
Diff: 1 *Page Ref: Sec. 24.3*

14) Two beams of coherent light travel different paths arriving at point P. If the maximum destructive interference is to occur at point P, the two beams must

A) travel paths that differ by a whole number of wavelengths.

B) travel paths that differ by an odd number of half-wavelengths.

Answer: B
Diff: 1 *Page Ref: Sec. 24.3*

15) At the first maxima on either side of the central bright spot in a double–slit experiment, light from each opening arrives

A) in phase.

B) 90° out of phase.

C) 180° out of phase.

D) none of the given answers

Answer: A
Diff: 1 *Page Ref: Sec. 24.3*

16) At the first minima on either side of the central bright spot in a double–slit experiment, light from each opening arrives

A) in phase.

B) 90° out of phase.

C) 180° out of phase.

D) none of the given answers

Answer: C
Diff: 1 *Page Ref: Sec. 24.3*

17) At the second maxima on either side of the central bright spot in a double–slit experiment, light from

A) each opening travels the same distance.

B) one opening travels twice as far as light from the other opening.

C) one opening travels one wavelength of light farther than light from the other opening.

D) one opening travels two wavelengths of light farther than light from the other opening.

Answer: D
Diff: 2 *Page Ref: Sec. 24.3*

18) In a Young's double slit experiment, if the separation between the slits decreases, what happens to the distance between the interference fringes?

A) It decreases.

B) It increases.

C) It remains the same.

D) There is not enough information to determine.

Answer: B
Diff: 2 *Page Ref: Sec. 24.3*

19) In a double–slit experiment, it is observed that the distance between adjacent maxima on a remote screen is 1.0 cm. What happens to the distance between adjacent maxima when the slit separation is cut in half?

A) It increases to 2.0 cm.

B) It increases to 4.0 cm.

C) It decreases to 0.50 cm.

D) It decreases to 0.25 cm.

Answer: A
Diff: 1 *Page Ref: Sec. 24.3*

20) One beam of coherent light travels path P_1 in arriving at point Q and another coherent beam travels path P_2 in arriving at the same point. If these two beams are to interfere destructively, the path difference $P_1 - P_2$ must be equal to

A) an odd number of half–wavelengths.

B) zero.

C) a whole number of wavelengths.

D) a whole number of half–wavelengths.

Answer: A
Diff: 1 *Page Ref: Sec. 24.3*

21) If a wave from one slit of a Young's double slit experiment arrives at a point on the screen one–half wavelength behind the wave from the other slit, which is observed at that point?

A) bright fringe

B) dark fringe

C) gray fringe

D) multi–colored fringe

Answer: B
Diff: 2 *Page Ref: Sec. 24.3*

22) Why would it be impossible to obtain interference fringes in a double–slit experiment if the separation of the slits is less than the wavelength of the light used?

A) The very narrow slits required would generate many different wavelengths, thereby washing out the interference pattern.

B) The two slits would not emit coherent light.

C) The fringes would be too close together.

D) In no direction could a path difference as large as one wavelength be obtained, and this is needed if a bright fringe, in addition to the central fringe, is to be observed.

Answer: D
Diff: 1 *Page Ref: Sec. 24.3*

23) The separation between adjacent maxima in a double-slit interference pattern using monochromatic light is

A) greatest for red light.

B) greatest for green light.

C) greatest for blue light.

D) the same for all colors of light.

Answer: A
Diff: 1 *Page Ref: Sec. 24.3*

24) The principle which explains why a prism separates white light into different colors is

A) refraction.

B) polarization.

C) dispersion.

D) total internal reflection.

Answer: C
Diff: 1 *Page Ref: Sec. 24.4*

25) The principle which allows a rainbow to form is

A) refraction.

B) polarization.

C) dispersion.

D) total internal reflection.

Answer: C
Diff: 1 *Page Ref: Sec. 24.4*

26) White light is

A) light of wavelength 550 nm, in the middle of the visible spectrum.

B) a mixture of all frequencies.

C) a mixture of red, green, and blue light.

D) the term used to describe very bright light.

E) the opposite (or complementary color) of black light.

Answer: B
Diff: 1 *Page Ref: Sec. 24.4*

27) Light with wavelength slightly shorter than 400 nm is called

A) ultraviolet light.

B) visible light.

C) infrared light.

D) none of the given answers

Answer: A
Diff: 1 *Page Ref: Sec. 24.4*

28) Light with wavelength slightly longer than 750 nm is called

A) ultraviolet light.

B) visible light.

C) infrared light.

D) none of the given answers

Answer: C

Diff: 1 *Page Ref: Sec. 24.4*

29) Which color of light undergoes the greatest refraction when passing from air to glass?

A) red

B) yellow

C) green

D) violet

Answer: D

Diff: 2 *Page Ref: Sec. 24.4*

30) Which color of light undergoes the smallest refraction when passing from air to glass?

A) red

B) yellow

C) green

D) violet

Answer: A

Diff: 2 *Page Ref: Sec. 24.4*

31) A beam of white light is incident on a thick glass plate with parallel sides, at an angle between $0°$ and $90°$ with the normal. Which color emerges from the other side first?

A) red

B) green

C) violet

D) None of the given; all colors emerge at the same time.

Answer: D

Diff: 3 *Page Ref: Sec. 24.4*

32) A person gazes at a very distant light source. If she now holds up two fingers, with a very small gap between them, and looks at the light source, she will see

A) the same thing as without the fingers, but dimmer.

B) a series of bright spots.

C) a sequence of closely spaced bright lines.

D) a hazy band of light varying from red at one side to blue or violet at the other.

Answer: C

Diff: 1 *Page Ref: Sec. 24.5*

33) In a single slit diffraction experiment, if the width of the slit increases, what happens to the width of the central maximum on a screen?

A) It increases.

B) It decreases.

C) It remains the same.

D) There is not enough information to determine.

Answer: B
Diff: 2 *Page Ref: Sec. 24.5*

34) Consider two diffraction gratings; one has 4000 lines per cm and the other one has 6000 lines per cm. Make a statement comparing the dispersion of the two gratings.

A) The 4000-line grating produces the greater dispersion.

B) The 6000-line grating produces the greater dispersion.

C) Both gratings produce the same dispersion, but the orders are sharper for the 4000-line grating.

D) Both gratings produce the same dispersion, but the orders are sharper for the 6000-line grating.

Answer: B
Diff: 1 *Page Ref: Sec. 24.6-24.7*

35) Consider two diffraction gratings with the same slit separation, the only difference being that one grating has 3 slits and the other 4 slits. If both gratings are illuminated with a beam of the same monochromatic light, make a statement concerning the separation between the orders.

A) The grating with 3 slits produces the greater separation between orders.

B) The grating with 4 slits produces the greater separation between orders.

C) Both gratings produce the same separation between orders.

D) Both gratings produce the same separation between orders, but the orders are better defined with the 4-slit grating.

Answer: D
Diff: 2 *Page Ref: Sec. 24.6-24.7*

36) The colors on an oil slick are caused by reflection and

A) diffraction.

B) interference.

C) refraction.

D) polarization.

Answer: B
Diff: 1 *Page Ref: Sec. 24.8*

37) We have seen that two monochromatic light waves can interfere constructively or destructively, depending on their phase difference. One consequence of this phenomenon is

A) the colors you see when white light is reflected from a soap bubble.

B) the appearance of a mirage in the desert.

C) a rainbow.

D) the way in which Polaroid sunglasses work.

E) the formation of an image by a converging lens, such as the lens in your eye.

Answer: A
Diff: 1 *Page Ref: Sec. 24.8*

38) When a beam of light, which is traveling in glass, strikes an air boundary, there is

A) a 90° phase change in the reflected beam.

B) no phase change in the reflected beam.

C) a 180° phase change in the reflected beam.

D) a 45° phase change in the reflected beam.

Answer: B
Diff: 1 *Page Ref: Sec. 24.8*

39) When a beam of light, which is traveling in air, is reflected by a glass surface, there is

A) a 90° phase change in the reflected beam.

B) no phase change in the reflected beam.

C) a 180° phase change in the reflected beam.

D) a 45° phase change in the reflected beam.

Answer: C
Diff: 1 *Page Ref: Sec. 24.8*

40) A soap film is being viewed in white light. As the film becomes very much thinner than the wavelength of blue light, the film

A) appears totally transparent because it reflects no visible light.

B) appears white because it reflects all wavelengths of visible light.

C) appears blue since all other colors are transmitted.

D) appears red since all other colors are transmitted.

Answer: A
Diff: 1 *Page Ref: Sec. 24.8*

41) In terms of the wavelength of light in magnesium fluoride, what is the minimum thickness of magnesium fluoride coating that must be applied to a glass lens to make it non-reflecting for that wavelength? (The index of refraction of magnesium fluoride is intermediate to that of glass and air.)

A) one-fourth wavelength

B) one-half wavelength

C) one wavelength

D) There is no minimum thickness.

Answer: A
Diff: 2 *Page Ref: Sec. 24.8*

42) A convex lens is placed on a flat glass plate and illuminated from above with monochromatic red light. When viewed from above, concentric bands of red and dark are observed. What does one observe at the exact center of the lens where the lens and the glass plate are in direct contact?

A) a bright red spot

B) a dark spot

C) a rainbow of color

D) a bright spot that is some color other than red

Answer: B
Diff: 2 *Page Ref: Sec. 24.8*

43) What principle is responsible for the fact that certain sunglasses can reduce glare from reflected surfaces?

A) refraction

B) polarization

C) diffraction

D) total internal reflection

Answer: B
Diff: 1 *Page Ref: Sec. 24.10*

44) For a beam of light, the direction of polarization is defined as

A) the beam's direction of travel.

B) the direction of the electric field's vibration.

C) the direction of the magnetic field's vibration.

D) the direction that is mutually perpendicular to the electric and magnetic field vectors.

Answer: B
Diff: 1 *Page Ref: Sec. 24.10*

45) What is the process to obtain polarized light in a dichroic material like a Polaroid film?

A) reflection

B) refraction

C) selective absorption

D) scattering

Answer: C
Diff: 2 *Page Ref: Sec. 24.10*

46) When the transmission axes of two Polaroid films are perpendicular to each other, what is the percentage of the incident light which will pass the two films?

A) 0%

B) 25%

C) 50%

D) 75%

Answer: A
Diff: 2 *Page Ref: Sec. 24.10*

47) Sunlight reflected from the surface of a lake

A) is unpolarized.

B) tends to be polarized with its electric field vector parallel to the surface of the lake.

C) tends to be polarized with its electric field vector perpendicular to the surface of the lake.

D) has undergone refraction by the surface of the lake.

E) none of the given answers

Answer: B
Diff: 1 *Page Ref: Sec. 24.10*

48) The polarization of sunlight is greatest at

A) sunrise.

B) sunset.

C) both sunrise and sunset.

D) midday.

Answer: C
Diff: 2 *Page Ref: Sec. 24.10*

49) In which of the following is diffraction NOT exhibited?

A) viewing a light source through a small pinhole

B) examining a crystal by X-rays

C) using a microscope under maximum magnification

D) resolving two nearby stars with a telescope

E) determining the direction of polarization with a birefringent crystal

Answer: E
Diff: 2 *Page Ref: Sec. 24.10*

50) On a clear day, the sky appears to be more blue toward the zenith (overhead) than it does toward the horizon. This occurs because

A) the atmosphere is denser higher up than it is at the Earth's surface.

B) the temperature of the upper atmosphere is higher than it is at the Earth's surface.

C) the sunlight travels over a longer path at the horizon, resulting in more scattering.

D) none of the given answers

Answer: C
Diff: 2 *Page Ref: Sec. 24.12*

Quantitative Problems

1) A beam of light ($f = 5.0 \times 10^{14}$ Hz) enters a piece of glass ($n = 1.5$). What is the frequency of the light while it is in the glass?

A) 5.0×10^{14} Hz

B) 7.5×10^{14} Hz

C) 3.3×10^{14} Hz

D) none of the given answers

Answer: A
Diff: 1 *Page Ref: Sec. 24.1–24.2*

2) Light has a wavelength of 600 nm in a vacuum. It passes into glass, which has an index of refraction of 1.50. What is the wavelength of the light in the glass?

A) 600 nm

B) 500 nm

C) 400 nm

D) 300 nm

Answer: C
Diff: 1 *Page Ref: Sec. 24.1–24.2*

3) Light has wavelength 600 nm in a vacuum. It passes into glass, which has an index of refraction of 1.50. What is the frequency of the light inside the glass?

A) 3.3×10^{14} Hz

B) 5.0×10^{14} Hz

C) 3.3×10^{5} Hz

D) 5.0×10^{5} Hz

Answer: B
Diff: 1 *Page Ref: Sec. 24.1–24.2*

4) Light has a wavelength of 600 nm in a vacuum. It passes into glass, which has an index of refraction of 1.50. What is the speed of the light in the glass?

A) 3.0×10^8 m/s

B) 2.5×10^8 m/s

C) 2.0×10^8 m/s

D) 1.5×10^8 m/s

Answer: C
Diff: 1 *Page Ref: Sec. 24.1-24.2*

5) Light of wavelength 550 nm in vacuum is found to travel at 1.96×10^8 m/s in a certain liquid. Determine the index of refraction of the liquid.

A) 0.65

B) 1.53

C) 1.96

D) 5.50

Answer: B
Diff: 1 *Page Ref: Sec. 24.1-24.2*

6) Light of wavelength 550 nm in air is found to travel at 1.96×10^8 m/s in a certain liquid. Determine the frequency of the light in the liquid.

A) 5.5×10^{14} Hz

B) 3.6×10^{14} Hz

C) 5.5×10^5 Hz

D) 3.6×10^5 Hz

Answer: A
Diff: 2 *Page Ref: Sec. 24.1-24.2*

7) Light of wavelength 550 nm in air is found to travel at 1.96×10^8 m/s in a certain liquid. Determine the wavelength of the light in the liquid.

A) 550 nm

B) 359 nm

C) 281 nm

D) 303 nm

Answer: B
Diff: 2 *Page Ref: Sec. 24.1-24.2*

8) Two thin slits are 6.00 μm apart. Monochromatic light falls on these slits, and produces a fifth order interference fringe at an angle of 32.3°. What is the wavelength of the light?

A) 164 nm

B) 416 nm

C) 614 nm

D) 641 nm

Answer: D

Diff: 1 *Page Ref: Sec. 24.3*

9) Light of wavelength 575 nm falls on a double-slit and the third order bright fringe is seen at an angle of 6.5°. What is the separation between the double slits?

A) 5.0 μm

B) 10 μm

C) 15 μm

D) 20 μm

Answer: C

Diff: 2 *Page Ref: Sec. 24.3*

10) In a Young's double slit experiment, if the separation between the two slits is 0.050 mm and the distance from the slits to a screen is 2.5 m, find the spacing between the first-order and second-order bright fringes for light with wavelength of 600 nm.

A) 1.5 cm

B) 3.0 cm

C) 4.5 cm

D) 6.0 cm

Answer: B

Diff: 2 *Page Ref: Sec. 24.3*

11) In a double-slit experiment, the slit separation is 2.0 mm, and two wavelengths, 750 nm and 900 nm, illuminate the slits. A screen is placed 2.0 m from the slits. At what distance from the central maximum on the screen will a bright fringe from one pattern first coincide with a bright fringe from the other?

A) 1.5 mm

B) 3.0 mm

C) 4.5 mm

D) 6.0 mm

Answer: C

Diff: 2 *Page Ref: Sec. 24.3*

12) Two thin slits are 0.050 mm apart. Monochromatic light of wavelength 634 nm falls on the slits. If there is a screen 6.0 m away, how far apart are adjacent interference fringes?

A) 0.76 mm

B) 7.6 mm

C) 7.6 cm

D) 76 cm

Answer: C
Diff: 2 *Page Ref: Sec. 24.3*

13) A monochromatic light is incident on a Young's double slit setup that has a slit separation of 30.0 μm. The resultant bright fringe separation is 2.15 cm on a screen 1.20 m from the double slit. What is the separation between the third-order bright fringe and the zeroth-order bright fringe?

A) 8.60 cm

B) 7.35 cm

C) 6.45 cm

D) 4.30 cm

Answer: C
Diff: 2 *Page Ref: Sec. 24.3*

14) A parallel light beam containing two wavelengths, 480 nm and 700 nm, strikes a plain piece of glass at an angle of incidence of 60°. The index of refraction of the glass is 1.4830 at 480 nm and 1.4760 at 700 nm. Determine the angle between the two beams in the glass.

A) 0.10°

B) 0.15°

C) 0.20°

D) 0.25°

Answer: C
Diff: 2 *Page Ref: Sec. 24.4*

15) A ray of light consisting of blue light (wavelength 480 nm) and red light (wavelength 670 nm) is incident on a thick piece of glass at 80°. What is the angular separation between the refracted red and refracted blue beams while they are in the glass? (The respective indices of refraction for the blue light and the red light are 1.4636 and 1.4561.)

A) 0.27°

B) 0.33°

C) 0.34°

D) 0.46°

Answer: A
Diff: 2 *Page Ref: Sec. 24.4*

16) 350 nm of light falls on a single slit of width 0.20 mm. What is the angular width of the central diffraction peak?

A) 0.10°

B) 0.15°

C) 0.20°

D) 0.30°

Answer: C
Diff: 2 *Page Ref: Sec. 24.5*

17) A single slit, which is 0.050 mm wide, is illuminated by light of 550 nm wavelength. What is the angular separation between the first two minima on either side of the central maximum?

A) 0.36°

B) 0.47°

C) 0.54°

D) 0.63°

Answer: D
Diff: 2 *Page Ref: Sec. 24.5*

18) Light of wavelength 687 nm is incident on a single slit 0.75 mm wide. At what distance from the slit should a screen be placed if the second dark fringe in the diffraction pattern is to be 1.7 mm from the center of the screen?

A) 0.39 m

B) 0.93 m

C) 1.1 m

D) 1.9 m

Answer: B
Diff: 2 *Page Ref: Sec. 24.5*

19) Light of wavelength 610 nm is incident on a slit 0.20 mm wide and the diffraction pattern is produced on a screen that is 1.5 m from the slit. What is the width of the central maximum?

A) 0.34 cm

B) 0.68 cm

C) 0.92 cm

D) 1.2 cm

Answer: C
Diff: 2 *Page Ref: Sec. 24.5*

20) Light of wavelength 580 nm is incident on a slit of width 0.300 mm. An observing screen is placed 2.00 m from the slit. Find the position of the first order dark fringe from the center of the screen.

A) 0.26 mm

B) 1.9 mm

C) 3.9 mm

D) 7.7 mm

Answer: C
Diff: 2 *Page Ref: Sec. 24.5*

21) Light of wavelength 580 nm is incident on a slit of width 0.300 mm. An observing screen is placed 2.00 m from the slit. Find the width of the central maximum.

A) 0.26 mm

B) 1.9 mm

C) 3.9 mm

D) 7.7 mm

Answer: D
Diff: 2 *Page Ref: Sec. 24.5*

22) When light illuminates a grating with 7000 lines per centimeter, its second order maximum is at 62.4°. What is the wavelength of the light?

A) 336 nm

B) 363 nm

C) 633 nm

D) 752 nm

Answer: C
Diff: 1 *Page Ref: Sec. 24.6–24.7*

23) A diffraction grating has 5000 lines per cm. The angle between the central maximum and the fourth order maximum is 47.2°. What is the wavelength of the light?

A) 138 nm

B) 183 nm

C) 367 nm

D) 637 nm

Answer: C
Diff: 2 *Page Ref: Sec. 24.6–24.7*

24) Monochromatic light is incident on a grating that is 75 mm wide and ruled with 50,000 lines. The second-order maximum is seen at 32.5°. What is the wavelength of the incident light?

A) 202 nm

B) 403 nm

C) 605 nm

D) 806 nm

Answer: B
Diff: 2 *Page Ref: Sec. 24.6–24.7*

25) In a diffraction experiment, light of 600 nm wavelength produces a first-order maximum 0.350 mm from the central maximum on a distant screen. A second monochromatic source produces a third-order maximum 0.870 mm from the central maximum when it passes through the same diffraction grating. What is the wavelength of the light from the second source?

A) 479 nm

B) 497 nm

C) 749 nm

D) 794 nm

Answer: B
Diff: 2 *Page Ref: Sec. 24.6–24.7*

26) A diffraction grating has 6000 lines per centimeter ruled on it. What is the angular separation between the second and the third orders on the same side of the central order when the grating is illuminated with a beam of light of wavelength 550 nm?

A) 20.5°

B) 30.5°

C) 40.5°

D) 50.5°

Answer: C
Diff: 2 *Page Ref: Sec. 24.6–24.7*

27) White light is spread out into spectral hues by a grating. If the grating has 2000 lines per centimeter, at what angle will red light (640 nm) appear in the first order?

A) 3.57°

B) 7.35°

C) 11.2°

D) 13.4°

Answer: B
Diff: 2 *Page Ref: Sec. 24.6–24.7*

28) A He-Ne laser (632.8 nm) is used to calibrate a grating. If the first-order maximum occurs at 20.5°, what is the grating constant (the distance between the slits)?

A) 1.81 μm

B) 2.20 μm

C) 3.62 μm

D) 4.52 μm

Answer: A
Diff: 2 *Page Ref: Sec. 24.6–24.7*

29) Monochromatic light of wavelength 500 nm is incident normally on a grating. If the third-order maximum of the diffraction pattern is observed at 32.0°, what is the grating constant (distance between the slits)?

A) 0.93 μm

B) 1.4 μm

C) 2.8 μm

D) 8.5 μm

Answer: C
Diff: 2 *Page Ref: Sec. 24.6–24.7*

30) Monochromatic light of wavelength 500 nm is incident normally on a grating. If the third-order maximum of the diffraction pattern is observed at 32.0°, how many total number of maxima can be seen?

A) 5

B) 7

C) 10

D) 11

Answer: D
Diff: 3 *Page Ref: Sec. 24.6–24.7*

31) A glass plate 2.5 cm long is separated from another glass plate at one end by a strand of someone's hair (diameter 0.010 mm). How far apart are the adjacent interference bands when viewed with light of wavelength 600 nm?

A) 0.25 mm

B) 0.50 mm

C) 0.75 mm

D) 1.0 mm

Answer: C
Diff: 2 *Page Ref: Sec. 24.8*

32) A soap bubble has an index of refraction of 1.33. What minimum thickness of this bubble will ensure maximum reflectance of normally incident 530 nm wavelength light?

A) 24.9 nm

B) 99.6 nm

C) 199 nm

D) 398 nm

Answer: B
Diff: 2 *Page Ref: Sec. 24.8*

33) Light of wavelength 500 nm illuminates a soap film (n = 1.33). What is the minimum thickness of film that will give an interference when the light is incident normally on it?

A) 24 nm

B) 94 nm

C) 188 nm

D) 376 nm

Answer: B
Diff: 2 *Page Ref: Sec. 24.8*

34) What is the minimum thickness of a nonreflecting film coating (n = 1.30) on a glass lens (n = 1.50) for wavelength 500 nm?

A) 250 nm

B) 192 nm

C) 167 nm

D) 96.2 nm

Answer: D
Diff: 2 *Page Ref: Sec. 24.8*

35) An ideal polarizer is placed in a beam of unpolarized light and the intensity of the transmitted light is 1. A second ideal polarizer is placed in the beam with its referred direction rotated 40° to that of the first polarizer. What is the intensity of the beam after it has passed through both polarizers?

A) 0.77

B) 0.64

C) 0.59

D) 0.41

Answer: C
Diff: 1 *Page Ref: Sec. 24.10*

36) A polarizer (with its preferred direction rotated 30° to the vertical) is placed in a beam of unpolarized light of intensity 1. After passing through the polarizer, the beam's intensity is

A) 0.25.

B) 0.50.

C) 0.87.

D) 0.75.

Answer: B
Diff: 2 *Page Ref: Sec. 24.10*

37) A beam of unpolarized light in air strikes a flat piece of glass at an angle of 57.3°. If the reflected beam is completely polarized, what is the index of refraction of the glass?

A) 1.50

B) 1.52

C) 1.54

D) 1.56

Answer: D
Diff: 2 *Page Ref: Sec. 24.10*

38) Unpolarized light is passed through a polarizer–analyzer combination. The transmission axes of the polarizer and the analyzer are at 30.0° to each other. What percentage of the unpolarized light gets through the combination?

A) 37.5%

B) 50%

C) 75%

D) 100%

Answer: A
Diff: 2 *Page Ref: Sec. 24–10*

39) How far above the horizon is the Moon when its image reflected in calm water is completely polarized?

A) 36.9°

B) 43.2°

C) 46.8°

D) 53.1°

Answer: A
Diff: 2 *Page Ref: Sec. 24.10*

40) A beam of light passes through a polarizer and then an analyzer. In this process, the intensity of the light transmitted is reduced to 10% of the intensity incident on the analyzer. What is the angle between the axes of the polarizer and the analyzer?

A) 18°

B) 22°

C) 68°

D) 72°

Answer: D
Diff: 2 *Page Ref: Sec. 24.10*

41) What is the Brewster's angle for light traveling in vacuum and reflecting off a piece of glass of index of refraction 1.48?

A) 31.9°

B) 39.8°

C) 45.3°

D) 56.0°

Answer: D
Diff: 1 *Page Ref: Sec. 24.10*

Chapter 25 Optical Instruments

Conceptual Questions

1) The length of time the shutter is open and the film is exposed in a camera is determined by the

A) shutter speed.

B) *f*-stop.

C) focusing.

D) none of the given answers

Answer: A
Diff: 1 *Page Ref: Sec. 25.1*

2) The amount of light reaching the film in a camera is determined by the

A) shutter speed.

B) *f*-stop.

C) focusing.

D) none of the given answers

Answer: B
Diff: 1 *Page Ref: Sec. 25.1*

3) In a single-lens reflex camera the lens-film distance may be varied by sliding the lens forward or backward with respect to the camera housing. If, with such a camera, a fuzzy picture is obtained, this means that

A) the lens was too far from the film.

B) the lens was too close to the film.

C) too much light was incident on the film.

D) too little light was incident on the film.

E) none of the given answers

Answer: E
Diff: 2 *Page Ref: Sec. 25.1*

4) A camera lens that covers the film with a field of view that corresponds approximately to that of normal vision is referred to as a

A) normal lens.

B) telephoto lens.

C) wide-angle lens.

D) zoom lens.

Answer: A
Diff: 1 *Page Ref: Sec. 25.1*

5) A camera lens that acts like a telescope to magnify images is referred to as a

A) normal lens.

B) telephoto lens.

C) wide-angle lens.

D) zoom lens.

Answer: B
Diff: 1 *Page Ref: Sec. 25.1*

6) A camera lens that covers the film with a wider field of view than that of the eye and through which objects appear smaller is referred to as a

A) normal lens.

B) telephoto lens.

C) wide-angle lens.

D) zoom lens.

Answer: C
Diff: 1 *Page Ref: Sec. 25.1*

7) In which of the following ways is a camera different from the human eye?

A) The camera always forms an inverted image, the eye does not.

B) The camera always forms a real image, the eye does not.

C) The camera utilizes a fixed focal length lens, the eye does not.

D) For the camera, the image magnification is greater than one, but for the eye the magnification is less than one.

E) A camera cannot focus on objects at infinity but the eye can.

Answer: C
Diff: 2 *Page Ref: Sec. 25.2*

8) The principal refraction of light by the eye occurs at the

A) cornea.

B) lens.

C) retina.

D) iris.

Answer: A
Diff: 1 *Page Ref: Sec. 25.2*

9) The closest distance at which an eye can see objects clearly is

A) the near point.

B) the far point.

C) nearsightedness.

D) farsightedness.

Answer: A
Diff: 1 *Page Ref: Sec. 25.2*

10) The farthest distance at which an eye can see objects clearly is

A) the near point.

B) the far point.

C) nearsightedness.

D) farsightedness.

Answer: B
Diff: 1 *Page Ref: Sec. 25.2*

11) If a person's eyeball is too long from front to back, the person is likely to suffer from

A) spherical aberration.

B) nearsightedness.

C) farsightedness.

D) astigmatism.

Answer: B
Diff: 1 *Page Ref: Sec. 25.2*

12) Nearsightedness can usually be corrected with

A) converging lenses.

B) diverging lenses.

C) achromatic lenses.

D) cylindrical lenses.

Answer: B
Diff: 1 *Page Ref: Sec. 25.2*

13) If the human eyeball is too long from front to back, this gives rise to a vision defect that can be corrected by using

A) convex meniscus eyeglasses.

B) concave meniscus eyeglasses.

C) cylindrical eyeglasses.

D) contact lenses, but no ordinary lenses.

E) shaded glasses (i.e., something that will cause the iris to dilate more).

Answer: B
Diff: 2 *Page Ref: Sec. 25.2*

14) If a person's eyeball is too short from front to back, the person is likely to suffer from

A) astigmatism.

B) spherical aberration.

C) farsightedness.

D) nearsightedness.

Answer: C
Diff: 1 *Page Ref: Sec. 25.2*

15) Farsightedness can usually be corrected with

A) cylindrical lenses.

B) achromatic lenses.

C) diverging lenses.

D) converging lenses.

Answer: D

Diff: 1 *Page Ref: Sec. 25.2*

16) If the human eyeball is too short from front to back, this gives rise to a vision defect that can be corrected by using

A) convex meniscus eyeglasses.

B) concave meniscus eyeglasses.

C) cylindrical eyeglasses.

D) contact lenses, but no ordinary lenses.

E) shaded glasses (i.e., something that will cause the iris to dilate more).

Answer: A

Diff: 2 *Page Ref: Sec. 25.2*

17) What type of lens is a magnifying glass?

A) converging

B) diverging

C) spherical

D) cylindrical

Answer: A

Diff: 1 *Page Ref: Sec. 25.3*

18) An important reason for using a very large diameter objective in an astronomical telescope is

A) to increase the magnification.

B) to increase the resolution.

C) to form a virtual image, which is easier to look at.

D) to increase the width of the field of view.

E) to increase the depth of the field of view.

Answer: B

Diff: 1 *Page Ref: Sec. 25.4*

19) Consider the image formed by a refracting telescope. Suppose an opaque screen is placed in front of the lower half of the objective lens. What effect will this have?

A) The top half of the image will be blacked out.

B) The lower half of the image will be blacked out.

C) The entire image will be blacked out, since the entire lens is needed to form an image.

D) The image will appear as it would if the objective were not blocked, but it will be dimmer.

E) There will be no noticeable difference in the appearance of the image with the objective partially blocked or not.

Answer: D
Diff: 2 *Page Ref: Sec. 25.4*

20) Assuming the film used has uniform sensitivity throughout the visible spectrum, in which of the following cases would you be able to best distinguish between two closely spaced stars? (The lens referred to is the objective lens of the telescope used.)

A) use a large lens and blue light

B) use a large lens and red light

C) use a small lens and blue light

D) use a small lens and red light

Answer: A
Diff: 2 *Page Ref: Sec. 25.4*

21) A refracting telescope has a magnification m. If the objective focal length is doubled and the eyepiece focal length is halved, what is the new magnification?

A) 4m

B) 2m

C) m/2

D) m/4

Answer: A
Diff: 2 *Page Ref: Sec. 25.4*

22) With what color light would you expect to be able to see the greatest detail when using a microscope?

A) red, because of its long wavelength

B) yellow, because of its right wavelength

C) blue, because of its shorter wavelength

D) Color does not matter.

Answer: C
Diff: 2 *Page Ref: Sec. 25.5*

23) Spherical lenses suffer from

A) both spherical and chromatic aberration.

B) spherical aberration, but not chromatic aberration.

C) chromatic aberration, but not spherical aberration.

D) neither spherical nor chromatic aberration.

Answer: A
Diff: 1 *Page Ref: Sec. 25.6*

24) Spherical mirrors suffer from

A) both spherical and chromatic aberration.

B) spherical aberration, but not chromatic aberration.

C) chromatic aberration, but not spherical aberration.

D) neither spherical nor chromatic aberration.

Answer: B
Diff: 1 *Page Ref: Sec. 25.6*

25) The resolving power of a microscope refers to the ability to

A) distinguish objects of different colors.

B) form clear images of two points that are very close together.

C) form a very large image.

D) form a very bright image.

Answer: B
Diff: 1 *Page Ref: Sec. 25.7–25.9*

26) If the diameter of a radar dish is doubled, what happens to its resolving power assuming that all other factors remain unchanged? Its resolving power

A) quadruples.

B) doubles.

C) halves.

D) is reduced to one-quarter its original value.

Answer: B
Diff: 2 *Page Ref: Sec. 25.7–25.9*

Quantitative Problems

1) A near-sighted person has a far point of 18 cm. What lens (in diopters) will allow this person to see distant objects clearly?

A) +5.6 D

B) -5.6 D

C) +0.056 D

D) -0.056 D

Answer: B
Diff: 2 *Page Ref: Sec. 25.2*

2) A person cannot see clearly objects more than 70.0 cm away. What power of lens should be prescribed if the glass is to be worn 1.00 cm in front of the eye?

A) 1.45 D

B) -1.45 D

C) 0.0145 D

D) -0.0145 D

Answer: B
Diff: 2 *Page Ref: Sec. 25.2*

3) A nearsighted person wears glasses whose lenses have power of -0.15 D. What is the person's far point if the glasses are very close to the eyes?

A) 1.5 m

B) 3.3 m

C) 6.0 m

D) 6.7 m

Answer: D
Diff: 2 *Page Ref: Sec. 25.2*

4) What power lens is needed to correct for farsightedness where the uncorrected near point is 75 cm?

A) +2.7 D

B) -2.7 D

C) +5.3 D

D) -5.3 D

Answer: A
Diff: 2 *Page Ref: Sec. 25.2*

5) The near point of a farsighted person is 100 cm. She places reading glasses close to her eyes, and with them she can comfortably read a newspaper at a distance of 25 cm. What lens power is required?

A) +2.5 D

B) +3.0 D

C) +3.2 D

D) –2.0 D

Answer: B
Diff: 2 *Page Ref: Sec. 25.2*

6) A farsighted person can read a newspaper held 25 cm from his eyes, if he wears glasses of +3.33 diopters. What is this person's near point?

A) 4.2 cm

B) 25 cm

C) 31 cm

D) 1.5 m

Answer: D
Diff: 2 *Page Ref: Sec. 25.2*

7) A magnifying lens has a focal length of 10 cm. A person has a near point of 25 cm. What is the magnification of the lens for that person when their eyes are focused at infinity?

A) 1.5

B) 2.5

C) 3.5

D) 4.5

Answer: B
Diff: 2 *Page Ref: Sec. 25.3*

8) A magnifying lens has a focal length of 10 cm. A person has a near point of 25 cm. What is the magnification of the lens for that person when their eyes are focused at their near point?

A) 1.5

B) 2.5

C) 3.5

D) 4.5

Answer: C
Diff: 2 *Page Ref: Sec. 25.3*

9) A magnifying glass has a focal length of 7.0 cm. What is the magnification if the image is viewed by a relaxed eye?

A) 1.6

B) 2.6

C) 3.6

D) 4.6

Answer: C
Diff: 2 *Page Ref: Sec. 25.3*

10) A person uses a converging lens of focal length 5.0 cm as a magnifying glass. What is the maximum possible magnification?

A) 4.0

B) 5.0

C) 6.0

D) 7.0

Answer: C
Diff: 2 *Page Ref: Sec. 25.3*

11) A person uses a converging lens of focal length 5.0 cm as a magnifying glass. What is the magnification if the person's eye is relaxed?

A) 4.0

B) 5.0

C) 6.0

D) 7.0

Answer: B
Diff: 2 *Page Ref: Sec. 25.3*

12) You have available lenses of focal lengths 2.0 cm, 4.0 cm, 8.0 cm, and 16.0 cm. If you were to use any two of these lenses to build a telescope, what is the maximum magnification you could achieve?

A) 2.0

B) 4.0

C) 6.0

D) 8.0

Answer: D
Diff: 1 *Page Ref: Sec. 25.4*

13) You have available lenses of focal lengths 2.0 cm, 4.0 cm, 8.0 cm, and 16 cm. If you were to use any two of these lenses to build a telescope, what is the lens separation for the maximum magnification telescope?

A) 10.0 cm

B) 12.0 cm

C) 18.0 cm

D) 24.0 cm

Answer: C
Diff: 1 *Page Ref: Sec. 25.4*

14) The objective of a telescope has a focal length of 200 cm and its eyepiece has a focal length of 1.0 cm. What is the magnification of this telescope when viewing an object at infinity?

A) 20

B) 0.0050

C) 200

D) none of the given answers

Answer: A
Diff: 1 *Page Ref: Sec. 25.4*

15) A student constructs an astronomical telescope with a magnification of 10. If the telescope has a converging lens of focal length 50 cm, what is the focal length of the eyepiece?

A) 2.5 cm

B) 5.0 cm

C) 10 cm

D) 25 cm

Answer: B
Diff: 2 *Page Ref: Sec. 25.4*

16) A student constructs an astronomical telescope with a magnification of 10. If the telescope has a converging lens of focal length 50 cm, what is the resulting length of the telescope?

A) 53 cm

B) 55 cm

C) 60 cm

D) 75 cm

Answer: B
Diff: 2 *Page Ref: Sec. 25.4*

17) A person is designing a 10X telescope. If the telescope is limited to a length of 20 cm, what is the approximate focal length of the objective?

A) 16 cm

B) 17 cm

C) 18 cm

D) 19 cm

Answer: C
Diff: 2 *Page Ref: Sec. 25.4*

18) A microscope has an objective lens of focal length 1.4 mm and an eyepiece of focal length 20 mm, adjusted for minimum eyestrain. A blood sample is placed 1.5 mm from the objective. How far apart are the lenses?

A) 20 mm

B) 21 mm

C) 23 mm

D) 41 mm

Answer: D
Diff: 2 *Page Ref: Sec. 25.5*

19) A microscope has an objective lens of focal length 1.4 mm and an eyepiece of focal length 20 mm, adjusted for minimum eyestrain. A blood sample is placed 1.5 mm from the objective. What is the overall magnification?

A) 18

B) 37

C) 180

D) 370

Answer: D
Diff: 2 *Page Ref: Sec. 25.5*

20) A compound microscope has an objective with a focal length of 3.00 mm and an eyepiece of focal length 6.00 cm. If the two lenses are separated by 40.0 cm, what is the total magnification?

A) 27.8

B) 55.6

C) 278

D) 556

Answer: D
Diff: 2 *Page Ref: Sec. 25.5*

21) A compound microscope has a 18-cm barrel and an objective with a focal length of 8.0 mm. What is the focal length of the eyepiece to give a total magnification of 240?

A) 0.13 cm

B) 1.5 cm

C) 1.9 cm

D) 2.3 cm

Answer: D
Diff: 2 *Page Ref: Sec. 25.5*

22) A binary star system in the constellation Orion has an angular separation of 10^{-5} rad. If the wavelength of the light from the system is 500 nm, what is the smallest aperture (diameter) telescope that can just resolve the two stars?

A) 0.50 cm

B) 0.61 cm

C) 5.0 cm

D) 6.1 cm

Answer: D
Diff: 2 *Page Ref: Sec. 25.7-25.9*

23) A compound microscope is designed to resolve objects which are 0.010 mm apart. If the focal length of the objective is 4.0 cm and the wavelength of light used is 550 nm, what is the diameter of the objective?

A) 0.27 mm

B) 0.54 mm

C) 2.7 mm

D) 5.4 mm

Answer: C
Diff: 2 *Page Ref: Sec. 25.7-25.9*

24) The pupil of a person's eye changes from a diameter of 3.5 mm to 1.5 mm as the illumination is increased. By what factor does the minimum angle of resolution change?

A) 0.43

B) 0.65

C) 2.0

D) 2.3

Answer: D
Diff: 2 *Page Ref: Sec. 25.7-25.9*

25) The 2.4-m reflecting Hubble Space Telescope has been placed into Earth orbit by the space shuttle. What angular resolution could this telescope achieve if the wavelength is 500 nm?

A) 2.5×10^{-7} rad

B) 3.6×10^{-7} rad

C) 5.7×10^{-7} rad

D) 6.8×10^{-7} rad

Answer: A

Diff: 2 *Page Ref: Sec. 25.7-25.9*

Chapter 26 Special Theory of Relativity

Conceptual Questions

1) You are riding in a spaceship that has no windows, radios, or other means for you to observe or measure what is outside. You wish to determine if the ship is stopped or moving at constant velocity. What should you do?

A) You can determine if the ship is moving by determining the apparent velocity of light.

B) You can determine if the ship is moving by checking your precision time piece. If it's running slow, the ship is moving.

C) You can determine if the ship is moving either by determining the apparent velocity of light or by checking your precision time piece. If it's running slow, the ship is moving.

D) You should give up because you have taken on an impossible task.

Answer: D
Diff: 1 Page Ref: Sec. 26.1

2) The Michelson-Morley experiment was designed to measure

A) the relativistic mass of the electron.

B) the relativistic energy of the electron.

C) the velocity of the Earth relative to the ether.

D) the acceleration of gravity on the Earth's surface.

Answer: C
Diff: 1 Page Ref: Sec. 26.1

3) Michelson and Morley concluded from the results of their experiment that

A) the experiment was a failure since there was no detectable shift in the interference pattern.

B) the experiment was successful in not detecting a shift in the interference pattern.

C) the experiment was a failure since they detected a shift in the interference pattern.

D) the experiment was successful in detecting a shift in the interference pattern.

Answer: A
Diff: 1 Page Ref: Sec. 26.1

4) You can build an interferometer yourself if you use the following components:

A) a light source, a detector screen, a partially silvered mirror, a flat mirror, and a glass plate.

B) a light source, a detector screen, two partially silvered mirrors, and a glass plate.

C) a light source, a detector screen, two partially silvered mirrors, a flat mirror, and a glass plate.

D) a light source, a detector screen, a partially silvered mirror, two flat mirrors, and a glass plate.

Answer: D
Diff: 2 *Page Ref: Sec. 26.1*

5) State the relativity principle.

Answer: The basic laws of physics are the same in all inertial reference frames.
Diff: 1 *Page Ref: Sec. 26.1*

6) State the three unprovable assumptions of Galilean–Newtonian relativity.

Answer:
1. The lengths of objects are the same in all reference frames.
2. Time passes at the same rate in all reference frames.
3. The mass of an object, as well as all forces, are the same in all reference frames.

Diff: 1 *Page Ref: Sec. 26.1*

7) The theory of special relativity

A) is based on a complex mathematical analysis.

B) has not been verified by experiment.

C) does not agree with Newtonian mechanics.

D) does not agree with electromagnetic theory.

Answer: C
Diff: 1 *Page Ref: Sec. 26.2*

8) One of Einstein's postulates in formulating the special theory of relativity was that the laws of physics are the same in reference frames that

A) accelerate.

B) move at constant velocity with respect to an inertial frame.

C) oscillate.

D) are stationary, but not in moving frames.

Answer: B
Diff: 1 *Page Ref: Sec. 26.2*

9) State the first postulate of special relativity.

Answer: The laws of physics have the same form in all inertial reference frames.
or
There is no experiment you can do in an inertial reference frame to tell if you are at rest or moving uniformly at constant velocity.
Diff: 1 *Page Ref: Sec. 26.2*

10) State the second postulate of special relativity.

Answer: Light propagates through empty space with a definite speed *c* independent of the speed of the source or observer.

Diff: 1 *Page Ref: Sec. 26.2*

11) If you were to measure your pulse rate while in a spaceship moving away from the Sun at a speed close to the speed of light, you would find that it was

A) much faster than normal.

B) much slower than normal.

C) the same as it was here on Earth.

Answer: C

Diff: 2 *Page Ref: Sec. 26.4*

12) Relative to a stationary observer, a moving clock

A) always runs slower than normal.

B) always runs faster than normal.

C) keeps its normal time.

D) can do any of the above. It depends on the relative velocity between the observer and the clock.

Answer: A

Diff: 2 *Page Ref: Sec. 26.4*

13) The gamma factor is defined as $\gamma \equiv 1/\sqrt{1 - (v/c)^2}$, therefore gamma ($\gamma$)

A) can be zero.

B) can be any number less than or equal to one.

C) can be any number greater than or equal to one.

D) cannot equal one.

Answer: C

Diff: 1 *Page Ref: Sec. 26.4*

14) Suppose one twin takes a ride in a space ship traveling at a very high speed to a distant star and back again, while the other twin remains on Earth. The twin that remained on Earth predicts that the astronaut twin is

A) younger.

B) the same age.

C) older.

D) cannot be determined from the given information

Answer: A

Diff: 2 *Page Ref: Sec. 26.4*

15) Relative to a stationary observer, a moving object

A) appears shorter than normal.

B) appears longer than normal.

C) keeps its same length time.

D) can do any of the above. It depends on the relative velocity between the observer and the object.

Answer: A
Diff: 2 *Page Ref: Sec. 26.5*

16) An object moves in a direction parallel to its length with a velocity that approaches the velocity of light. The width of this object, as measured by a stationary observer,

A) approaches infinity.

B) approaches zero.

C) increases slightly.

D) does not change.

Answer: D
Diff: 2 *Page Ref: Sec. 26.5*

17) An object moves in a direction parallel to its length with a velocity that approaches the velocity of light. The length of this object, as measured by a stationary observer,

A) approaches infinity.

B) approaches zero.

C) increases slightly.

D) does not change.

Answer: B
Diff: 2 *Page Ref: Sec. 26.5*

18) As the speed of a particle approaches the speed of light, the mass of the particle

A) increases.

B) decreases.

C) remains the same.

D) approaches zero.

Answer: A
Diff: 2 *Page Ref: Sec. 26.7*

19) As the speed of a particle approaches the speed of light, the momentum of the particle

A) increases.

B) decreases.

C) remains the same.

D) approaches zero.

Answer: A
Diff: 2 *Page Ref: Sec. 26.7*

20) A spear is thrown by you at a very high speed. As it passes, you measure its length at one-half its normal length. From this measurement, you conclude that the moving spear's mass must be

A) one-half its rest mass.

B) twice its rest mass.

C) four times its rest mass.

D) none of the given answers

Answer: B
Diff: 2 Page Ref: Sec. 26.7

21) What happens to the kinetic energy of a speedy proton when its relativistic mass doubles?

A) It doubles.

B) It more than doubles.

C) It less than doubles.

D) It must increase, but it is impossible to say by how much.

Answer: B
Diff: 2 Page Ref: Sec. 26.9

22) What happens to the total relativistic energy of a speedy proton when its relativistic mass doubles?

A) It doubles.

B) It more than doubles.

C) It less than doubles.

D) It must increase, but it is impossible to say by how much.

Answer: A
Diff: 1 Page Ref: Sec. 26.9

23) Consider a particle of mass m and rest mass m_o. Which of the following is the correct expression for the kinetic energy of such a particle?

A) $m_o v^2/2$

B) $mv^2/2$

C) $mc^2 - m_o c^2$

D) $1/2(mc^2 - m_o c^2)$

Answer: C
Diff: 2 Page Ref: Sec. 26.9

24) Consider two spaceships, each traveling at 0.50c in a straight line. Ship A is moving directly away from the Sun and ship B is approaching the Sun. The science officers on each ship measure the velocity of light coming from the Sun. What do they measure for this velocity?

A) Ship A measures it as less than c, and ship B measures it as greater than c.

B) Ship B measures it as less than c, and ship A measures it as greater than c.

C) On both ships it is measured to be less than c.

D) On both ships it is measured to be exactly c.

Answer: D
Diff: 1 *Page Ref: Sec. 26.10*

25) Which of the following depends on the observer's frame of reference?

A) the mass of the proton

B) the length of a meter stick

C) the half-life of a muon

D) all of the given answers

Answer: D
Diff: 1 *Page Ref: Sec. 26.4-26.9*

26) As the velocity of your spaceship increases, you would observe

A) that your precision clock runs slower than normal.

B) that the length of your spaceship has decreased.

C) that your mass has increased.

D) all of the given answers

E) none of the given answers

Answer: E
Diff: 2 *Page Ref: Sec. 26.4-26.9*

Quantitative Problems

1) A boat can travel 4.0 m/s in still water. With what speed, relative to the shore, does it move in a river that is flowing at 1.0 m/s if the boat is heading upstream?

A) 3.0 m/s

B) 4.1 m/s

C) 4.8 m/s

D) 5.0 m/s

Answer: A
Diff: 1 *Page Ref: Sec. 26.1*

2) A boat can travel 4.0 m/s in still water. With what speed, relative to the shore, does it move in a river that is flowing at 1.0 m/s if the boat is heading downstream?

A) 3.0 m/s

B) 4.1 m/s

C) 4.8 m/s

D) 5.0 m/s

Answer: D
Diff: 1 *Page Ref: Sec. 26.1*

3) A boat can travel 4.0 m/s in still water. With what speed, relative to the shore, does it move in a river that is flowing at 1.0 m/s if the boat is heading straight across the river?

A) 3.0 m/s

B) 4.1 m/s

C) 4.8 m/s

D) 5.0 m/s

Answer: B
Diff: 1 *Page Ref: Sec. 26.1*

4) How fast should a moving clock travel if it is to be observed by a stationary observer as running at one-half its normal rate?

A) 0.50c

B) 0.65c

C) 0.78c

D) 0.87c

Answer: D
Diff: 2 *Page Ref: Sec. 26.4-26.5*

5) A spaceship takes a nonstop journey to a planet and returns in 10 hours according to a clock on the spaceship. If the speed of the spaceship is 0.80c, how much time has elapsed on the Earth?

A) 3.2 h

B) 7.0 h

C) 15 h

D) 17 h

Answer: D
Diff: 2 *Page Ref: Sec. 26.4-26.5*

6) A set of twins, Andrea and Courtney, are initially 10 years old. While Courtney remains on Earth, Andrea rides on a space ship which travels away from Earth at a speed of 0.6c for five years (as measured by Courtney), then turns around and comes back at 0.6c. When Andrea returns, Courtney is 20 years old. How old is Andrea upon her return?

A) 10 years

B) 12 years

C) 18 years

D) 20 years

Answer: C
Diff: 1 *Page Ref: Sec. 26.4–26.5*

7) One 20-year-old twin brother takes a space trip with a speed of 0.80c for 30 years according to a clock on the spaceship. Upon returning to the Earth, what is his own age and the age of the Earth-based twin brother?

A) 20; 30

B) 30; 50

C) 50; 70

D) 70; 90

Answer: C
Diff: 2 *Page Ref: Sec. 26.4–26.5*

8) A meter stick is moving toward you with a speed of 0.80c. What is its length?

A) zero

B) 0.40 m

C) 0.60 m

D) 1.0 m

Answer: C
Diff: 2 *Page Ref: Sec. 26.4–26.5*

9) How fast would a rocket ship have to move to contract to half of its proper length (as observed by a stationary object)?

A) 0.50c

B) 0.65c

C) 0.78c

D) 0.87c

Answer: D
Diff: 2 *Page Ref: Sec. 26.4–26.5*

10) The length of a spaceship is 10 m when it is at rest. If the spaceship travels by you with a speed of 0.70c, what length does it appear to you?

A) 5.5 m

B) 7.1 m

C) 12 m

D) 18 m

Answer: B
Diff: 2 *Page Ref: Sec. 26.4–26.5*

11) The closest star to our solar system is Alpha Centauri, which is 4.30 light years away. A spaceship with a constant speed of 0.800c relative to the Earth travels toward the star. What distance does the space ship travel according to a passenger on the ship?

A) 2.58 ly

B) 3.52 ly

C) 4.12 ly

D) 4.30 ly

Answer: A
Diff: 2 *Page Ref: Sec. 26.4–26.5*

12) The closest star to our solar system is Alpha Centauri, which is 4.30 light years away. A spaceship with a constant speed of 0.800c relative to the Earth travels toward the star. How much time would elapse on a clock on board the spaceship?

A) 3.23 y

B) 4.40 y

C) 5.15 y

D) 5.38 y

Answer: A
Diff: 2 *Page Ref: Sec. 26.4–26.5*

13) The closest star to our solar system is Alpha Centauri, which is 4.30 light years away. A spaceship with a constant speed of 0.800c relative to the Earth travels toward the star. How much time would elapse on a clock on the Earth?

A) 3.23 y

B) 4.40 y

C) 5.15 y

D) 5.38 y

Answer: D
Diff: 2 *Page Ref: Sec. 26.4–26.5*

14) An electron is traveling at 0.85c. What is its mass? (The rest mass is 9.11×10^{-31} kg.)

A) 1.4×10^{-29} kg

B) 7.2×10^{-30} kg

C) 1.7×10^{-30} kg

D) 2.4×10^{-30} kg

Answer: C
Diff: 2 *Page Ref: Sec. 26.7*

15) What is the speed of a proton if its mass is twice its rest mass?

A) 0.50c

B) 0.68c

C) 0.73c

D) 0.87c

Answer: D
Diff: 2 *Page Ref: Sec. 26.7*

16) If the velocity of your spaceship goes from 0.3 c to 0.6 c, then your mass will increase by

A) 19%.

B) 38%.

C) 100%.

D) 200%.

Answer: A
Diff: 2 *Page Ref: Sec. 26.7*

17) What is the momentum in kg•m/s of a proton when it is moving with a speed of 0.60c?

A) 1.2×10^{-19} kg•m/s

B) 1.5×10^{-19} kg•m/s

C) 3.0×10^{-19} kg•m/s

D) 3.8×10^{-19} kg•m/s

Answer: D
Diff: 2 *Page Ref: Sec. 26.7*

18) During a reaction, an element loses 4.8×10^{-28} kg of mass. How much energy (in Joules) is released?

A) 4.3×10^{-11} J

B) 1.4×10^{-19} J

C) 1.6×10^{-36} J

D) 5.3×10^{-45} J

Answer: A
Diff: 1 *Page Ref: Sec. 26.9*

19) During a reaction, 1.7×10^{-4} J of energy is released. What change of mass would cause this?

A) 5.1×10^{-4} kg

B) 1.5×10^{-13} kg

C) 4.8×10^{-18} kg

D) 1.9×10^{-21} kg

Answer: D

Diff: 1 *Page Ref: Sec. 26.9*

20) How much energy would be released if 2.0 kg of material was lost during a reaction?

A) 1.8×10^{17} J

B) 1.5×10^{16} J

C) 6.0×10^{8} J

D) 4.7×10^{-8} J

Answer: A

Diff: 1 *Page Ref: Sec. 26.9*

21) The amount of energy equivalent to two kilogram of mass at rest is

A) 18×10^{16} J.

B) 3.0×10^{8} J.

C) 9.0×10^{16} J.

D) none of the given answers

Answer: A

Diff: 1 *Page Ref: Sec. 26.9*

22) The atomic bomb that was dropped on Nagasaki in 1945 killed 140,000 people, helping to end World War II on the next day. It released energy equivalent to that of 20,000 tons of TNT explosive. How much mass was converted to energy when this took place? (1000 tons of TNT = 4.3×10^{12} J) Incidentally, modern H-bombs have energy yields 1000 times as much!

A) 1 g

B) 10 g

C) 100 g

D) 1 kg

Answer: A

Diff: 1 *Page Ref: Sec. 26.9*

23) The kinetic energy of a proton is 80% of its total energy. What is the speed of the proton?

A) 0.02c

B) 0.87c

C) 0.98c

D) 1.0c

Answer: C

Diff: 2 *Page Ref: Sec. 26.9*

24) The kinetic energy of a proton is 80% of its total energy. What is the momentum in kg•m/s of the proton?

A) 5.0×10^{-19} kg•m/s

B) 2.5×10^{-19} kg•m/s

C) 5.0×10^{-18} kg•m/s

D) 2.5×10^{-18} kg•m/s

Answer: D

Diff: 2 *Page Ref: Sec. 26.9*

25) What energy is released (in MeV) during a reaction in which 1.67×10^{-25} kg of material is converted to energy?

A) 5.0×10^{-14} MeV

B) 4.1×10^{-7} MeV

C) 3.1×10^{-4} MeV

D) 9.4×10^{4} MeV

Answer: D

Diff: 2 *Page Ref: Sec. 26.9*

26) How much mass is lost during a reaction in which 1.7×10^{8} MeV of energy is released?

A) 1.8×10^{-8} kg

B) 5.7×10^{-9} kg

C) 1.9×10^{-17} kg

D) 3.0×10^{-22} kg

Answer: D

Diff: 2 *Page Ref: Sec. 26.9*

27) What is the total energy of an electron moving with a speed of 0.95c?

A) 2.6×10^{-13} J

B) 8.2×10^{-14} J

C) 1.1×10^{-13} J

D) 1.2×10^{-14} J

Answer: A

Diff: 2 *Page Ref: Sec. 26.9*

28) How many joules of energy are required to accelerate one kilogram of mass from rest to a velocity of 0.866 c?

A) 1.8×10^{17} J

B) 9.0×10^{16} J

C) 3.0×10^{3} J

D) none of the given answers

Answer: B

Diff: 2 *Page Ref: Sec. 26.9*

29) In a nuclear plant, 10^{17} J of energy is available from mass conversion. How much mass was lost?

A) 0.1 kg

B) 1 kg

C) 10 kg

D) 100 kg

Answer: B
Diff: 2 *Page Ref: Sec. 26.9*

30) An electron is accelerated through 100 kV. By what factor has its mass increased with respect to its rest mass?

A) 1.20

B) 1.55

C) 4.25

D) 8.00

Answer: A
Diff: 2 *Page Ref: Sec. 26.9*

31) You are in a rocket traveling away from the Sun at 0.95c. You measure the speed of light from the Sun to be

A) 0.05c.

B) 0.95c.

C) 1.0c.

D) cannot be determined without knowing the frequency of the light

Answer: C
Diff: 1 *Page Ref: Sec. 26.10*

32) Two spaceships are traveling through space at 0.60 c relative to the Earth. If the ships are headed directly toward each other, what is their approach velocity, as measured by a person on either craft?

A) 1.2c

B) c

C) 0.60c

D) none of the given answers

Answer: D
Diff: 1 *Page Ref: Sec. 26.10*

33) A fast spaceship is traveling with a speed of 0.80c. How fast would light travel from the headlights of the ship relative to a stationary observer?

A) 0.20c

B) 0.80c

C) 1.0c

D) 1.8c

Answer: C
Diff: 2 *Page Ref: Sec. 26.10*

34) A spaceship moves away from the Earth with a speed of 0.80c. The spaceship then fires a missile with a speed of 0.50c relative to the spaceship. What is the velocity of the missile measured by observers on the Earth if the missile is fired away from the Earth?

A) 0.30c

B) 0.50c

C) 0.93c

D) 1.3c

Answer: C
Diff: 2 *Page Ref: Sec. 26.10*

35) A spaceship moves away from the Earth with a speed of 0.80c. The spaceship then fires a missile with a speed of 0.50c relative to the spaceship. What is the velocity of the missile measured by observers on the Earth if the missile is fired toward the Earth?

A) 0.30c

B) 0.50c

C) 0.93c

D) 1.3c

Answer: B
Diff: 2 *Page Ref: Sec. 26.10*

Chapter 27 Early Quantum Theory and Models of the Atom

Conceptual Questions

1) In a pair of accelerating plates, such as found inside a CRT, the electrons are emitted

A) from the cathode which is positive, toward the anode which is positive.

B) from the cathode which is negative, toward the anode which is positive.

C) from the anode which is positive, toward the cathode which is negative.

D) from the anode which is negative, toward the cathode which is positive.

Answer: B
Diff: 1 *Page Ref: Sec. 27.1*

2) A blackbody is an ideal system that

A) absorbs 100% of the light incident upon it, but cannot emit light of its own (i.e., a "black" body).

B) emits 100% of the light it generates, but cannot absorb radiation of its own.

C) either absorbs 100% of the light incident upon it, or emits 100% of the radiation it generates.

D) absorbs 50% of the light incident upon it, and emits 50% of the radiation it generates.

Answer: C
Diff: 1 *Page Ref: Sec. 27.2*

3) Which color in the visible spectrum is associated with the lowest temperature?

A) blue

B) green

C) orange

D) red

Answer: D
Diff: 2 *Page Ref: Sec. 27.2*

4) Planck's constant

A) sets an upper limit to the amount of energy that can be absorbed or emitted.

B) sets a lower limit to the amount of energy that can be absorbed or emitted.

C) relates mass to energy.

D) none of the given answers

Answer: B
Diff: 2 *Page Ref: Sec. 27.2*

5) The ratio of energy to frequency for a given photon gives

A) its amplitude.

B) its velocity.

C) Planck's constant.

D) its work function.

Answer: C

Diff: 1 Page Ref: Sec. 27.2

6) The fundamental SI units of Planck's constant are

A) kg•m / s.

B) kg•m2 / s.

C) kg•m / s2.

D) kg•m2 / s2.

Answer: B

Diff: 2 Page Ref: Sec. 27,2

7) Planck's constant has a value of

A) 1.055×10^{-34} J•s.

B) 6.626×10^{-34} J•s.

C) 8.85×10^{-12} J•s.

D) 8.988×10^{9} J•s.

Answer: B

Diff: 1 Page Ref: Sec. 27.2

8) A photon is a particle that

A) has zero electric charge.

B) has zero electric field associated with it.

C) cannot travel in a vacuum.

D) has a velocity in a vacuum that varies with the photon frequency.

Answer: A

Diff: 1 Page Ref: Sec. 27.3–27.4

9) Which of the following is an accurate statement?

A) In vacuum, ultraviolet photons travel faster than infrared photons.

B) Photons can have positive or negative charge.

C) An ultraviolet photon has more energy than an infrared photon.

D) Photons do not have momentum (i.e., they cannot exert pressure on things).

Answer: C

Diff: 1 Page Ref: Sec. 27.3–27.4

10) What is a photon?

A) an electron in an excited state

B) a small packet of electromagnetic energy that has particle-like properties

C) one form of a nucleon, one of the particles that makes up the nucleus

D) an electron that has been made electrically neutral

Answer: B
Diff: 1 *Page Ref: Sec. 27.3–27.4*

11) The energy of a photon depends on

A) its amplitude.

B) its velocity.

C) its frequency.

D) none of the given answers

Answer: C
Diff: 1 *Page Ref: Sec. 27.3–27.4*

12) If the wavelength of a photon is halved, by what factor does its energy change?

A) 4

B) 2

C) 1/4

D) 1/2

Answer: B
Diff: 2 *Page Ref: Sec. 27.3–27.4*

13) Which color of light has the lowest energy photons?

A) red

B) yellow

C) green

D) blue

Answer: A
Diff: 1 *Page Ref: Sec. 27.3–27.4*

14) The photoelectric effect is explainable assuming

A) that light has a wave nature.

B) that light has a particle nature.

C) that light has a wave nature and a particle nature.

D) none of the above

Answer: B
Diff: 1 *Page Ref: Sec. 27.3–27.4*

15) In order for a photon to eject an electron from a metal's surface in the photoelectric effect, the photon's

A) frequency must be greater than a certain minimum value.

B) speed must be greater than a certain minimum value.

C) wavelength must be greater than a certain minimum value.

D) momentum must be zero.

Answer: A
Diff: 1 *Page Ref: Sec. 27.3–27.4*

16) The kinetic energy of the photoelectron depends on which of the following?

A) intensity of light

B) duration of illumination

C) wavelength of light

D) angle of illumination

Answer: C
Diff: 2 *Page Ref: Sec. 27.3–27.4*

17) A beam of red light and a beam of violet light each deliver the same power on a surface. For which beam is the number of photons hitting the surface per second the greatest?

A) the red beam

B) the violet beam

C) The number of photons per second is the same for both beams.

D) This cannot be answered without knowing just what the light intensity is.

Answer: A
Diff: 2 *Page Ref: Sec. 27.3–27.4*

18) A metal surface is illuminated with blue light and electrons are ejected at a given rate each with a certain amount of energy. If the intensity of the blue light is increased, electrons are ejected

A) at the same rate, but with more energy per electron.

B) at the same rate, but with less energy per electron.

C) at an increased rate with no change in energy per electron.

D) at a reduced rate with no change in energy per electron.

Answer: C
Diff: 2 *Page Ref: Sec. 27.3–27.4*

19) A beam of X-rays of frequency f is incident upon a substance that scatters the beam in various directions. If we measure the frequency of the scattered X-rays, we will find

A) X-rays with frequency less than f.

B) X-rays with frequency greater than f.

C) only X-rays with frequency f.

D) X-rays with frequencies ranging from less than f to greater than f.

Answer: A
Diff: 2 *Page Ref: Sec. 27.5*

20) A beam of X-rays of wavelength λ is incident upon a substance that scatters the beam in various directions. If we measure the wavelength of the scattered X-rays, we will find

A) X-rays with wavelength less than λ.

B) X-rays with wavelength greater than λ.

C) only X-rays with wavelength λ.

D) X-rays which range in wavelength from less than λ to greater than λ.

Answer: B
Diff: 2 *Page Ref: Sec. 27.5*

21) When a photon is scattered from an electron, there will be an increase in its

A) energy.

B) frequency.

C) wavelength.

D) momentum.

Answer: C
Diff: 2 *Page Ref: Sec. 27.5*

22) In the Compton effect, as the scattering angle increases, the frequency of the X-rays scattered at that angle

A) increases.

B) decreases.

C) does not change.

D) varies randomly.

Answer: B
Diff: 2 *Page Ref: Sec. 27.5*

23) In a Compton scattering experiment, what scattering angle produces the greatest change in wavelength?

A) zero degrees

B) 90°

C) 180°

D) none of the given answers

Answer: C
Diff: 2 *Page Ref: Sec. 27.5*

24) When the accelerating voltage in an X-ray tube is doubled, the minimum wavelength of the X-rays

A) is increased to twice the original value.

B) is increased to four times the original value.

C) is decreased to one-half the original value.

D) is decreased to one-fourth the original value.

Answer: C
Diff: 2 *Page Ref: Sec. 27.5*

25) When a proton passes through matter, it is possible for it to interact with the matter in such a way that an electron and a positron are produced; this interaction is referred to as

A) the photoelectric effect.

B) the Compton effect.

C) pair production.

D) none of the given answers

Answer: C
Diff: 2 *Page Ref: Sec. 27.6*

26) As a particle travels faster, its de Broglie wavelength

A) increases.

B) decreases.

C) remains constant.

D) could be any of the given answers; it depends on other factors.

Answer: B
Diff: 2 *Page Ref: Sec. 27.8*

27) When an electron is accelerated to a higher speed, there is a decrease in its

A) energy.

B) frequency.

C) wavelength.

D) momentum.

Answer: C
Diff: 2 *Page Ref: Sec. 27.8*

28) Which one of the following would tend to have the smallest wavelength if they are moving with the same speed?

A) electron

B) proton

C) baseball

D) bowling ball

Answer: D

Diff: 2 *Page Ref: Sec. 27.8*

29) The reason the wavelike nature of a moving baseball is not noticed in everyday life is that

A) it doesn't have a wavelike nature.

B) its wavelength is too small.

C) its frequency is too small.

D) its energy is too small.

E) No one pays attention to such things except for the Mets; and they can't hit a curve ball anyway.

Answer: B

Diff: 1 *Page Ref: Sec. 27.8*

30) What advantage might an electron microscope have over a light microscope?

A) Electrons are more powerful.

B) Shorter wavelengths are possible.

C) Longer wavelengths are possible.

D) none of the given answers

Answer: B

Diff: 1 *Page Ref: Sec. 27.9*

31) The part of an electron microscope that plays the same role as the lenses do in an optical microscope is

A) the vacuum chamber.

B) the coils.

C) the cathode.

D) the deflector plates.

Answer: B

Diff: 1 *Page Ref: Sec. 27.9*

32) Which of the following microscopes is capable of "photographing" individual atoms?

A) light microscope

B) scanning tunneling microscope

C) transmission electron microscope

D) scanning electron microscope

Answer: B
Diff: 2 *Page Ref: Sec. 27.9*

33) According to the Bohr model of the atom, the angular momentum of an electron around the nucleus

A) could equal any positive value.

B) must equal an integral multiple of h.

C) must equal an integral multiple of $h/2\pi$.

D) decreases with time, eventually becoming zero.

Answer: C
Diff: 1 *Page Ref: Sec. 27.12*

34) When an electron jumps from an orbit where n = 4 to one where n = 2

A) a photon is emitted.

B) a photon is absorbed.

C) two photons are emitted.

D) two photons are absorbed.

E) none of the given answers

Answer: A
Diff: 1 *Page Ref: Sec. 27.12*

35) The distance between adjacent orbit radii in a hydrogen atom

A) increases with increasing values of n.

B) decreases with increasing values of n.

C) remains constant for all values of n.

D) varies randomly with increasing values of n.

Answer: A
Diff: 2 *Page Ref: Sec. 27.12*

36) The energy difference between adjacent orbit radii in a hydrogen atom

A) increases with increasing values of n.

B) decreases with increasing values of n.

C) remains constant for all values of n.

D) varies randomly with increasing values of n.

Answer: B
Diff: 2 *Page Ref: Sec. 27.12*

Quantitative Problems

1) What is the wavelength corresponding to the most intense light emitted by a giant star of surface temperature 5000 K?

A) 576 nm

B) 578 nm

C) 580 nm

D) 582 nm

Answer: C
Diff: 1 *Page Ref: Sec. 27.2*

2) What is the frequency of the most intense radiation from an object with temperature 100°C?

A) 2.9×10^{-5} Hz

B) 3.9×10^{13} Hz

C) 1.0×10^{13} Hz

D) 1.0×10^{11} Hz

Answer: B
Diff: 2 *Page Ref: Sec. 27.2*

3) How much energy is carried by a photon with frequency 110 GHz?

A) 1.1×10^{-20} J

B) 1.4×10^{-22} J

C) 7.3×10^{-23} J

D) 1.3×10^{-25} J

Answer: C
Diff: 1 *Page Ref: Sec. 27.3–27.4*

4) How much energy is carried by a photon with a frequency of 100,000 GHz?

A) 4.73×10^{-42} J

B) 4.37×10^{-24} J

C) 6.63×10^{-24} J

D) 6.63×10^{-20} J

Answer: D
Diff: 1 *Page Ref: Sec. 27.3–27.4*

5) What frequency of electromagnetic radiation has energy 4.7×10^{-25} J?

A) 710 kHz

B) 4.7 MHz

C) 710 MHz

D) 1.4 GHz

Answer: C
Diff: 1 *Page Ref: Sec. 27.3–27.4*

6) What frequency of electromagnetic radiation has an energy of 58.1 μeV?

A) 1.4 MHz

B) 711 MHz

C) 7.1 GHz

D) 14 GHz

Answer: D
Diff: 1 *Page Ref: Sec. 27.3–27.4*

7) What is the photon energy of red light having wavelength 640 nm?

A) 1.13×10^{-19} J

B) 1.31×10^{-19} J

C) 3.11×10^{-19} J

D) 1.94×10^{-19} J

Answer: C
Diff: 2 *Page Ref: Sec. 27.3–27.4*

8) How much energy, in joules, is carried by a photon of wavelength 660 nm?

A) 1.46×10^{-48} J

B) 3.01×10^{-19} J

C) 6.63×10^{-34} J

D) none of the given answers

Answer: B
Diff: 2 *Page Ref: Sec. 27.3–27.4*

9) At what rate are photons emitted by a 50-W sodium vapor lamp? (Assume that the lamp's light is monochromatic and of wavelength 589 nm.)

A) 1.0×10^{20}/s

B) 1.5×10^{20}/s

C) 2.0×10^{20}/s

D) 2.5×10^{20}/s

Answer: B
Diff: 2 *Page Ref: Sec. 27.3–27.4*

10) A metal has a work function of 4.5 eV. Find the maximum kinetic energy of the photoelectrons if the wavelength of light is 250 nm.

A) zero

B) 0.37 eV

C) 0.46 eV

D) 0.53 eV

Answer: C
Diff: 2 *Page Ref: Sec. 27.3–27.4*

11) When light of wavelength 350 nm is incident on a metal surface, the stopping potential of the photoelectrons is 0.500 eV. What is the work function of the metal?

A) 0.500 eV

B) 3.04 eV

C) 3.54 eV

D) 4.12 eV

Answer: B
Diff: 2 *Page Ref: Sec. 27.3–27.4*

12) When light of wavelength 350 nm is incident on a metal surface, the stopping potential of the photoelectrons is 0.500 eV. What is the threshold frequency?

A) 3.47×10^{14} Hz

B) 3.74×10^{14} Hz

C) 4.73×10^{14} Hz

D) 7.34×10^{14} Hz

Answer: D
Diff: 2 *Page Ref: Sec. 27.3–27.4*

13) When light of wavelength 350 nm is incident on a metal surface, the stopping potential of the photoelectrons is 0.500 eV. What is the maximum kinetic energy of the electron?

A) 0.500 eV

B) 3.04 eV

C) 3.54 eV

D) 4.12 eV

Answer: A
Diff: 2 *Page Ref: Sec. 27.3–27.4*

14) A monochromatic light is incident on the surface of a metal with work function 2.50 eV. If a 1.0-V stopping potential is required to make the photocurrent zero, what is the wavelength of light?

A) 354 nm

B) 423 nm

C) 497 nm

D) 744 nm

Answer: A
Diff: 2 *Page Ref: Sec. 27.3–27.4*

15) If the scattering angle in Compton's scattering is 90°. What is the wavelength shift?

A) 1.22×10^{-12} m

B) 2.43×10^{-12} m

C) 3.65×10^{-12} m

D) 4.85×10^{-12} m

Answer: B
Diff: 2 *Page Ref: Sec. 27.5*

16) X-rays of wavelength 0.20 nm are scattered by a metal. The wavelength shift is observed to be 2.0×10^{-12} m at a certain scattering angle measured relative to the incoming X-ray. What is the scattering angle?

A) 20°

B) 40°

C) 60°

D) 80°

Answer: D
Diff: 2 *Page Ref: Sec. 27.5*

17) X-rays with a wavelength of 0.00100 nm are scattered by free electrons at 130°. What is the kinetic energy of each recoil electron?

A) 2.5 MeV

B) 5.0 MeV

C) 7.5 MeV

D) 10 MeV

Answer: B
Diff: 3 *Page Ref: Sec. 27.5*

18) What is the wavelength of the matter wave associated with a ball of mass 0.50 kg moving with a speed of 25 m/s?

A) 3.5×10^{-35} m

B) 5.3×10^{-35} m

C) 3.5×10^{-33} m

D) 5.3×10^{-33} m

Answer: B
Diff: 1 *Page Ref: Sec. 27.8*

19) What is the de Broglie wavelength of a ball of mass 200 g moving with a speed of 30 m/s?

A) 1.1×10^{-34} m

B) 2.2×10^{-34} m

C) 4.5×10^{-28} m

D) 6.7×10^{-27} m

Answer: A
Diff: 1 *Page Ref: Sec. 27.8*

20) What is the wavelength of the matter wave associated with an electron moving with a speed of 2.5×10^{7} m/s?

A) 29 pm

B) 35 pm

C) 47 pm

D) 53 pm

Answer: A
Diff: 1 *Page Ref: Sec. 27.8*

21) An electron is accelerated through a potential difference of 150 V. What is its wavelength?

A) 0.1 nm

B) 1 nm

C) 1 mm

D) 1 cm

Answer: A
Diff: 2 *Page Ref: Sec. 27.8*

22) An electron is accelerated by a potential difference of 100 V. What is its wavelength?

A) 0.122 nm

B) 0.212 nm

C) 0.221 nm

D) 0.313 nm

Answer: A
Diff: 2 *Page Ref: Sec. 27.8*

23) An electron is accelerated by a potential difference of 100 V. What is its momentum in kg•m/s?

A) 3.45×10^{-24}

B) 3.54×10^{-24}

C) 4.53×10^{-24}

D) 5.43×10^{-24}

Answer: D
Diff: 2 *Page Ref: Sec. 27.8*

24) An electron is accelerated by a potential difference of 100 V. What is its kinetic energy?

A) 1.26×10^{-17} J

B) 1.62×10^{-17} J

C) 2.16×10^{-17} J

D) 2.61×10^{-17} J

Answer: B
Diff: 2 *Page Ref: Sec. 27.8*

25) A person of mass 50 kg has a wavelength of 4.4×10^{-36} m when running. How fast is she running?

A) 2.0 m/s

B) 3.0 m/s

C) 4.0 m/s

D) 5.0 m/s

Answer: B
Diff: 2 *Page Ref: Sec. 27.8*

26) An electron has a wavelength of 0.123 nm. What is its energy in eV? (This energy is not in the relativistic region.)

A) 20 eV

B) 60 eV

C) 80 eV

D) 100 eV

Answer: D
Diff: 2 *Page Ref: Sec. 27.8*

27) If r_1 is the smallest orbital radius around a single proton, then r_6 is equal to

A) $36r_1$.

B) $12r_1$.

C) $6r_1$.

D) $2.45r_1$.

Answer: A
Diff: 1 *Page Ref: Sec. 27.12*

28) The electron of a hydrogen atom makes a transition from the n = 5 state to the n = 2 state. What is the wavelength of the emitted photon?

A) 344 nm

B) 434 nm

C) 443 nm

D) 523 nm

Answer: B
Diff: 2 *Page Ref: Sec. 27.12*

29) The binding energy of the hydrogen atom in its ground state is -13.6 eV. What is the energy when it is in the n = 5 state?

A) 2.72 eV

B) -2.72 eV

C) 0.544 eV

D) -0.544 eV

Answer: D
Diff: 2 *Page Ref: Sec. 27.12*

30) A hydrogen atom in the ground state absorbs a photon of energy 12.09 eV. To which state will the electron make a transition?

A) n = 2

B) n = 3

C) n = 4

D) n = 5

Answer: B
Diff: 2 *Page Ref: Sec. 27.12*

31) What is the ionization energy of the neutral hydrogen atom?

A) 27.2 eV

B) 13.6 eV

C) 6.8 eV

D) none of the given answers

Answer: B
Diff: 1 *Page Ref: Sec. 27.12*

32) What is the ionization energy of singly ionized helium?

A) 54.4 eV

B) 27.2 eV

C) 13.6 eV

D) none of the given answers

Answer: A
Diff: 1 *Page Ref: Sec. 27.12*

33) In making a transition from state $n = 1$ to state $n = 2$, the hydrogen atom must

A) absorb a photon of energy 10.2 eV.

B) emit a photon of energy 10.2 eV.

C) absorb a photon of energy 13.58 eV.

D) emit a photon of energy 13.58 eV.

Answer: A
Diff: 2 *Page Ref: Sec. 27.12*

34) In state $n = 1$, the energy of the hydrogen atom is -13.58 eV. What is its energy in state $n = 2$?

A) -6.79 eV

B) -4.53 eV

C) -3.40 eV

D) -1.51 eV

Answer: C
Diff: 1 *Page Ref: Sec. 27.12*

35) The wavelength of a ruby laser is 694.3 nm. What is the energy difference between the two energy states involved in laser action?

A) 1.537 eV

B) 1.646 eV

C) 1.786 eV

D) 1.812 eV

Answer: C
Diff: 2 *Page Ref: Sec. 27.12*

36) An electron is moving about a single proton in an orbit characterized by $n = 4$. How many of the electron's de Broglie wavelengths fit into the circumference of this orbit?

A) 1

B) 2

C) 4

D) 16

Answer: C
Diff: 1 *Page Ref: Sec. 27.13*

Chapter 28 Quantum Mechanics of Atoms

Conceptual Questions

1) The probability of finding an electron in a hydrogen atom is directly proportional to its

A) energy.

B) momentum.

C) wave function.

D) square of the wave function.

Answer: D

Diff: 2 *Page Ref: Sec. 28.2*

2) State Heisenberg's Uncertainty Principle.

Answer: The position and momentum of a particle cannot both be measured precisely at the same time.

Diff: 1 *Page Ref: Sec. 28.3*

3) The reason the position of a particle cannot be specified with infinite precision is the

A) exclusion principle.

B) uncertainty principle.

C) photoelectric effect.

D) principle of relativity.

Answer: B

Diff: 1 *Page Ref: Sec. 28.3*

4) If the accuracy in measuring the position of a particle increases, the accuracy in measuring its velocity will

A) increase.

B) decrease.

C) remain the same.

D) be uncertain.

Answer: B

Diff: 2 *Page Ref: Sec. 28.3*

5) If the accuracy in measuring the velocity of a particle increases, the accuracy in measuring its position will

A) increase.

B) decrease.

C) remain the same.

D) be uncertain.

Answer: B
Diff: 2 *Page Ref: Sec. 28.3*

6) The quantity "h-bar" has a value of

A) 1.055×10^{-34} J•s.

B) 6.626×10^{-34} J•s.

C) 8.85×10^{-12} J•s.

D) 8.988×10^{9} J•s.

Answer: A
Diff: 1 *Page Ref: Sec. 28.3*

7) The principal quantum number can have any integer value ranging from

A) $-\infty$ to $+\infty$.

B) 0 to ∞.

C) 1 to ∞.

D) 1 to 100.

Answer: C
Diff: 1 *Page Ref: Sec. 28.6*

8) The orbital quantum number can have any integer value ranging from

A) 0 to n.

B) 0 to (n–1).

C) 1 to n.

D) 1 to (n+1).

Answer: B
Diff: 1 *Page Ref: Sec. 28.6*

9) The magnetic quantum number can have any integer value ranging from

A) –n to +n.

B) $-l$ to $+l$.

C) 0 to n.

D) 0 to l.

Answer: B
Diff: 1 *Page Ref: Sec. 28.6*

10) The spin quantum number can have values of

A) $-\frac{1}{2}$, -1, 0, +1, $+\frac{1}{2}$.

B) $-\frac{1}{2}$, -1, +1, $+\frac{1}{2}$.

C) $-\frac{1}{2}$, 0, $+\frac{1}{2}$.

D) $-\frac{1}{2}$, $+\frac{1}{2}$.

Answer: D
Diff: 1 *Page Ref: Sec. 28.6*

11) If $l = 4$, which one of the following is a possible quantum number for n?

A) 0

B) 2

C) 4

D) 8

Answer: D
Diff: 2 *Page Ref: Sec. 28.6*

12) If n = 5, which one of the following is not an allowed magnetic quantum number?

A) 0

B) 2

C) 4

D) 5

Answer: D
Diff: 2 *Page Ref: Sec. 28.6*

13) The wave equation for hydrogen has solutions only if the three quantum numbers n, l, and m_l meet certain conditions. One of these conditions specifies that n

A) can be any real number.

B) can be any non-negative integer.

C) can be any integer.

D) can be any positive integer.

Answer: D
Diff: 2 *Page Ref: Sec. 28.6*

14) The wave equation for hydrogen has solutions only if the three quantum numbers n, *l*, and m_l meet certain conditions. One of these conditions specifies that l

A) is either zero or +1.

B) is either equal to or less than n–1.

C) is a positive integer.

D) has an absolute value that is either equal to or less than n.

Answer: B
Diff: 2 *Page Ref: Sec. 28.6*

15) The wave equation for hydrogen has solutions only if the three quantum numbers n, *l*, and m_l meet certain conditions. One of these conditions specifies that m_l

A) has an absolute value either equal to or less than l.

B) is equal to or less than n.

C) is equal to or greater than 1.

D) can be any integer.

Answer: A
Diff: 2 *Page Ref: Sec. 28.6*

16) In the ground state, the quantum numbers (n, *l*, m_l, m_s) for hydrogen are, respectively,

A) 1, 1, 1, 1.

B) 1, 0, 0, 0.

C) 1, 0, 0, ±1/2.

D) 1, 1, 1, ±1/2.

Answer: C
Diff: 2 *Page Ref: Sec. 28.6*

17) According to the selection rule, when a photon is emitted or absorbed, transitions can only occur between state with values of *l* that differ by

A) four units.

B) three units.

C) two units.

D) one unit.

Answer: D
Diff: 2 *Page Ref: Sec. 28.6*

18) The number of electrons in a neutral atom is called its

A) principal quantum number.

B) orbital quantum number.

C) magnetic quantum number.

D) atomic number.

Answer: D
Diff: 1   *Page Ref: Sec. 28.7*

19) State the Pauli exclusion principle.

Answer: No two electrons in an atom can occupy the same quantum state.
Diff: 1   *Page Ref: Sec. 28.7*

20) In terms of an atom's electron configuration, the letters K, L, M, and N refer to

A) different shells with n equal to 1, 2, 3, or 4 respectively.

B) different sub shells with l equal to 1, 2, 3, or 4 respectively.

C) the four possible levels for the magnetic quantum number.

D) the four possible quantum numbers.

Answer: A
Diff: 2   *Page Ref: Sec. 28.8*

21) What is the maximum number of electrons that can occupy the g sub shell?

A) 10

B) 14

C) 18

D) 22

Answer: C
Diff: 2   *Page Ref: Sec. 28.8*

22) How many possible sets of quantum numbers or electron states are there in the 5f sub shell?

A) 2

B) 8

C) 10

D) 14

Answer: D
Diff: 2   *Page Ref: Sec. 28.8*

23) The elements in the periodic table that have completely filled shells or subshells are referred to as

A) noble gases.

B) halogens.

C) alkali metals.

D) transition elements.

Answer: A
Diff: 1 *Page Ref: Sec. 28.8*

24) The elements in the periodic table which lack one electron from a filled shell are referred to as

A) noble gases.

B) halogens.

C) alkali metals.

D) transition elements.

Answer: B
Diff: 1 *Page Ref: Sec. 28.8*

25) The elements in the periodic table which have a single outer *s* electron are referred to as

A) noble gases.

B) halogens.

C) alkali metals.

D) transition elements.

Answer: C
Diff: 1 *Page Ref: Sec. 28.8*

26) The word LASER is an acronym for

A) Light Altered Spectra of Energy Radiated.

B) Latent Source of Enhanced Radiation.

C) Light Amplification by the Stimulated Emission of Radiation.

D) Light Absorbed States of Energetic Resonance.

Answer: C
Diff: 1 *Page Ref: Sec. 28.11*

27) In order to produce a hologram, one needs, in addition to an object and a piece of photographic film,

A) a beam of monochromatic light and a mirror.

B) a beam of monochromatic light and a lens.

C) a beam of coherent light and a lens.

D) a beam of coherent light and a mirror.

Answer: D
Diff: 1 *Page Ref: Sec. 28.12*

28) When a hologram is illuminated with a beam of coherent light, it produces

A) both a real and a virtual image.

B) only a real image of the object.

C) only a virtual image of the object.

D) none of the given answers

Answer: A

Diff: 2 *Page Ref: Sec. 28.12*

Quantitative Problems

1) An electron inside a hydrogen atom is confined to within a space of about 0.110 nm. If the electron mass is 9.11×10^{-31} kg, what is the uncertainty in the electron's velocity?

A) 1.05×10^{6} m/s

B) 1.50×10^{6} m/s

C) 1.05×10^{8} m/s

D) 1.50×10^{8} m/s

Answer: A

Diff: 1 *Page Ref: Sec. 28.3*

2) Suppose that the speed of an electron traveling 2000 m/s is known to an accuracy of 1 part in 10^{5} (i.e., within 0.001%). What is the greatest possible accuracy within which we can determine the position of this electron?

A) 2.9 mm

B) 5.8 mm

C) 8.7 mm

D) 1.2 cm

Answer: B

Diff: 2 *Page Ref: Sec. 28.3*

3) A measurement of an electron's speed is 2.0×10^{6} m/s and has an uncertainty of 10%. What is the minimum uncertainty in position?

A) 0.29 nm

B) 0.58 nm

C) 0.87 nm

D) 1.2 nm

Answer: B

Diff: 2 *Page Ref: Sec. 28.3*

4) A baseball has mass 143 g and speed 45.0 m/s, with the speed known to within 0.100%. What is the minimum uncertainty in the position of the baseball?

A) 1.56×10^{-32} m

B) 1.65×10^{-32} m

C) 1.56×10^{-30} m

D) 1.65×10^{-30} m

Answer: B
Diff: 2 *Page Ref: Sec. 28.3*

5) The energy of an electron state has an uncertainty of about 0.500 eV. What is the uncertainty in the life-time of the level?

A) 1.32×10^{-15} s

B) 8.28×10^{-15} s

C) 1.32×10^{-11} s

D) 8.28×10^{-11} s

Answer: A
Diff: 2 *Page Ref: Sec. 28.3*

6) An electron is known to be confined to a region of width 0.1 nm. What is an approximate expression for the least kinetic energy it could have, in eV?

A) 2.7 eV

B) 3.2 eV

C) 3.8 eV

D) 4.3 eV

Answer: C
Diff: 2 *Page Ref: Sec. 28.3*

7) The radius of a typical nucleus is about 5.0×10^{-15} m. Assuming this to be the uncertainty in the position of a proton in the nucleus, estimate the uncertainty in the proton's energy (in eV).

A) 0.4 MeV

B) 0.6 MeV

C) 0.8 MeV

D) 1.0 MeV

Answer: C
Diff: 3 *Page Ref: Sec. 28.3*

8) A hydrogen atom is in the 6h state. Determine the principal quantum number.

A) 0

B) 5

C) 6

D) 7

Answer: C
Diff: 2 *Page Ref: Sec. 28.6–28.8*

9) A hydrogen atom is in the 6h state. How many electrons are allowed in this state?

A) 22

B) 18

C) 14

D) 10

Answer: A
Diff: 2 *Page Ref: Sec. 28.6–28.8*

10) A hydrogen atom is in the 6h state. Which of the following could be an orbital quantum number?

A) 5

B) 6

C) 7

D) 8

Answer: A
Diff: 2 *Page Ref: Sec. 28.6–28.8*

11) A hydrogen atom is in the 6h state. Which one of the following is not a magnetic quantum number?

A) 0

B) 2

C) 4

D) 6

Answer: D
Diff: 2 *Page Ref: Sec. 28.6–28.8*

12) In a hydrogen atom, a given electron has $n = 7$. How many values can l have?

A) 6

B) 7

C) 15

D) 98

Answer: B
Diff: 2 *Page Ref: Sec. 28.6–28.8*

13) In a hydrogen atom, a given electron has $l = 7$. How many values can m_l have?

A) 6

B) 7

C) 15

D) 98

Answer: C
Diff: 2 *Page Ref: Sec. 28.6–28.8*

14) In a hydrogen atom, an electron with n = 7 can exist in how many different quantum states?

A) 6

B) 7

C) 15

D) 98

Answer: D
Diff: 2 *Page Ref: Sec. 28.6–28.8*

15) Consider ground-state helium holding two electrons in orbit. If one of the electrons has quantum numbers (n, l, m_l, m_s) of 1, 0, 0, -1/2 respectively, the quantum numbers for the other electron will be

A) 1, 1, 0, -1/2.

B) 1, 0, 0, +1/2.

C) 1, 1, 1, +1/2.

D) none of the given answers

Answer: B
Diff: 2 *Page Ref: Sec. 28.6–28.8*

16) How many electrons will fit into a 4f sub shell?

A) 3

B) 4

C) 7

D) 14

Answer: D
Diff: 1 *Page Ref: Sec. 28.6–28.8*

17) The values of n and l for a 4f sub shell are

A) n = 4, $l = 4$.

B) n = 4, $l = 3$.

C) n = 3, $l = 3$.

D) n = 4, $l = 2$.

Answer: B
Diff: 1 *Page Ref: Sec. 28.6–28.8*

18) A neutral atom has electron configuration $1s^2 2s^2 2p^6 3s^2 3p^2$. What element is this?

A) carbon

B) nitrogen

C) silicon

D) germanium

Answer: C

Diff: 1 *Page Ref: Sec. 28.6–28.8*

19) A neutral atom has an electron configuration of $1s^2 2s^2 2p^6 3s^2 3p^2$. What is its atomic number?

A) 5

B) 11

C) 14

D) 20

Answer: C

Diff: 1 *Page Ref: Sec. 28.6–28.8*

20) A neutral atom has an electron configuration of $1s^2 2s^2 2p^6$. If a neutral atom holds one additional electron, what is the ground state configuration?

A) $1s^2 2s^2 2p^6 3s^1$

B) $1s^2 2s^2 2p^7$

C) $1s^2 2s^3 2p^6$

D) none of the given answers

Answer: A

Diff: 1 *Page Ref: Sec. 28.6–28.8*

21) What is the electron configuration for Li which has three electrons?

A) $1s^3$

B) $1s^1 2s^2$

C) $1s^2 2s^1$

D) $1s^2 1p^1$

Answer: C

Diff: 2 *Page Ref: Sec. 228.6–8.8*

22) High-energy photons are used to bombard an unknown metal. The strongest peak is found for X-rays with an energy of 66 keV. What is the atomic number of the metal?

A) 80

B) 81

C) 82

D) 83

Answer: C

Diff: 2 *Page Ref: Sec. 28.9*

23) What is the shortest-wavelength X-ray photon emitted in an X-ray tube subject to 50 kV?

A) 0.025 nm

B) 0.25 nm

C) 2.5 nm

D) none of the given answers

Answer: A
Diff: 2 *Page Ref: Sec. 28.9*

24) In a ruby laser, an electron jumps from a higher energy level to a lower one. If the energy difference between the two levels is 1.8 eV, what is the wavelength of the emitted photon?

A) 469 nm

B) 649 nm

C) 694 nm

D) 964 nm

Answer: C
Diff: 2 *Page Ref: Sec. 28.11*

Chapter 29 Molecules and Solids

Conceptual Questions

1) Covalent bonding is caused by

A) the sharing of electrons between atoms.

B) the transfer of electrons between atoms.

C) unequal charge distributions around neutral molecules.

D) atoms bonding to hydrogen molecules.

Answer: A
Diff: 1 *Page Ref: Sec. 29.1*

2) Ionic bonding is caused by

A) the sharing of electrons between atoms.

B) the transfer of electrons between atoms.

C) unequal charge distributions around neutral molecules.

D) atoms bonding to hydrogen molecules.

Answer: B
Diff: 1 *Page Ref: Sec. 29.1*

3) The bond energy for a hydrogen molecule is

A) 2.5 eV

B) 3.5 eV

C) 4.5 eV

D) 5.5 eV

Answer: C
Diff: 1 *Page Ref: Sec. 29.1*

4) Van der Waals bonding is caused by

A) the sharing of electrons between atoms.

B) the transfer of electrons between atoms.

C) unequal charge distribution around neutral molecules.

D) atoms bonding to hydrogen molecules.

Answer: C
Diff: 1 *Page Ref: Sec. 29.3*

5) In general, which of the following is the strongest bond?

A) hydrogen bond

B) van der Waals bond

C) ionic bond

D) covalent bond

Answer: C
Diff: 1 *Page Ref: Sec. 29.3*

6) In general, which of the following is the weakest bond?

A) hydrogen bond

B) van der Waals bond

C) ionic bond

D) covalent bond

Answer: B
Diff: 1 *Page Ref: Sec. 29.3*

7) For a diatomic quantum mechanical rotator, the energy difference between adjacent energy levels

A) increases as L increases.

B) decreases as L increases.

C) is constant for all L.

D) varies randomly as L increases.

Answer: A
Diff: 2 *Page Ref: Sec. 29.4*

8) A diatomic quantum mechanical rotator in the L = 1 quantum state has energy E. The same rotator in the L = 2 quantum state will have energy

A) 2E.

B) 3E.

C) 6E.

D) none of the given answers

Answer: B
Diff: 1 *Page Ref: Sec. 29.4*

9) In its lowest quantum state, the energy of a diatomic harmonic oscillator is

A) (1/4)hf.

B) (1/2)hf.

C) hf.

D) (3/2)hf.

Answer: B
Diff: 1 *Page Ref: Sec. 29.4*

10) For a diatomic quantum mechanical vibrator, the energy difference between adjacent quantum states

A) increases as v increases.

B) decreases as v increases.

C) is constant for all values of v.

D) varies randomly as v increases.

Answer: C
Diff: 2 *Page Ref: Sec. 29.4*

11) In its lowest quantum state, a diatomic quantum mechanical rotator has a rotational energy of

A) zero.

B) $h/2\pi I$.

C) $h/\pi I$.

D) none of the given answers

Answer: A
Diff: 1 *Page Ref: Sec. 29.4*

12) A diatomic quantum mechanical vibrator in its ground state has energy E. This same vibrator in its third state has energy

A) E.

B) 3E.

C) 5E.

D) 7E.

Answer: C
Diff: 2 *Page Ref: Sec. 29.4*

13) Metallic bonding is caused by

A) the sharing of electrons by all atoms.

B) the transfer of electrons between atoms.

C) unequal charge distributions around neutral molecules.

D) atoms bonding to hydrogen molecules.

Answer: A
Diff: 1 *Page Ref: Sec. 29.5*

14) In a good conductor, the highest energy band containing electrons is

A) only partially filled.

B) completely filled.

Answer: A
Diff: 1 *Page Ref: Sec. 29.6*

15) In a good insulator, the highest energy band containing electrons, called the valence band, is
   A) only partially filled.
   B) completely filled.

Answer: B
Diff: 1 *Page Ref: Sec. 29.6*

16) An n-type semiconductor is produced by
   A) doping the host crystal with donor impurities.
   B) doping the host crystal with accepter impurities.
   C) pure crystals of germanium.
   D) none of the given answers

Answer: A
Diff: 1 *Page Ref: Sec. 29.7*

17) A p-type semiconductor is produced by
   A) doping the host crystal with donor impurities.
   B) doping the host crystal with accepter impurities.
   C) pure crystals of germanium.
   D) none of the given answers

Answer: B
Diff: 1 *Page Ref: Sec. 29.7*

18) In a p-type semiconductor, a hole is
   A) a donor atom.
   B) an extra electron supplied by a donor atom.
   C) a missing atom in the crystalline structure.
   D) a region where an electron is missing.

Answer: D
Diff: 1 *Page Ref: Sec. 29.7*

19) When a voltage is applied across a p-type semiconductor, the holes
   A) are destroyed.
   B) move toward the positive electrode.
   C) move toward the negative electrode.
   D) do not move.

Answer: C
Diff: 1 *Page Ref: Sec. 29.7*

20) If a battery is connected to a diode with the positive terminal to the *p* side and the negative terminal to the *n* side, then diode is said to be

A) forward biased.

B) reversed biased.

Answer: A
Diff: 1 *Page Ref: Sec. 29.8*

21) A simple junction transistor consists of three semiconductor sections consisting of

A) *pnp* semiconductors.

B) *npn* semiconductors.

C) either *pnp* or *npn* semiconductors.

D) none of the given answers

Answer: A
Diff: 1 *Page Ref: Sec. 29.9*

Quantitative Problems

1) A diatomic quantum mechanical oscillator has a moment of inertia of 7.73×10^{-45} kg•m2. What is the rotational energy in the quantum state characterized by L = 2?

A) 2.27×10^{-5} eV

B) 2.72×10^{-5} eV

C) 7.22×10^{-5} eV

D) 8.71×10^{-5} eV

Answer: B
Diff: 1 *Page Ref: Sec. 29.4*

2) A diatomic molecule has 2.6×10^{-5} eV of rotational energy in the L = 2 quantum state. What is the rotational energy in the L = 1 quantum state?

A) 3.4×10^{-6} eV

B) 5.3×10^{-6} eV

C) 7.8×10^{-6} eV

D) 8.7×10^{-6} eV

Answer: D
Diff: 2 *Page Ref: Sec. 29.4*

3) A diatomic molecule has 18×10^{-5} eV of rotational energy in the L = 2 quantum state. What is the rotational energy in the L = 0 quantum state?

A) 9.0×10^{-5} eV

B) 6.0×10^{-5} eV

C) 3.0×10^{-5} eV

D) 0 eV

Answer: D
Diff: 2 *Page Ref: Sec. 29.4*

4) Estimate the rotational energy (in eV) for a diatomic hydrogen molecule in the L = 2 quantum state. (The equilibrium separation for the H_2 molecule is 0.075 nm.)

A) 0.011 eV

B) 0.022 eV

C) 0.033 eV

D) 0.044 eV

Answer: D
Diff: 3 *Page Ref: Sec. 29.4*

5) A diatomic molecule is vibrating in the $v = 1$ quantum state with a frequency of 2.0×10^{13} Hz. What is the energy of vibration?

A) 0.041 eV

B) 0.083 eV

C) 0.12 eV

D) 0.17 eV

Answer: C
Diff: 1 *Page Ref: Sec. 29.4*

6) The energy gap between the valence and conduction bands in a certain semiconductor is 1.25 eV. What is the threshold wavelength for optical absorption in this substance?

A) 599 nm

B) 959 nm

C) 873 nm

D) 995 nm

Answer: D
Diff: 2 *Page Ref: Sec. 29.6*

Chapter 30 Nuclear Physics and Radioactivity

Conceptual Questions

1) Which of the atomic particles has the least mass?

A) electron

B) proton

C) neutron

D) nucleon

Answer: A

Diff: 1 *Page Ref: Sec. 30.1*

2) The mass of an atom is

A) approximately equally divided between neutrons, protons, and electrons.

B) evenly divided between the nucleus and the surrounding electron cloud.

C) concentrated in the cloud of electrons surrounding the nucleus.

D) concentrated in the nucleus.

Answer: D

Diff: 1 *Page Ref: Sec. 30.1*

3) The hydrogen nucleus consists of

A) a single proton.

B) a single neutron.

C) one proton and one neutron.

D) one proton and two neutrons.

Answer: A

Diff: 1 *Page Ref: Sec. 30.1*

4) An atom's atomic number is determined by the number of

A) neutrons in its nucleus.

B) nucleons in its nucleus.

C) protons in its nucleus.

D) alpha particles in its nucleus.

Answer: C

Diff: 1 *Page Ref: Sec. 30.1*

5) An atom's mass number is determined by the number of

A) neutrons in its nucleus.

B) nucleons in its nucleus.

C) protons in its nucleus.

D) alpha particles in its nucleus.

Answer: B
Diff: 1 *Page Ref: Sec. 30.1*

6) If an atom's atomic number is given by Z, its atomic mass by A, and its neutron number by N, which of the following is correct?

A) N = A + Z

B) N = Z - A

C) N = A - Z

D) none of the given answers

Answer: C
Diff: 1 *Page Ref: Sec. 30.1*

7) When a neutron is emitted from an unstable nucleus, the atomic mass number of the nucleus

A) increases by 1.

B) decreases by 1.

C) does not change.

D) none of the given answers

Answer: B
Diff: 1 *Page Ref: Sec. 30.1*

8) The number of protons in an atom is

A) zero.

B) equal to the number of neutrons.

C) equal to the number of electrons.

D) the same for all elements.

Answer: C
Diff: 1 *Page Ref: Sec. 30.1*

9) There is a limit to the size of a stable nucleus because of

A) the limited range of the strong nuclear force.

B) the weakness of the electrostatic force.

C) the weakness of the gravitational force.

D) none of the given answers

Answer: A
Diff: 2 *Page Ref: Sec. 30.1*

10) Atoms with the same atomic number but with different numbers of neutrons are referred to as

A) nucleons.

B) nuclides.

C) isotopes.

D) none of the given answers

Answer: C
Diff: 1 *Page Ref: Sec. 30.1*

11) Isotopes of an element have nuclei with

A) the same number of protons, but different numbers of neutrons.

B) the same number of protons, and the same number of neutrons.

C) a different number of protons, and a different number of neutrons.

D) a different number of protons, and the same number of neutrons.

Answer: A
Diff: 1 *Page Ref: Sec. 30.1*

12) The atomic mass unit is defined as

A) the mass of a proton.

B) the mass of an electron.

C) the mass of a hydrogen-1 atom.

D) one twelfth the mass of a carbon-12 atom.

Answer: D
Diff: 1 *Page Ref: Sec. 30.1*

13) Compared to the masses of its separate protons and neutrons, the total mass of a stable nucleus is always

A) less.

B) the same.

C) greater.

D) zero.

Answer: A
Diff: 2 *Page Ref: Sec. 30.2*

14) When nucleons join to form a stable nucleus, energy is

A) destroyed.

B) absorbed.

C) released.

D) not transferred.

Answer: C
Diff: 1 *Page Ref: Sec. 30.2*

15) The binding energy of a nucleus is contributed to

A) radioactivity.

B) alpha decay.

C) too many neutrons.

D) mass defect.

Answer: D
Diff: 1 *Page Ref: Sec. 30.2*

16) The binding energy per nucleon is

A) directly proportional to atomic number.

B) inversely proportional to atomic number.

C) the same for all atoms.

D) none of the given answers

Answer: D
Diff: 2 *Page Ref: Sec. 30.2*

17) The binding energy per nucleon

A) increases steadily as we go to heavier elements.

B) decreases steadily as we go to heavier elements.

C) is approximately constant throughout the periodic table, except for very light nuclei.

D) has a maximum near iron in the periodic table.

Answer: D
Diff: 2 *Page Ref: Sec. 30.2*

18) Which of the following statements concerning the nuclear force is false?

A) The nuclear force is very short-ranged.

B) The nuclear force is very weak and much smaller in relative magnitude than the electrostatic and gravitational forces.

C) The nuclear force is attractive and not repulsive.

D) The nuclear force acts on both protons and neutrons.

Answer: B
Diff: 1 *Page Ref: Sec. 30.2*

19) Compared to the electrostatic force, the nuclear force between adjacent protons in a nucleus is

A) much weaker.

B) about the same size.

C) only slightly larger.

D) much larger.

Answer: D
Diff: 2 *Page Ref: Sec. 30.2*

20) Alpha rays can penetrate

A) air only.

B) a piece of paper.

C) several millimeters of aluminum.

D) several centimeters of lead.

Answer: B

Diff: 2 *Page Ref: Sec. 30.3–30.7*

21) Beta rays can penetrate

A) air only.

B) a piece of paper.

C) several millimeters of aluminum.

D) several centimeters of lead.

Answer: C

Diff: 2 *Page Ref: Sec. 30.3–30.7*

22) Gamma rays can penetrate

A) air only.

B) a piece of paper.

C) several millimeters of aluminum.

D) several centimeters of lead.

Answer: D

Diff: 2 *Page Ref: Sec. 30.3–30.7*

23) An α particle is also known as

A) an electron.

B) a positron.

C) a helium nucleus.

D) a photon.

Answer: C

Diff: 1 *Page Ref: Sec. 30.3–30.7*

24) A β^- particle is also known as

A) an electron.

B) a positron.

C) a helium nucleus.

D) a photon.

Answer: A

Diff: 1 *Page Ref: Sec. 30.3–30.7*

25) A β^+ particle is also known as

A) an electron.

B) a positron.

C) a helium nucleus.

D) a photon.

Answer: B
Diff: 1 *Page Ref: Sec. 30.3–30.7*

26) A gamma ray is also known as

A) an electron.

B) a positron.

C) a helium nucleus.

D) a photon.

Answer: D
Diff: 1 *Page Ref: Sec. 30.3–30.7*

27) An alpha particle will be attracted to a

A) gamma ray.

B) proton.

C) positive charge.

D) negative charge.

Answer: D
Diff: 1 *Page Ref: Sec. 30.3–30.7*

28) Alpha particles have an atomic mass equal to

A) 1.

B) 2.

C) 4.

D) 6.

Answer: C
Diff: 1 *Page Ref: Sec. 30.3–30.7*

29) When an alpha particle is emitted from an unstable nucleus, the atomic mass number of the nucleus

A) increases by 2.

B) decreases by 2.

C) increases by 4.

D) decreases by 4.

Answer: D
Diff: 1 *Page Ref: Sec. 30.3–30.7*

30) When an alpha particle is emitted from an unstable nucleus, the atomic number of the nucleus

A) increases by 2.

B) decreases by 2.

C) increases by 4.

D) decreases by 4.

Answer: B
Diff: 1 *Page Ref: Sec. 30.3–30.7*

31) The expression $(M_X - M_Y - M_a) \times 931.5$ represents

A) the binding energy of the nucleus X.

B) the binding energy of the nucleus Y.

C) the energy released when nucleus X undergoes alpha decay.

D) the energy released when nucleus Y undergoes alpha decay.

Answer: C
Diff: 2 *Page Ref: Sec. 30.3–30.7*

32) In beta decay

A) a proton is emitted.

B) a neutron is emitted.

C) an electron is emitted.

D) an electron decays into another particle.

Answer: C
Diff: 1 *Page Ref: Sec. 30.3–30.7*

33) During β^+ decay

A) a neutron is transformed to a proton.

B) a proton is transformed to a neutron.

C) a neutron is ejected from the nucleus.

D) a proton is ejected from the nucleus.

Answer: B
Diff: 1 *Page Ref: Sec. 30.3–30.7*

34) During β^- decay

A) a neutron is transformed to a proton.

B) a proton is transformed to a neutron.

C) a neutron is ejected from the nucleus.

D) a proton is ejected from the nucleus.

Answer: A
Diff: 1 *Page Ref: Sec. 30.3–30.7*

35) When a β^+ particle is emitted from an unstable nucleus, the atomic number of the nucleus

A) increases by 1.

B) decreases by 1.

C) does not change.

D) none of the given answers

Answer: B
Diff: 2 *Page Ref: Sec. 30.3–30.7*

36) When a β^- particle is emitted from an unstable nucleus, the atomic number of the nucleus

A) increases by 1.

B) decreases by 1.

C) does not change.

D) none of the given answers

Answer: A
Diff: 2 *Page Ref: Sec. 30.3–30.2*

37) When a β^- particle is emitted from an unstable nucleus, the atomic mass number of the nucleus

A) increases by 1.

B) decreases by 1.

C) does not change.

D) none of the given answers

Answer: C
Diff: 1 *Page Ref: Sec. 30.3–30.7*

38) The existence of the neutrino was postulated in order to explain

A) alpha decay.

B) gamma emission.

C) beta decay.

D) fission.

Answer: C
Diff: 2 *Page Ref: Sec. 30.3–30.7*

39) Which of the following is most nearly the same as a gamma ray?

A) an alpha particle

B) a beta ray

C) visible light

D) a proton

E) a neutron

Answer: C
Diff: 1 *Page Ref: Sec. 30.3–30.7*

40) When a gamma ray is emitted from an unstable nucleus,

A) the number of neutrons and the number of protons drop by two.

B) the number of neutrons drops by one and the number of protons increases by one.

C) there is no change in either the number of neutrons or the number of protons.

D) none of the given answers

Answer: C
Diff: 1 *Page Ref: Sec. 30.3–30.7*

41) Which particle has the most mass?

A) alpha

B) beta

C) electron

D) gamma

Answer: A
Diff: 2 *Page Ref: Sec. 30.3–30.7*

42) In all three types of radioactive decay, what value is conserved in addition to electric charge, energy, and momentum?

A) atomic number

B) neutron number

C) nucleon number

D) none of the given answers

Answer: C
Diff: 2 *Page Ref: Sec. 31.1–31.3*

43) What happens to the half–life of a radioactive substance as it decays?

A) It remains constant.

B) It increases.

C) It decreases.

D) It could do any of these.

Answer: A
Diff: 1 *Page Ref: Sec. 30.8–30.11*

44) In radioactive dating, carbon–14 is often used. This nucleus emits a single beta particle when it decays. When this happens, the resulting nucleus is

A) still carbon–14.

B) boron–14.

C) nitrogen–14.

D) carbon–15.

E) carbon–13.

Answer: C
Diff: 2 *Page Ref: Sec. 30.8–30.11*

45) The type of detector that uses a magnetic field to curve charged particles is a

A) Geiger tube.

B) scintillation counter.

C) cloud chamber.

D) bubble chamber.

E) spark chamber.

Answer: D
Diff: 2 *Page Ref: Sec. 30.13*

46) The type of detector that uses liquid hydrogen is a

A) Geiger tube.

B) scintillation counter.

C) cloud chamber.

D) bubble chamber.

E) spark chamber.

Answer: D
Diff: 2 *Page Ref: Sec. 30.13*

47) Cloud chambers have been replaced by bubble chambers because

A) the radioactive clouds were too dangerous to work with.

B) the density of fluids is greater than the density of vapors.

C) bubble chambers tend to be larger and more expensive.

D) gamma rays are visible in bubble chambers, but not in cloud chambers.

Answer: B
Diff: 2 *Page Ref: Sec. 30.13*

Quantitative Problems

1) An element with atomic mass number of 14 and atomic number 6 has how many protons?

A) 6

B) 8

C) 14

D) 20

Answer: A
Diff: 1 *Page Ref: Sec. 30.1*

2) An element with atomic mass number of 14 and atomic number 6 has how many neutrons?

A) 6

B) 8

C) 14

D) 20

Answer: B

Diff: 1 *Page Ref: Sec. 30.1*

3) The atomic number and mass number for calcium 39 are 20 and 39, respectively. How many nucleons are in one atom?

A) 1

B) 19

C) 20

D) 39

Answer: D

Diff: 1 *Page Ref: Sec. 30.1*

4) The atomic number and mass number for calcium 39 are 20 and 39, respectively. How many electrons are in one atom?

A) 1

B) 19

C) 20

D) 39

Answer: C

Diff: 1 *Page Ref: Sec. 30.1*

5) The atomic number and mass number for calcium 39 are 20 and 39, respectively. How many protons are in one atom?

A) 1

B) 19

C) 20

D) 39

Answer: C

Diff: 1 *Page Ref: Sec. 30.1*

6) The atomic number and mass number for calcium 39 are 20 and 39, respectively. How many neutrons are in one atom?

A) 1

B) 19

C) 20

D) 39

Answer: B
Diff: 1 *Page Ref: Sec. 30.1*

7) In a $^{93}_{41}$Nb nucleus, the number of protons, neutrons, and electrons is

A) 41, 52, 93.

B) 41, 52, 52.

C) 41, 52, 41.

D) 41, 52, 0.

Answer: D
Diff: 1 *Page Ref: Sec. 30.1*

8) How many protons are there in the carbon-14 nucleus?

A) none

B) 1

C) 6

D) 8

E) 14

Answer: C
Diff: 1 *Page Ref: Sec. 30.1*

9) If an element of atomic number 15 has an isotope of mass number 32,

A) the number of neutrons in the nucleus is 15.

B) the number of neutrons in the nucleus is 17.

C) the number of protons in the nucleus is 17.

D) the number of nucleons in the nucleus is 15.

Answer: B
Diff: 1 *Page Ref: Sec. 30.1*

10) Calculate the binding energy of ^{4}He.

A) 28.3 MeV

B) 20.4 MeV

C) 14.2 MeV

D) 7.80 MeV

Answer: C
Diff: 2 *Page Ref: Sec. 30.2*

11) How much energy is required to remove one proton from ^{9}Be?

A) 16.9 MeV

B) 19.6 MeV

C) 58.2 MeV

D) 82.5 MeV

Answer: A
Diff: 2 *Page Ref: Sec. 30.2*

12) An element with atomic number 88 goes through alpha decay. Its atomic number is now

A) 80.

B) 84.

C) 86.

D) 88.

Answer: C
Diff: 1 *Page Ref: Sec. 30.3–30.7*

13) An atom has 98 protons and 249 nucleons. If it undergoes alpha decay, what are the number of protons and neutrons, respectively, in the daughter nucleus?

A) 100, 245

B) 94, 247

C) 96, 245

D) 100, 249

Answer: C
Diff: 2 *Page Ref: Sec. 30.3–30.7*

14) A carbon–14 nucleus decays to a nitrogen–14 nucleus by beta decay. How much energy (in MeV) is released if carbon–14 has a mass of 14.003242 u and nitrogen–14 has a mass of 14.003074 u?

A) 0.0157 MeV

B) 0.157 MeV

C) 1.57 MeV

D) 15.7 MeV

Answer: B
Diff: 2 *Page Ref: Sec. 30.3–30.7*

15) An element with atomic number 6 undergoes β^- decay. Its atomic number is now

A) 7.

B) 6.

C) 5.

D) 2.

Answer: A
Diff: 1 *Page Ref: Sec. 30.3–30.7*

16) If the half-life of a material is 45 years, how much will be left after 100 years?

A) more than 1/2

B) less than 1/2

C) more than 1/4

D) less than 1/4

Answer: D
Diff: 1 *Page Ref: Sec. 30.8–30.11*

17) If 4.0×10^{18} atoms decay with a half-life of 2.3 years, how many are remaining after 3.7 years?

A) 2.5×10^{18}

B) 1.7×10^{18}

C) 1.3×10^{18}

D) 1.1×10^{18}

Answer: C
Diff: 2 *Page Ref: Sec. 30.8–30.11*

18) What is the probability that an atom will decay this year if its half-life is 247 years?

A) 0.0017

B) 0.0028

C) 0.017

D) 0.071

Answer: B
Diff: 2 *Page Ref: Sec. 30.8–30.11*

19) A Thallium source was certified at 10 μCi ten years ago. What is its activity now if the half-life is 3.7 years?

A) 4.7 μCi

B) 3.3 μCi

C) 1.5 μCi

D) 1.0 μCi

Answer: C
Diff: 2 *Page Ref: Sec. 30.8–30.11*

20) A radioactive sample has a half-life of 10 min. What fraction of the sample is left after 40 min?

A) 1/2

B) 1/4

C) 1/8

D) 1/16

Answer: D
Diff: 2 *Page Ref: Sec. 30.8–30.11*

21) The half-life of radioactive iodine-137 is 8.0 days. How many iodine nuclei are necessary to produce an activity of 1.0 μCi?

A) 2.9×10^9

B) 4.6×10^9

C) 3.7×10^{10}

D) 7.6×10^{12}

Answer: C
Diff: 2 *Page Ref: Sec. 30.8-30.11*

22) A radioactive substance with a half-life of 3.0 days has an initial activity of 0.24 Ci. What is its activity after 6.0 days?

A) 0.12 Ci

B) 0.48 Ci

C) 0.06 Ci

D) none of the given answers

Answer: C
Diff: 2 *Page Ref: Sec. 30.8-30.11*

23) The radioactivity due to carbon-14 measured in a piece of a wooden casket from an ancient burial site was found to produce 20 counts per minute from a given sample, whereas the same amount of carbon from a piece of living wood produced 160 counts per minute. The half-life of carbon-14, a beta emitter, is 5730 years. Thus we would estimate the age of the artifact to be about

A) 5,700 years.

B) 11,500 years.

C) 14,800 years.

D) 17,200 years.

E) 23,000 years.

Answer: D
Diff: 2 *Page Ref: Sec. 30.8-30.11*

24) How long would it take 4.0×10^{20} atoms to decay to 1.0×10^{19} atoms if their half-life was 14.7 years?

A) 29.4 years

B) 58.8 years

C) 78.2 years

D) 147 years

Answer: C
Diff: 3 *Page Ref: Sec. 30.8-30.11*

25) How long will it take a 4.5 Ci sample of material to reach an activity level of 0.14 Ci if the half-life is 435 years?

A) 14,478 years

B) 3245 years

C) 2178 years

D) 1993 years

Answer: C
Diff: 3 *Page Ref: Sec. 30.8–30.11*

Chapter 31 Nuclear Energy; Effects and Uses of Radiation

Conceptual Questions

1) When a target nucleus is bombarded by an appropriate beam of particles, it is possible to produce

A) a less massive nucleus, but not a more massive one.

B) a more massive nucleus, but not a less massive one.

C) a nucleus with smaller atomic number, but not one with a greater atomic number.

D) a nucleus with greater atomic number, but not one with a smaller atomic number.

E) a nucleus with either greater or smaller atomic number.

Answer: E
Diff: 2 *Page Ref: Sec. 31.1-31.3*

2) The mass of a proton is 1.6726×10^{-27} kg and the mass of a neutron is 1.6749×10^{-27} kg. A proton captures a neutron forming a deuterium nucleus. One would expect the mass of this nucleus to be

A) equal to $(1.6726 + 1.6749) \times 10^{-27}$ kg.

B) less than $(1.6726 + 1.6749) \times 10^{-27}$ kg.

C) greater than $(1.6726 + 1.6749) \times 10^{-27}$ kg.

D) any of these; it depends on the energy released during the capture.

Answer: B
Diff: 2 *Page Ref: Sec. 31.1-31.3*

3) In a nuclear reaction, what value is conserved in addition to electric charge, energy, and momentum?

A) atomic number

B) neutron number

C) nucleon number

D) none of the given answers

Answer: C
Diff: 2 *Page Ref: Sec. 31.1-31.3*

4) A proton strikes an oxygen–18 nucleus producing fluorine–18 and another particle. What other particle is produced by this nuclear reaction?

A) a neutron

B) an alpha particle

C) an β^- particle

D) an β^+ particle

Answer: A
Diff: 1 *Page Ref: Sec. 31.1–31.3*

5) A nuclear reaction is said to be exothermic if the total kinetic energy is

A) less after the reaction than before.

B) equal both before and after the reaction.

C) greater after the reaction than before.

D) zero after the reaction.

Answer: C
Diff: 2 *Page Ref: Sec. 31.1–31.3*

6) A nuclear reaction is said to be endothermic if the total kinetic energy is

A) less after the reaction than before.

B) equal both before and after the reaction.

C) greater after the reaction than before.

D) zero after the reaction.

Answer: A
Diff: 2 *Page Ref: Sec. 31.1–31.3*

7) The process during which a heavy nucleus such as uranium splits into two intermediate–sized nuclei after being struck by a neutron is referred to as

A) nuclear fission.

B) nuclear fusion.

Answer: A
Diff: 1 *Page Ref: Sec. 31.1–31.3*

8) The process during which small nuclei combine to form larger ones is referred to as

A) nuclear fission.

B) nuclear fusion.

Answer: B
Diff: 1 *Page Ref: Sec. 31.1–31.3*

9) How does the total mass of the products of a nuclear fission reaction compare to the mass of the original elements?

A) greater

B) less

C) the same

D) varies according to the reaction

Answer: B
Diff: 1 *Page Ref: Sec. 31.1–31.3*

10) How does the mass of the products of a nuclear fusion reaction compare to the mass of the original elements?

A) greater

B) less

C) the same

D) varies according to the reaction

Answer: B
Diff: 1 *Page Ref: Sec. 31.1–31.3*

11) When light elements such as hydrogen undergo fusion,

A) there is a loss of mass.

B) there is an increase in mass.

C) there is no change in mass.

D) electric charge can be annihilated.

Answer: A
Diff: 1 *Page Ref: Sec. 31.1–31.3*

12) The fuel for nuclear fission is

A) H.

B) He.

C) U.

D) any radioactive material.

Answer: C
Diff: 2 *Page Ref: Sec. 31.1–31.3*

13) The fuel for nuclear fusion in the center of the Sun is

A) H.

B) He.

C) U.

D) any radioactive material.

Answer: A
Diff: 2 *Page Ref: Sec. 31.1–31.3*

14) The energy radiated by a star, such as the Sun, results from

A) beta decay.

B) alpha decay.

C) fission reactions.

D) fusion reactions.

Answer: D
Diff: 1 *Page Ref: Sec. 31.1–31.3*

15) What is the source of the energy the Sun radiates to us?

A) chemical reactions

B) nuclear fission reactions

C) nuclear fusion reactions

D) magnetic explosions

E) cosmic rays

Answer: C
Diff: 1 *Page Ref: Sec. 31.1–31.3*

16) What is the principle difference between a hydrogen bomb and a uranium bomb?

A) A uranium bomb is an atomic bomb, and a hydrogen bomb is a nuclear bomb.

B) A uranium bomb utilizes a fission reaction whereas a hydrogen bomb utilizes a fusion reaction.

C) Both work on the same principle, but the hydrogen bomb has a higher yield.

D) A hydrogen bomb converts mass into energy, whereas a uranium bomb does not.

E) One results in radioactive fallout, and the other does not.

Answer: B
Diff: 1 *Page Ref: Sec. 31.1–31.3*

17) One sometimes hears reference to a "20-kiloton" bomb. What does this mean?

A) It means 20,000 tons of nuclear explosive is used in the bomb.

B) It means that the number of "fissile" nuclei is equal to the number of trinitrotoluene molecules in 20,000 tons of TNT explosive.

C) It means that the total weight of the bomb (not just the uranium) is 20,000 tons.

D) It means that the energy released by the bomb is equal to the energy released when 20,000 tons of TNT is exploded.

E) This refers to the maximum pressure generated by the bomb when it explodes.

Answer: D
Diff: 1 *Page Ref: Sec. 31.1–31.3*

18) What is the meaning of the term "critical mass"?

A) This refers to the mass of the "critical" elements in a reactor, i.e., the uranium or plutonium.

B) This refers to the minimum amount of fissionable material required to sustain a chain reaction.

C) This is the amount of mass needed to make a power reactor economically feasible.

D) This is the material which is just on the verge of becoming radioactive.

Answer: B
Diff: 1 *Page Ref: Sec. 31.1–31.3*

19) A chain reaction can occur

A) in any uranium core.

B) when critical mass is reached.

C) in the center of the Sun.

D) when the coolant is too hot.

Answer: B
Diff: 2 *Page Ref: Sec. 31.1–31.3*

20) The chief hazard of radiation damage to living cells is

A) due to ionization.

B) due to heating.

C) due to the creation of chemical impurities.

D) the creation of new isotopes within the body.

Answer: A
Diff: 1 *Page Ref: Sec. 31.4*

21) What is necessary to stop beta particles?

A) air alone

B) paper

C) metal foil

D) thick metal

Answer: C
Diff: 1 *Page Ref: Sec. 31.4*

22) What is created in pair production?

A) a proton and a positron

B) an electron and an antiproton

C) an electron and a positron

D) an electron and a photon

Answer: C
Diff: 1 *Page Ref: Sec. 31.4*

23) All of the following are units used to describe radiation dosage in humans except

A) curie.

B) rad.

C) rem.

D) RBE.

E) sievert.

Answer: A
Diff: 2 *Page Ref: Sec. 31.5*

24) A unit that measures the effective dose of radiation in a human is the

A) curie.

B) RBE.

C) rad.

D) rem.

Answer: D
Diff: 2 *Page Ref: Sec. 31.5*

Quantitative Problems

1) When lead-207 ($Z = 82$) is bombarded with neutrons, it can change into

A) lead-208.

B) lead-206.

C) tellurium-208 ($Z = 81$).

D) bismuth-208 ($Z = 83$).

Answer: A
Diff: 1 *Page Ref: Sec. 31.1–31.3*

2) In the fission reaction $^{235}U + ^{1}n \rightarrow ^{141}Ba + ^{92}Kr$ + neutrons, the number of neutrons produced is

A) zero.

B) 1.

C) 2.

D) 3.

Answer: D
Diff: 2 *Page Ref: Sec. 31.1–31.3*

3) Complete the following nuclear reaction:

$^{16}_{8}O + ^{1}_{0}n \rightarrow$ ________ $+ ^{4}_{2}He$

A) ^{12}C

B) ^{13}C

C) ^{14}C

D) ^{15}C

Answer: B

Diff: 2 *Page Ref: Sec. 31.1–31.3*

4) Complete the following nuclear reaction:

$^{16}_{8}O + ^{4}_{2}He \rightarrow$ ________ $+ ^{19}_{10}Ne$

A) ^{1}p

B) ^{1}n

C) ^{2}H

D) ^{3}H

Answer: B

Diff: 2 *Page Ref: Sec. 31.1–31.3*

5) Complete the following nuclear reaction:

$^{38}_{19}K + ^{1}_{1}H \rightarrow$ ________ $+ ^{38}_{20}Ca$

A) ^{1}p

B) ^{1}n

C) ^{2}H

D) ^{3}H

Answer: B

Diff: 2 *Page Ref: Sec. 31.1–31.3*

6) Complete the following nuclear reaction:

$^{3}_{1}H + ^{3}_{1}H \rightarrow$ ________ $+ ^{4}_{2}He$

A) $2(^{1}p)$

B) $2(^{1}n)$

C) ^{2}H

D) ^{3}H

Answer: B

Diff: 2 *Page Ref: Sec. 31.1–31.3*

7) Complete the following nuclear reaction:

$^{27}_{13}Al$ (α, n) ________

A) 28P

B) 29P

C) 30P

D) 31P

Answer: C
Diff: 2 *Page Ref: Sec. 31.1–31.3*

8) The Q value for a particular reaction is –2.4 MeV, and the reaction's threshold energy is 9.60 MeV. What is the ratio of the mass of the incident particle to the mass of the stationary target nucleus?

A) –0.75

B) 0.25

C) 3

D) 4

E) 5

Answer: C
Diff: 2 *Page Ref: Sec. 31.1–31.3*

9) Find the Q value of the following reaction:

$$^{14}_{7}N + ^{4}_{2}He \rightarrow ^{17}_{8}O + ^{1}_{1}H$$

(14.003074 u) (4.002603) (16,999131 u) (1.007825 u)

A) –0.001279 u

B) –0.002179 u

C) –0.007219 u

D) –.0.009721 u

Answer: A
Diff: 1 *Page Ref: Sec. 31.1–31.3*

10) What is the Q value for the following reaction?

^{7}Li	+	^{1}p	=	^{4}He	+	^{4}He
(7.016005)		(1.007825)		(4.002603)		(4.002603)

A) 13.57 MeV

B) 15.37 MeV

C) 17.35 MeV

D) 17.53 MeV

Answer: C

Diff: 2 *Page Ref: Sec. 31.1–31.3*

11) What is the Q-value of the following reaction?

^{14}N	+	^{4}He	=	^{1}p	+	^{17}O
(14.003074)		(4.002603)		(1.007825)		(16.999131)

A) 1.191 MeV

B) -1.191 MeV

C) 1.279×10^{-3} MeV

D) -1.279×10^{-3} MeV

Answer: B

Diff: 2 *Page Ref: Sec. 31.1–31.3*

12) What is the energy of reaction of the process $^{9}_{4}Be\ (\alpha, n)\ ^{12}_{6}C$?

A) 3.66 Mev

B) 5.60 MeV

C) 5.70 MeV

D) 6.11 MeV

E) 6.34 MeV

Answer: C

Diff: 2 *Page Ref: Sec. 31.1–31.3*

13) What is the energy released (positive) or absorbed (negative) in the following reaction?

^{3}H	+	^{3}H	=	^{4}He	+	$2(^{1}n)$
(3.016049)		(3.016049)		(4.002603)		(1.008665)

A) 0.0122 MeV

B) -0.0122 MeV

C) 11.3 MeV

D) -11.3 MeV

Answer: C

Diff: 2 *Page Ref: Sec. 31.1–31.3*

14) An X-ray technician takes an average of ten X-rays per day and receives 2.5 mrad per X-ray. What is the total dose the technician receives in 250 working days?

A) 2.50 rem

B) 5.00 rem

C) 6.25 rem

D) 7.75 rem

Answer: C
Diff: 2 *Page Ref: Sec. 31.5*

Chapter 32 Elementary Particles

Conceptual Questions

1) What happens to the cyclotron frequency of a charged particle if its speed doubles?

A) It triples.

B) It doubles.

C) It halves.

D) It does not change.

Answer: D
Diff: 1 *Page Ref: Sec. 32.1*

2) What happens to the cyclotron frequency of a charged particle if the radius of its path doubles?

A) It triples.

B) It doubles.

C) It halves.

D) It does not change.

Answer: D
Diff: 1 *Page Ref: Sec. 32.1*

3) The Feynman diagram shows two electrons approaching each other, interacting, and then leaving each other. What particle is being exchanged during the interaction?

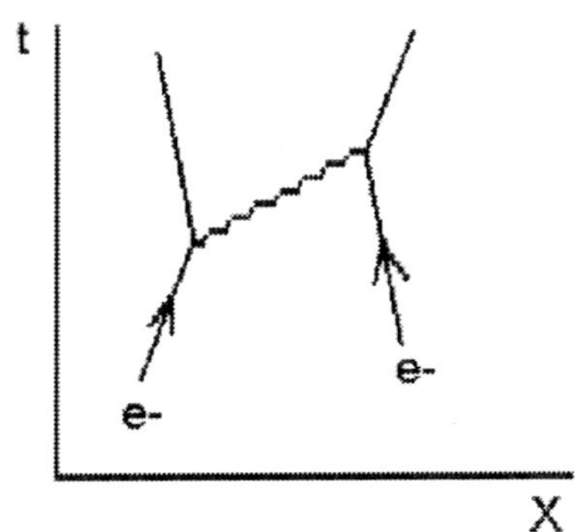

FIGURE 32-1

A) pion

B) virtual photon

C) neutrino

D) W particle

Answer: B
Diff: 2 *Page Ref: Sec. 32.2-32.6*

4) The Feynman diagram shows the weak interaction of a neutrino (ν) and a neutron (n), mediated by a W^+ particle. The interaction produces an electron (e^-) and another particle. What is the other particle?

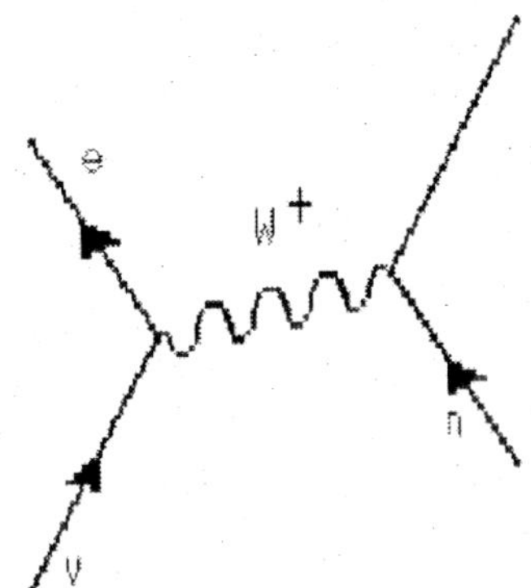

FIGURE 32-2

A) a positron (e^+)

B) a pion (π^+)

C) a proton (p)

D) a quark

E) an anti-neutron

Answer: C
Diff: 2 *Page Ref: Sec. 32.2-32.6*

5) A positively charged electron is

A) called a proton.

B) called a positron.

C) also called an electron.

D) not found in nature.

Answer: B
Diff: 1 *Page Ref: Sec. 32.2-32.6*

6) What effect does an increase in the mass of the virtual exchange particle have on the range of the force it mediates?

A) decreases it

B) increases it

C) has no appreciable effect

D) decreases charged particle interactions and increases neutral particle interactions

Answer: A
Diff: 2 *Page Ref: Sec. 32.3-32.6*

7) An exchange particle for the weak force is the

A) photon.

B) meson.

C) W.

D) graviton.

Answer: C

Diff: 2 Page Ref: Sec. 32.2–32.6

8) The exchange particles for the weak force are very massive (about 100 times as massive as a proton). This would lead one to expect that the weak force would

A) act over a very long range.

B) act over a very short range.

C) only act on very massive particles.

D) be transmitted at the speed of light.

Answer: B

Diff: 2 Page Ref: Sec. 32.2–32.6

9) The exchange particle for quarks is called

A) the stickon.

B) the gluon.

C) the epoxyon.

D) the epsilon.

Answer: B

Diff: 2 Page Ref: Sec. 32.2–32.6

10) A particle that travels at the speed of light

A) has never been observed.

B) must have zero rest mass.

C) must have a very large rest mass.

D) has infinite energy.

Answer: B

Diff: 1 Page Ref: Sec. 32.2–32.6

11) One reason a photon could not create an odd number of electrons and positrons is that such a process would

A) not conserve charge.

B) not conserve energy.

C) require photon energies that are not attainable.

D) result in the creation of mass.

Answer: A

Diff: 1 Page Ref: Sec. 32.2–32.6

12) Is the following decay permissible? $\Sigma^+ \rightarrow \Lambda^\circ + \pi^+$

A) yes

B) No, because charge is not conserved.

C) No, because mass is created.

D) No, because lepton number is not conserved.

Answer: C
Diff: 2 *Page Ref: Sec. 32.2–32.6*

13) Is the following decay allowed? $\Sigma^+ \rightarrow p + \pi^+$

A) yes

B) No, because charge is not conserved.

C) No, because mass is created.

D) No, because lepton number is not conserved.

Answer: B
Diff: 2 *Page Ref: Sec. 32.2–32.6*

14) Is the following decay allowed? $\pi^\circ \rightarrow \mu^+ + \nu\mu$

A) yes

B) No, because charge is not conserved.

C) No, because mass is created.

D) No, because lepton number is not conserved.

Answer: B
Diff: 2 *Page Ref: Sec. 32.2–32.6*

15) The neutrino has

A) enormous rest mass, positive charge, and spin quantum number 1/2.

B) negligible rest mass, negative charge, and spin quantum number 1.

C) negligible rest mass, no charge, and spin quantum number 1/2.

D) none of the given answers

Answer: C
Diff: 2 *Page Ref: Sec. 32.2–32.6*

16) An electron is an example of

A) a lepton.

B) a meson.

C) a baryon.

D) a gauge boson.

Answer: A
Diff: 2 *Page Ref: Sec. 32.2–32.6*

17) A proton is an example of

A) a lepton.

B) a meson.

C) a baryon.

D) a gauge boson.

Answer: C
Diff: 2 *Page Ref: Sec. 32.2–32.6*

18) A neutron is an example of

A) a lepton.

B) a meson.

C) a baryon.

D) a gauge boson.

Answer: C
Diff: 2 *Page Ref: Sec. 32.2–32.6*

19) A photon is an example of

A) a lepton.

B) a meson.

C) a baryon.

D) a gauge boson.

Answer: D
Diff: 2 *Page Ref: Sec. 32.2–32.6*

20) Particles that do not interact via the strong force but do interact via the weak nuclear force (and presumably by the much weaker gravitation force) are called

A) gauge bosons.

B) leptons.

C) baryons.

D) mesons.

Answer: B
Diff: 2 *Page Ref: Sec. 32.2–32.6*

21) Hadrons are divided into two subgroups called

A) baryons and leptons.

B) leptons and mesons.

C) mesons and baryons.

D) nucleons and gauge bosons.

Answer: C
Diff: 2 *Page Ref: Sec. 32.2–32.6*

22) A quark is

A) a constituent of a nucleon.

B) a constituent of a hadron.

C) an elementary particle.

D) all of the given answers

Answer: D
Diff: 1 *Page Ref: Sec. 32.7–32.11*

23) What is the quark composition of a Λ°?

A) uud

B) uus

C) uds

D) uss

Answer: C
Diff: 2 *Page Ref: Sec. 32.7–32.11*

24) A distinctive feature of quarks is that they

A) have zero rest mass.

B) have zero charge.

C) have fractional electric charge.

D) are always observed singly, since they do not readily interact with other particles.

Answer: C
Diff: 1 *Page Ref: Sec. 32.7–32.11*

25) The charge of some quarks and antiquarks is

A) e/4.

B) e/3.

C) e/2.

D) e.

Answer: B
Diff: 2 *Page Ref: Sec. 32.7–32.11*

26) When a quark emits or absorbs a gluon, the quark changes

A) its charge.

B) its mass.

C) its color.

D) into an antiquark.

Answer: C
Diff: 2 *Page Ref: Sec. 32.7–32.11*

27) The number of types of quarks is

A) 2.

B) 3.

C) 6.

D) 8.

Answer: C

Diff: 2 *Page Ref: Sec. 32.7-32.11*

28) Which of the following is not considered to be one of the four fundamental forces?

A) the gravity force

B) the meson force

C) the weak nuclear force

D) the strong nuclear force

E) the electromagnetic force

Answer: B

Diff: 2 *Page Ref: Sec. 32.7-32.11*

29) A significant step in "unifying" the forces of nature was the discovery that two of the so-called fundamental forces were two parts of a single force. The two forces that were so unified were

A) the electromagnetic force and the weak force.

B) the electromagnetic force and the strong nuclear force.

C) the electromagnetic force and the gravity force.

D) the weak force and the strong nuclear force.

Answer: A

Diff: 2 *Page Ref: Sec. 32.7-32.11*

30) The grand unified theory (GUT) is a sought-after model that would unify three of the four forces of nature. Which force is the one it would not include?

A) gravitational

B) strong

C) weak

D) electromagnetic

Answer: A

Diff: 2 *Page Ref: Sec. 32.7-32.11*

Quantitative Problems

1) What is the wavelength for a beam of 1.4 GeV electrons?

A) 8.8×10^{-14} m

B) 8.8×10^{-15} m

C) 8.8×10^{-16} m

D) 8.8×10^{-17} m

Answer: C
Diff: 2 *Page Ref: Sec. 32.1*

2) A cyclotron operates at 10 MHz. What magnetic field is needed to accelerate protons?

A) 0.12 T

B) 0.25 T

C) 0.66 T

D) 1.5 T

Answer: C
Diff: 1 *Page Ref: Sec. 32.1*

3) A cyclotron of radius 0.25 m accelerates protons in a 1.7-T magnetic field. What is the frequency for the applied alternating voltage?

A) 0.26 MHz

B) 2.6 MHz

C) 26 MHz

D) 260 MHz

Answer: C
Diff: 2 *Page Ref: Sec. 32.1*

4) A cyclotron of radius 0.25 m accelerates protons in a 1.7-T magnetic field. What is the kinetic energy of the protons when they leave the cyclotron?

A) 7.8 keV

B) 8.7 keV

C) 7.8 MeV

D) 8.7 MeV

Answer: D
Diff: 2 *Page Ref: Sec. 32.1*

5) A deuteron has the same charge as a proton but approximately twice the proton mass. Suppose deuterons are being accelerated in a cyclotron in an orbit of radius 75 cm at a frequency of 8.0 Mhz. What magnetic field is needed?

A) 0.011 T

B) 0.11 T

C) 1.1 T

D) 11 T

Answer: C
Diff: 2 *Page Ref: Sec. 32.1*

6) Suppose you were to try to create a proton–antiproton pair by annihilation of a very high energy photon. The proton and the anti–proton have the same masses, but opposite charges. What energy photon would be required?

A) 1.022 MeV

B) 1880 MeV

C) 940 MeV

D) 223 MeV

Answer: B
Diff: 1 *Page Ref: Sec. 32.2–32.6*

7) When a positronium atom (electron + positron) decays, it emits two photons. What are the energies of the photons?

A) 0.511 MeV and 1.022 MeV

B) 0.225 MeV and 0.285 MeV

C) 0.256 MeV and 0.256 MeV

D) 0.511 MeV and 0.511 MeV

Answer: D
Diff: 1 *Page Ref: Sec. 32.2–32.6*

8) The π° meson has a mass of 264 times that of an electron. What is the range of the force mediated by this particle?

A) 1.5×10^{-10} m

B) 1.5×10^{-12} m

C) 1.5×10^{-14} m

D) 1.5×10^{-15} m

Answer: D
Diff: 2 *Page Ref: Sec. 32.2–32.6*